Edexcel GCSE
Mathematics

16+

Series Director: Keith Pledger
Series Editor: Graham Cumming

Authors: Julie Bolter   Jean Linsky   Kevin Tanner   Brian Western

With: Gareth Cole   Gill Dyer   Michael Flowers   Karen Hughes
Peter Jolly   Joan Knott   Graham Newman   Rob Pepper
Joe Petran   Keith Pledger   Rob Summerson

ALWAYS LEARNING

PEARSON

Published by Pearson Education Limited, a company incorporated in England and Wales, having its registered office at Edinburgh Gate, Harlow, Essex, CM20 2JE. Registered company number: 872828

Edexcel is a registered trademark of Edexcel Limited

Text © Gill Dyer, Keith Pledger and Pearson Education Limited 2011.

The rights of Julie Bolter, Gareth Cole, Gill Dyer, Michael Flowers, Karen Hughes, Peter Jolly, Joan Knott, Jean Linsky, Graham Newman, Rob Pepper, Joe Petran, Keith Pledger, Rob Summerson, Kevin Tanner and Brian Western to be identified as the authors of this Work have been asserted by them in accordance with the Copyright, Designs and Patent Act, 1988.

First published 2011

13 12 11
10 9 8 7 6 5 4 3 2 1

British Library Cataloguing in Publication Data
A catalogue record for this book is available from the British Library

ISBN 978 1 44690 003 1

Copyright notice
All rights reserved. No part of this publication may be reproduced in any form or by any means (including photocopying or storing it in any medium by electronic means and whether or not transiently or incidentally to some other use of this publication) without the written permission of the copyright owner, except in accordance with the provisions of the Copyright, Designs and Patents Act 1988 or under the terms of a licence issued by the Copyright Licensing Agency, Saffron House, 6–10 Kirby Street, London EC1N 8TS (www.cla.co.uk). Applications for the copyright owner's written permission should be addressed to the publisher.

Typeset by Techset, Gateshead
Printed in Great Britain at Scotprint, Haddington

Disclaimer
This material has been published on behalf of Edexcel and offers high-quality support for the delivery of Edexcel qualifications.
This does not mean that the material is essential to achieve any Edexcel qualification, nor does it mean that it is the only suitable material available to support any Edexcel qualification. Edexcel material will not be used verbatim in setting any Edexcel examination or assessment. Any resource lists produced by Edexcel shall include this and other appropriate resources.
Copies of official specifications for all Edexcel qualifications may be found on the Edexcel website: www.edexcel.com

CONTENTS

Number

Algebra

Geometry and measure

Statistics and probability

Detailed contents

Sections shown in light blue cover content that will be examined at Higher tier only.

About this book

Edexcel GCSE Mathematics 16+ is specially designed to help you get the grade you need in your one-year GCSE Maths course, whether you are taking Foundation tier or Higher tier. Carefully structured, it can be used with Specification A (Linear) or Specification B (Modular).

Section objectives show what you'll be practising

Key points to understand and remember

Clear worked examples show successful exam techniques in action

Self-assessment checklist to check your skills

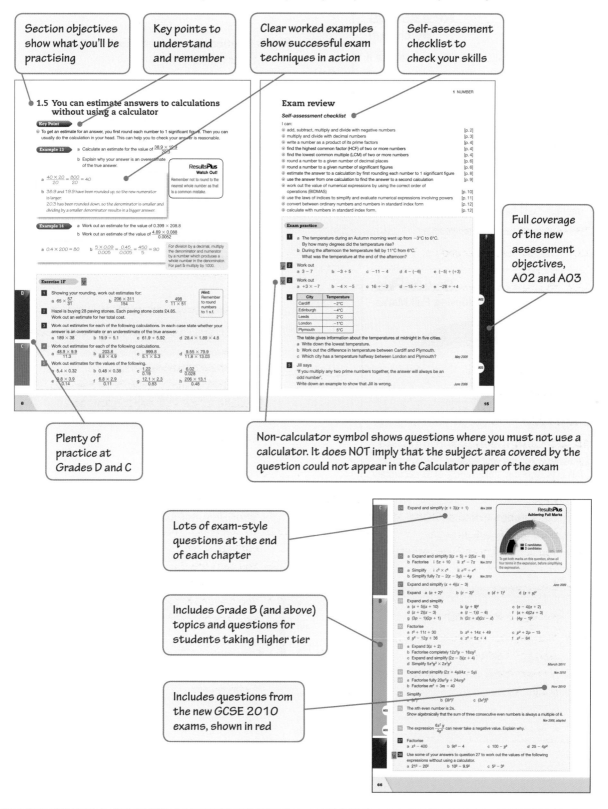

Full coverage of the new assessment objectives, AO2 and AO3

Plenty of practice at Grades D and C

Non-calculator symbol shows questions where you must not use a calculator. It does NOT imply that the subject area covered by the question could not appear in the Calculator paper of the exam

Lots of exam-style questions at the end of each chapter

Includes Grade B (and above) topics and questions for students taking Higher tier

Includes questions from the new GCSE 2010 exams, shown in red

ResultsPlus

ResultsPlus features throughout the book combine exam performance data with examiner insight to give you more information on how to succeed.

Results**Plus**
Watch Out!

Students sometimes forget that the factors of a number always include 1 and the number itself.

Avoid the common pitfalls and misconceptions that examiners frequently see students make.

Results**Plus**
Exam Tip

To decrease a quantity, the multiplier will be less than 1.

Exam techniques, advice, useful checks and methods to help remember key facts.

Results**Plus**
Achieving Full Marks

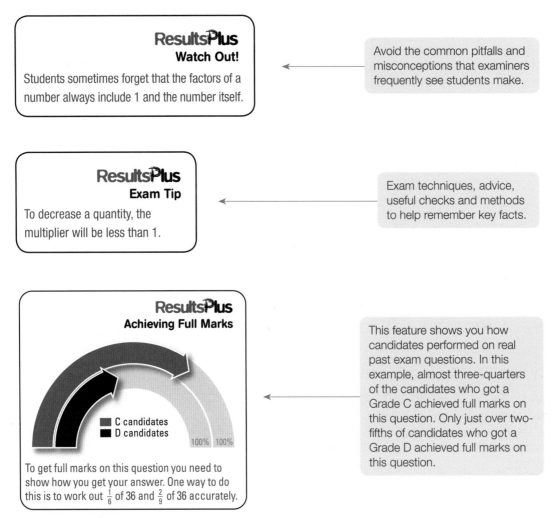

■ C candidates
■ D candidates

100%   100%

To get full marks on this question you need to show how you get your answer. One way to do this is to work out $\frac{1}{6}$ of 36 and $\frac{2}{9}$ of 36 accurately.

This feature shows you how candidates performed on real past exam questions. In this example, almost three-quarters of the candidates who got a Grade C achieved full marks on this question. Only just over two-fifths of candidates who got a Grade D achieved full marks on this question.

If you have taken Edexcel GCSE Mathematics before, use your ResultsPlus report to help you focus on the areas you need:

	Analysis	Exam docs	Skills map		Select skills map:	GCSE Mathematics (1380/2381) F content	▼	

▼ Expand skills map   Show skills: All skills tested ▼

GCSE Mathematics (1380/2381) F content	Mean score	Percentage	Edexcel Ave	Key
⊟ ▲ Numbers and Algebra	93/107	87%	(59%)	▲
⊟ ▲ AO2/1 Numbers and the number system; solving numerical problems; calculations	57/65	88%	(63%)	Over 70%
⊞ ▲ AO2/1A Number	20/21	95%	(81%)	●
⊞ ▲ AO2/1B Calculations	6/6	100%	(38%)	35 - 70%
⊞ ▲ AO2/1C Powers and indices	2/2	100%	(69%)	■
⊞ ▲ AO2/1D Fractions	1/1	100%	(88%)	Under 35%
⊟ ● AO2/1E Calculations with fractions	6/11	55%	(45%)	
▲ Work out the fraction of quantities	2/2	100%	(61%)	Untested
▲ Write equivalent fractions to a given fraction	2/2	100%	(77%)	
● Calculate with fractions	2/4	50%	(33%)	
■ Add and subtract fractions when one denominator is a multiple of another	0/2	0%	(23%)	
■ Multiply and divide fractions: no mixed numbers	0/1	0%	(42%)	
⊞ ▲ AO2/1F Decimals and percentages	6/8	75%	(57%)	

Preparation for the exam

Questions in the exam will test the **new assessment objectives**:

Assessment objective	What it is	What this means	Range of marks in the exam
AO1	Recall and use your knowledge of the prescribed content	Standard questions testing your knowledge of each topic	45–55%
AO2	Select and apply mathematical methods in a range of contexts	Deciding what method you need to use to get to the correct solution to a problem	25–35%
AO3	Interpret and analyse problems and generate strategies to solve them	Deciding how to solve a problem and explaining why	15–25%

This book has hundreds of practice questions on all the assessment objectives.

AO1 questions

Every question in the exams will test AO1, either as a standalone question or embedded within an AO2 or AO3 question. Likewise, all the questions in this book give you practice at AO1.

What does an AO2 question look like?

7   An MP3 player usually costs £130. In a sale all prices are reduced by $\frac{2}{5}$.
     Work out the sale price of the MP3 player. ◄

> You need to read and understand the question. Then decide what method to use to get the correct answer.

What does an AO3 question look like?

6   Ben says that an increase of 40% followed by an increase of 20% is the same as an increase of 60%.
     Is Ben correct? You must give a reason for your answer.

> Here you need to read and analyse the question. Then use your maths knowledge to solve the problem.

Functional elements

Some questions in the exam will test your ability to apply maths in everyday, real life situations. The number of marks for functional elements depends on which tier you are taking:

GCSE tier	Range of marks in the exam
Foundation	30–40%
Higher	20–30%

3   Paul makes green paint by mixing 2 parts of yellow paint with 3 parts of blue paint.
     Paul has 500 ml of yellow paint and 1 litre of blue paint.
     What is the maximum amount of green paint that Paul can make? ◄

> This question has **functional elements**.

Quality of written communication (QWC)

There will also be marks for showing your working properly and explaining clearly. You need to
- use the correct mathematical notation and vocabulary to show you can communicate effectively
- organise the relevant information logically.

> The asterisk tells you that this is a **QWC** question.

*16   Rachael is a sales manager.
     Last year, Rachael had a 10% pay rise. This year, she had a 5% pay rise.
     Ziggy says, 'Rachael has had a 15% pay rise over the two years.'
     Is Ziggy correct? Explain your answer.

Geometric shapes

Angles

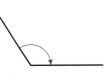

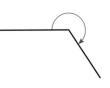

Acute angle
Less than a $\frac{1}{4}$ turn

Obtuse angle
More than a $\frac{1}{4}$ turn

Reflex angle
More than a $\frac{1}{2}$ turn

Right angle
$\frac{1}{4}$ turn

Triangles

Equilateral triangle

All three sides are
the same length.
All three angles are 60°.

Isosceles triangle

Two of the sides are the
same length.
Two of the angles are equal.

Scalene triangle

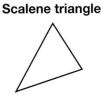

None of the sides or
angles are equal.

Right-angled triangle

One of the angles is 90°.

Obtuse-angled triangle

One of the angles is obtuse
(more than 90°)

Acute-angled triangle

All of the angles are acute
(less than 90°).

Quadrilaterals

Square

- All sides are the same length.
- All angles are 90°.
- The diagonals are equal in length and **bisect** each other at right angles.
- It has 4 lines of reflection symmetry.
- It has rotational symmetry of order 4.

Rectangle

- Opposite sides are the same length.
- All angles are 90°.
- The diagonals are equal in length and bisect each other.
- It has 2 lines of reflection symmetry.
- It has rotational symmetry of order 2.

Parallelogram

- Opposite sides are parallel and are the same length.
- The diagonals bisect each other.
- It has no lines of reflection symmetry.
- It has rotational symmetry of order 2.

Trapezium

- One pair of opposite sides are parallel.

Kite

- Two pairs of **adjacent** sides are equal.
- One pair of opposite angles are equal.
- Diagonals cross each other at right angles.
- It has 1 line of reflection symmetry.

Rhombus

- All sides are the same length.
- Opposite angles are equal.
- Diagonals bisect each other at right angles.
- It has 2 lines of reflection symmetry.
- It has rotational symmetry of order 2.

Regular polygons

Equilateral triangle (3 sides)   **Square** (4 sides)   **Pentagon** (5 sides)

Hexagon (6 sides)   **Heptagon** (7 sides)   **Octagon** (8 sides)   **Decagon** (10 sides)

Parts of a circle

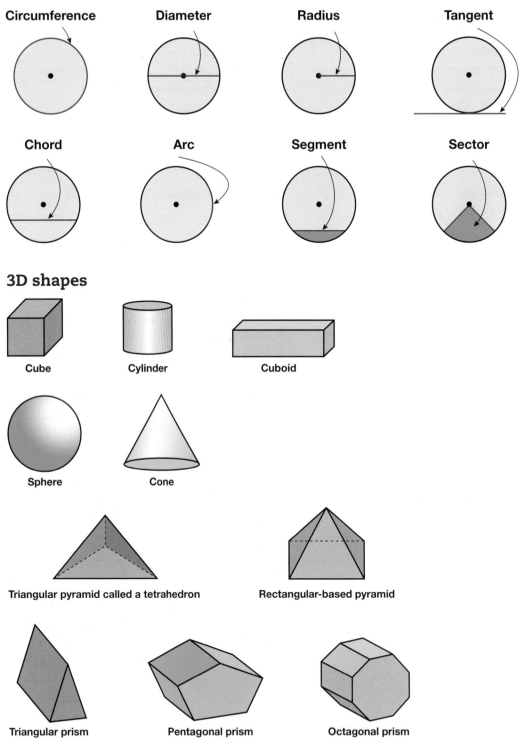

Circumference

Diameter

Radius

Tangent

Chord

Arc

Segment

Sector

3D shapes

Cube

Cylinder

Cuboid

Sphere

Cone

Triangular pyramid called a tetrahedron

Rectangular-based pyramid

Triangular prism

Pentagonal prism

Octagonal prism

Language in the exam

Here are the main instructions and other terms that you will come across in the exam.

You must show all your working...	You will lose marks if working is not shown.
Estimate...	Often means round numbers to 1 significant figure
Calculate...	Some working out is needed – so show it!
Work out OR Find...	A written or mental calculation is needed.
Write down...	Written working out is not usually required.
Give an exact value of...	No rounding or approximations.
Give your answer to an appropriate degree of accuracy...	If the numbers in the question are given to 2 decimal places, give your answer to 2 decimal places.
Give your answer in its simplest form...	Usually cancelling of a fraction or a ratio is required.
Simplify...	Algebra: collect like terms together.
Solve...	Usually means find the value of 'x' in an equation.
Factorise...	Put in brackets with common factors outside the brackets.
Expand...	Multiply out.
Measure...	Use a ruler or a protractor to accurately measure lengths or angles.
Draw an accurate diagram...	Use ruler and protractor; lengths must be exact, angles must be accurate.
Construct, using ruler and compasses...	The ruler is to be used as a straight edge and compasses must be used to draw arcs. Do not erase construction lines.
Sketch...	An accurate drawing is not required; freehand drawing will be accepted.
Diagram NOT accurately drawn...	Don't measure angles or sides.
Give reasons for your answer OR Explain why...	Worded explanations are required referring to the theory used.
Use your (the) graph...	Read values from your graph and use them.
Describe fully...	Usually transformations: • Reflection in a line (2 marks) • Rotation through an angle about a point (3 marks) • Enlargement of scale factor about a point (3 marks)
Give a reason for your answer...	Usually in angle questions, a written reason is required (e.g. angles in a triangle add up to 180°, or alternate angles etc.)

Geometry exam questions

In geometry questions, including QWC questions, you can be asked to give reasons for your answer or proof. This is often related to angles problems. In the exam you need to communicate clearly how you have used geometrical properties in solving the problem.

Here are some examples of clear statements:

Lines	Vertically opposite angles are equal.
	Angles on a straight line add up to 180°
	Angles at a point add up to 360°
Triangles and quadrilaterals	Angles in a triangle add up to 180°
	Base angles of an isosceles triangle are equal.
	Angles in an equilateral triangle are equal.
	Angles in a quadrilateral add up to 360°
	An exterior angle (of a triangle) is equal to the sum of the internal opposite angles.
Polygons	Exterior angles of a polygon add up to 360°.
	The interior and exterior angle of any polygon add up to 180°.
Parallel lines	Alternate angles are equal.
	Corresponding angles are equal.
	Allied angles add up to 180°.

Formulae sheets

Formulae: Foundation Tier

You must not write on this formulae page.
Anything you write on this formulae page will gain NO credit.

Area of trapezium $= \frac{1}{2}(a + b)h$

Volume of a prism $=$ area of cross section $\times$ length

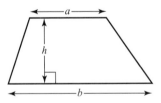

Formulae sheets

Formulae: Higher Tier

You must not write on this formulae page.
Anything you write on this formulae page will gain NO credit.

Volume of a prism = area of cross section × length

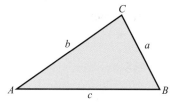

Area of trapezium = $\frac{1}{2}(a + b)h$

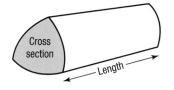

Volume of sphere = $\frac{4}{3}\pi r^3$

Surface area of sphere = $4\pi r^2$

Volume of cone = $\frac{1}{3}\pi r^2 h$

Curved surface area of cone = $\pi r l$

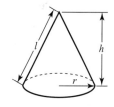

In any triangle ABC

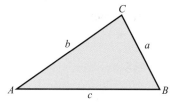

Sine Rule $\dfrac{a}{\sin A} = \dfrac{b}{\sin B} = \dfrac{c}{\sin C}$

Cosine Rule $a^2 = b^2 + c^2 - 2bc \cos A$

Area of triangle = $\frac{1}{2}ab \sin C$

The Quadratic Equation

The solutions of $ax^2 + bx + c = 0$
where $a \neq 0$, are given by

$$x = \frac{-b \pm \sqrt{(b^2 - 4ac)}}{2a}$$

1 NUMBER

1.1 You can calculate with negative numbers

Key Points

- Adding a negative number is the same as subtracting a positive number.
- Subtracting a negative number is the same as adding a positive number.
- The rules for multiplying and dividing are:
  - if the signs are the same the result is positive
  - if the signs are different the result is negative.

Example 1 Work out

a $-3 - -2$ b $4 + -2$

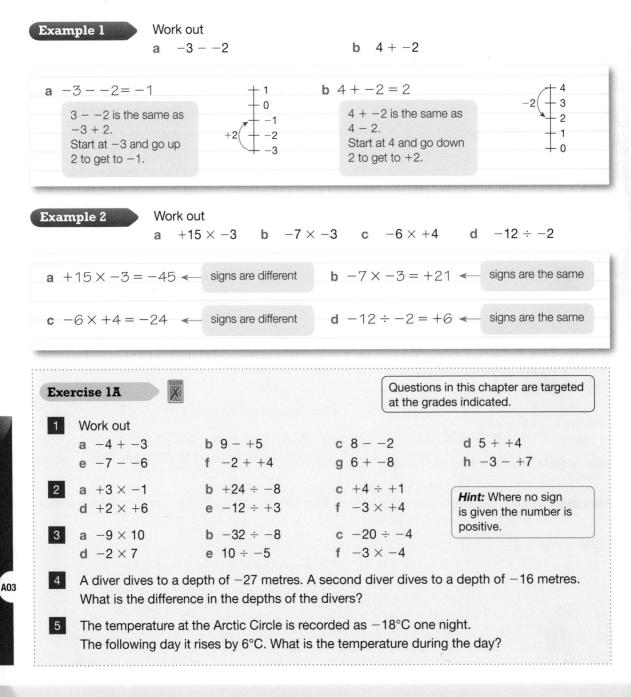

a $-3 - -2 = -1$

$3 - -2$ is the same as $-3 + 2$.
Start at -3 and go up 2 to get to -1.

b $4 + -2 = 2$

$4 + -2$ is the same as $4 - 2$.
Start at 4 and go down 2 to get to $+2$.

Example 2 Work out

a $+15 \times -3$ b -7×-3 c $-6 \times +4$ d $-12 \div -2$

a $+15 \times -3 = -45$ ← signs are different   b $-7 \times -3 = +21$ ← signs are the same

c $-6 \times +4 = -24$ ← signs are different   d $-12 \div -2 = +6$ ← signs are the same

Exercise 1A

Questions in this chapter are targeted at the grades indicated.

1 Work out
   a $-4 + -3$ b $9 - +5$ c $8 - -2$ d $5 + +4$
   e $-7 - -6$ f $-2 + +4$ g $6 + -8$ h $-3 - +7$

2 a $+3 \times -1$ b $+24 \div -8$ c $+4 \div +1$
   d $+2 \times +6$ e $-12 \div +3$ f $-3 \times +4$

   Hint: Where no sign is given the number is positive.

3 a -9×10 b $-32 \div -8$ c $-20 \div -4$
   d -2×7 e $10 \div -5$ f -3×-4

4 A diver dives to a depth of -27 metres. A second diver dives to a depth of -16 metres. What is the difference in the depths of the divers?

5 The temperature at the Arctic Circle is recorded as $-18°C$ one night. The following day it rises by $6°C$. What is the temperature during the day?

F

A03

1.2 You can multiply and divide decimals

Key Points

○ When multiplying, the total number of decimal places in the answer is the same as the total number of the decimal places in the question.

○ To divide decimals, multiply both numbers by 10, 100, 1000 etc. until you are dividing by a whole number.

Example 3 Work out 7.59×3.8.

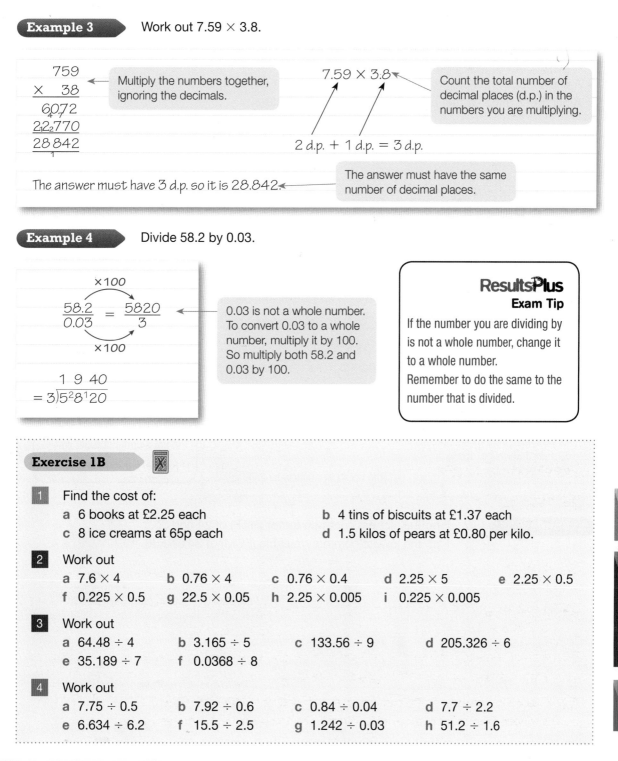

```
    759
×    38
   6072
  22770
  28842
```

Multiply the numbers together, ignoring the decimals.

7.59×3.8

Count the total number of decimal places (d.p.) in the numbers you are multiplying.

2 d.p. + 1 d.p. = 3 d.p.

The answer must have 3 d.p. so it is 28.842.

The answer must have the same number of decimal places.

Example 4 Divide 58.2 by 0.03.

$$\frac{58.2}{0.03} = \frac{5820}{3}$$

×100 (top and bottom)

0.03 is not a whole number. To convert 0.03 to a whole number, multiply it by 100. So multiply both 58.2 and 0.03 by 100.

```
        1 9 4 0
= 3)5²8¹20
```

ResultsPlus
Exam Tip

If the number you are dividing by is not a whole number, change it to a whole number. Remember to do the same to the number that is divided.

Exercise 1B

1 Find the cost of:
   a 6 books at £2.25 each
   b 4 tins of biscuits at £1.37 each
   c 8 ice creams at 65p each
   d 1.5 kilos of pears at £0.80 per kilo.

2 Work out
   a 7.6×4 b 0.76×4 c 0.76×0.4 d 2.25×5 e 2.25×0.5
   f 0.225×0.5 g 22.5×0.05 h 2.25×0.005 i 0.225×0.005

3 Work out
   a $64.48 \div 4$ b $3.165 \div 5$ c $133.56 \div 9$ d $205.326 \div 6$
   e $35.189 \div 7$ f $0.0368 \div 8$

4 Work out
   a $7.75 \div 0.5$ b $7.92 \div 0.6$ c $0.84 \div 0.04$ d $7.7 \div 2.2$
   e $6.634 \div 6.2$ f $15.5 \div 2.5$ g $1.242 \div 0.03$ h $51.2 \div 1.6$

G

F

E

1.3 You can understand and use factors, multiples and prime numbers

Key Points

- The factors of a number are whole numbers that divide exactly into the number. They include 1 and the number itself.
- The highest common factor (HCF) is the highest factor that is common to two or more numbers.
- Multiples of a number are the results of multiplying the number by a positive whole number.
- The lowest common multiple (LCM) is the lowest multiple that is common to two or more numbers.
- A prime number is a whole number greater than 1 whose only factors are 1 and the number itself.
- A prime factor is a factor that is also a prime number. For example, the prime factors of 18 are 2 and 3.
- A number can be written as a product of its prime factors.

Example 5   Find the common factors of 12 and 18.

The factors of 12 are 1, 2, 3, 4, 6, 12.
The factors of 18 are 1, 2, 3, 6, 9, 18.
1, 2, 3 and 6 are all factors of both 12 and 18.
They are the common factors of 12 and 18.

> **ResultsPlus**
> **Watch Out!**
> Students sometimes forget that the factors of a number always include 1 and the number itself.

Example 6   Write 36 as a product of its prime factors.

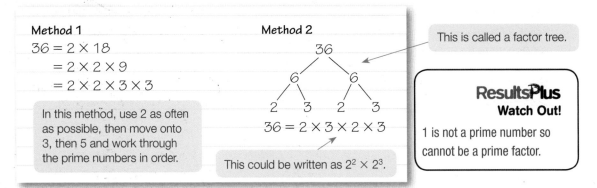

Method 1
36 = 2 × 18
   = 2 × 2 × 9
   = 2 × 2 × 3 × 3

In this method, use 2 as often as possible, then move onto 3, then 5 and work through the prime numbers in order.

Method 2

36 = 2 × 3 × 2 × 3

This could be written as $2^2 \times 2^3$.

> This is called a factor tree.

> **ResultsPlus**
> **Watch Out!**
> 1 is not a prime number so cannot be a prime factor.

Example 7   a   Find the highest common factor (HCF) of 24 and 36.
   b   Find the lowest common multiple (LCM) of 24 and 36.

a 24 = 2 × 2 × 2 × 3
   36 = 2 × 2 × 3 × 3
   2 × 2 × 3 = 12
   12 is the HCF

> Write each number in prime factor form.
> Pick out the factors common to both numbers.

b 24: 24, 48, 72, 96, 120
   36: 36, 72, 108
   The LCM of 24 and 36 is 72.

> Write a list of multiples for each number. The LCM is the lowest number that appears in both lists.

Exercise 1C

1 Find the common factors of:

a 4 and 6
b 10 and 15
c 24 and 36
d 10, 30 and 60
e 16 and 24
f 15 and 40
g 12 and 28
h 30 and 42
i 18 and 25.

2 Find all the prime factors of the following numbers.

a 30
b 25
c 42
d 39
e 105

3 Write these numbers as products of their prime factors.

a 45
b 36
c 28
d 80
e 72

4 Find the highest common factor of:

a 4 and 8
b 9 and 12
c 18 and 24
d 14 and 30
e 21 and 35.

5 Find the lowest common multiple of:

a 3 and 4
b 4 and 6
c 12 and 15
d 36 and 16
e 50 and 85.

6 Find the LCM and HCF of:

a 12 and 18
b 120 and 180
c 24 and 84
d 91 and 130
e 72 and 96
f 40 and 60.

7 Two lighthouses off the Cornish coast can be recognised by the different intervals between their flashes. One flashes every 24 seconds and the other every 40 seconds. A ship's captain sees them flash at the same time. How long will it be before this happens again?

8 The light on a motorway service vehicle flashes every 20 seconds. The light on a tractor flashes every 10 seconds. As they pass each other on a road, the lights flash together. How long will it be before this happens again?

9 The number 48 can be written in the form $2^n \times 3$. Find the value of n.

10 The number 84 can be written in the form $2^n \times m \times p$ where n, m and p are prime numbers. Find the values of n, m and p.

11 Burgers come in boxes of 8. Buns come in packets of 6.
What is the smallest number of boxes of burgers and packets of buns that Mrs Moore must buy if she wants to ensure that there is a bun for every burger?

12 Bertrand's theorem states that 'Between any two numbers n and $2n$, there always lies at least one prime number, providing n is bigger than 1'. Show that Bertrand's theorem is true:

a for $n = 10$
b for $n = 20$
c for $n = 34$.

* 13 Sally says that if you multiply two prime numbers then you will always get an odd number. Is Sally correct? Give a reason for your answer.

F

D

C

AO2

AO2

B

A

1.4 You can round a number to a given number of decimal places or significant figures

Key Points

● To round (or correct) to a given number of decimal places (d.p.), count that number of decimal places from the decimal point. Look at the next digit along. If it is 5 or more, you need to round up. If it is less than 5, round down.

● To round numbers to a given number of significant figures, count that number of digits from the first non-zero digit. If the next digit is 5 or more then you round up. Otherwise, you round down.

Example 8   Round the following numbers to one decimal place (1 d.p.).
    a 25.27   b 25.72   c 25.558

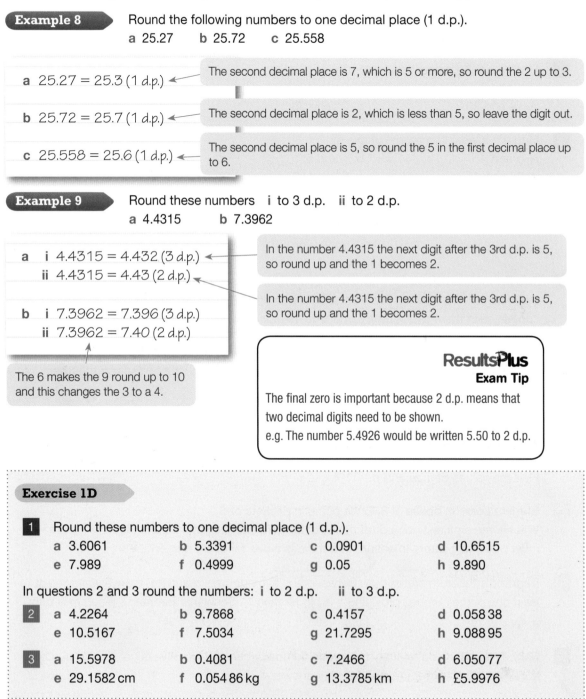

a 25.27 = 25.3 (1 d.p.)   ← The second decimal place is 7, which is 5 or more, so round the 2 up to 3.

b 25.72 = 25.7 (1 d.p.)   ← The second decimal place is 2, which is less than 5, so leave the digit out.

c 25.558 = 25.6 (1 d.p.) ← The second decimal place is 5, so round the 5 in the first decimal place up to 6.

Example 9   Round these numbers i to 3 d.p.   ii to 2 d.p.
    a 4.4315   b 7.3962

a   i 4.4315 = 4.432 (3 d.p.)   ← In the number 4.4315 the next digit after the 3rd d.p. is 5, so round up and the 1 becomes 2.
    ii 4.4315 = 4.43 (2 d.p.)

b   i 7.3962 = 7.396 (3 d.p.)   In the number 4.4315 the next digit after the 3rd d.p. is 5, so round up and the 1 becomes 2.
    ii 7.3962 = 7.40 (2 d.p.)

The 6 makes the 9 round up to 10 and this changes the 3 to a 4.

ResultsPlus
Exam Tip

The final zero is important because 2 d.p. means that two decimal digits need to be shown.
e.g. The number 5.4926 would be written 5.50 to 2 d.p.

Exercise 1D

1 Round these numbers to one decimal place (1 d.p.).
    a 3.6061   b 5.3391   c 0.0901   d 10.6515
    e 7.989   f 0.4999   g 0.05   h 9.890

In questions 2 and 3 round the numbers: i to 2 d.p.   ii to 3 d.p.

2 a 4.2264   b 9.7868   c 0.4157   d 0.058 38
       e 10.5167   f 7.5034   g 21.7295   h 9.088 95

3 a 15.5978   b 0.4081   c 7.2466   d 6.050 77
       e 29.1582 cm   f 0.054 86 kg   g 13.3785 km   h £5.9976

F

E

Example 10 Write these numbers to 1 significant figure (1 s.f.).
a 32   b 452   c 0.0878

a 32 to 1 significant figure is 30.

The first digit is in the tens column, so you need to round to the nearest ten. 32 to the nearest ten is 30.

b 452 to 1 significant figure is 500.

The first digit is in the hundreds column, so round to the nearest hundred.

c 0.0878 to 1 significant figure is 0.09.

The first non-zero digit is in the hundredths column, so round to the nearest hundredth.

Example 11 Write the following numbers correct to:
a 3 significant figures   b 2 significant figures.
i 2788   ii 4.7084   iii 0.006 675

a i 2790 (3 s.f.)   ii 4.71 (3 s.f.)   iii 0.006 68 (3 s.f.)

b i 2800 (2 s.f.)   ii 4.7 (2 s.f.)   iii 0.0067 (2 s.f.)

Example 12 Write the following numbers correct to 2 significant figures.
a 7995   b 4.996   c 0.000 99

a 8000 (2 s.f.)

b 5.0 (2 s.f.)

Note the difference between 5 (1 significant figure) and 5.0 (2 significant figures).

c 0.0010 (2 s.f.)

ResultsPlus
Exam Tip

Although there may only be one non-zero figure in your answer, the numbers could still be correct to 2 significant figures.

Exercise 1E

1   Write down these numbers to 1 significant figure (1 s.f.).
    a 41   b 709   c 287   d 0.348   e 21 899
    f 0.007 41   g 973   h 4.6   i 13.309   j 19.07

2   Round these numbers to 2 significant figures (2 s.f.).
    a 0.061 78   b 0.1649   c 96.303   d 41.475
    e 734.56   f 0.079 47   g 5.6853   h 586.47

3   Round these numbers to 3 significant figures (3 s.f.).
    a 0.014 84   b 2222.8   c 76.249   d 0.3798
    e 8.3846   f 35.959   g 187.418   h 0.066 63
    i 218 736   j 3 989 375   k 307 096   l 25 555

4   The fastest lap time in a motor race Grand Prix was 83.345 seconds.
    Write this time to 3 significant figures.

E

1.5 You can estimate answers to calculations without using a calculator

Key Point

◉ To get an estimate for an answer, you first round each number to 1 significant figure. Then you can usually do the calculation in your head. This can help you to check your answer is reasonable.

Example 13

a Calculate an estimate for the value of $\dfrac{38.9 \times 19.9}{20.3}$

b Explain why your answer is an overestimate of the true answer.

a $\dfrac{40 \times 20}{20} = \dfrac{800}{20} = 40$

b 38.9 and 19.9 have been rounded up, so the new numerator is larger.
20.3 has been rounded down, so the denominator is smaller and dividing by a smaller denominator results in a bigger answer.

> **ResultsPlus**
> **Watch Out!**
> Remember not to round to the nearest whole number as that is a common mistake.

Example 14

a Work out an estimate for the value of 0.399×208.8

b Work out an estimate of the value of $\dfrac{4.89 \times 0.088}{0.0052}$

a $0.4 \times 200 = 80$

b $\dfrac{5 \times 0.09}{0.005} = \dfrac{0.45}{0.005} = \dfrac{450}{5} = 90$

> For division by a decimal, multiply the denominator and numerator by a number which produces a whole number in the denominator. For part **b** multiply by 1000.

Exercise 1F

1. Showing your rounding, work out estimates for:

   a $65 \times \dfrac{57}{31}$

   b $\dfrac{206 \times 311}{154}$

   c $\dfrac{498}{11 \times 51}$

   > **Hint:** Remember to round numbers to 1 s.f.

2. Hazel is buying 28 paving stones. Each paving stone costs £4.85. Work out an estimate for her total cost.

3. Work out estimates for each of the following calculations. In each case state whether your answer is an overestimate or an underestimate of the true answer.

   a 189×38

   b $19.9 \div 5.1$

   c $61.9 \div 5.92$

   d $28.4 \times 1.89 \times 4.8$

4. Work out estimates for each of the following calculations.

   a $\dfrac{48.9 \times 9.9}{11.3}$

   b $\dfrac{203.8}{9.8 \times 4.9}$

   c $\dfrac{999.8}{5.1 \times 5.3}$

   d $\dfrac{9.55 \times 79.9}{11.8 \times 13.03}$

5. Work out estimates for the values of the following.

   a 5.4×0.32

   b 0.48×0.38

   c $\dfrac{1.22}{0.19}$

   d $\dfrac{6.02}{0.028}$

   e $\dfrac{9.8 \times 3.9}{0.14}$

   f $\dfrac{6.8 \times 2.9}{0.11}$

   g $\dfrac{12.1 \times 2.3}{0.83}$

   h $\dfrac{206 \times 13.1}{0.48}$

1.6 You can use one calculation to find the answer to another

◉ The answer to one calculation can often be used to find the answer to a second calculation.

Example 15 Given that $3.8 \times 5.2 = 19.76$, find the values of each of the following.
  a 38×5.2 b 380×0.52

$38 = 3.8 \times 10$

a 38×5.2 $= 3.8 \times 10 \times 5.2$ ◄
     $= (3.8 \times 5.2) \times 10$ ◄ Rearrange the terms and substitute the known answer.
     $= 19.76 \times 10$
     $= 197.6$ ◄ You can check the answer by estimating. 38×5.2 is roughly 40×5, which is 200.

$380 = 3.8 \times 100$ and $0.52 = 5.2 \div 10$

b $380 \times 0.52 = 3.8 \times 100 \times 5.2 \div 10$ ◄
     $= (3.8 \times 5.2) \times 100 \div 10$ ◄ Rearrange the terms and substitute the known answer.
     $= 19.76 \times 10$
     $= 197.6$ ◄ You can check the answer by estimating. 380×0.52 is roughly 400×0.5, which is 200.

Example 16 Given that $\dfrac{40.8}{8.5} = 4.8$, find the value of each of the following.
  a $\dfrac{408}{8.5}$ b $\dfrac{40.8}{85}$

$408 = 40.8 \times 10$

a $\dfrac{408}{8.5}$ $= \dfrac{40.8 \times 10}{8.5}$ ◄
     Rearrange the terms and substitute the known answer.
     $= \left(\dfrac{40.8}{8.5}\right) \times 10$ ◄
     You can check the answer by estimating. $408 \div 8.5$ is roughly $400 \div 8$, which is 50.
     $= 4.8 \times 10$
     $= 48$ ◄

$85 = 8.5 \times 10$

b $\dfrac{40.8}{85}$ $= \dfrac{40.8}{8.5 \times 10}$ ◄
     Rearrange the terms and substitute the known answer. Multiplying the bottom number by 10 is the same as dividing the top number by 10.
     $= \left(\dfrac{40.8}{8.5}\right) \div 10$ ◄
     $= 4.8 \div 10$
     $= 0.48$ ◄ You can check the answer by estimating. $40.8 \div 85$ is roughly $40 \div 80$, which is 0.5.

Exercise 1G

1 Given that $6.4 \times 2.8 = 17.92$, work out   a 64×28 b 640×2.8 c 0.64×28

2 Given that $\dfrac{18.3}{1.25} = 14.64$, work out   a $\dfrac{183}{1.25}$ b $\dfrac{1.83}{1.25}$ c $\dfrac{0.183}{1.25}$

3 Given that $13.2 \times 5.5 = 72.6$, work out
    a 132×5.5 b 1.32×0.55 c 0.132×55 d $\dfrac{72.6}{13.2}$

4 Given that $\dfrac{30.4}{4.75} = 6.4$, work out   a $\dfrac{30.4}{47.5}$ b $\dfrac{3.04}{4.75}$ c $\dfrac{304}{4.75}$ d $\dfrac{30.4}{6.4}$

D

1.7 You understand the order of operations

Key Points

- **BIDMAS** gives the order in which operations should be carried out.

- Remember that B I D M A S stands for

  B rackets — If there are brackets, work out the value of the expression inside the brackets first.

  I ndices — Indices include powers, square roots and cube roots.

  D ivide
  M ultiply — If there are no brackets, do dividing and multiplying before adding and subtracting, no matter where they come in the expression.

  A dd
  S ubtract — If an expression has only adding and subtracting then work it out from left to right.

Example 17   Work out $3 + 2 \times 5 - 1$

$$3 + 2 \times 5 - 1 = 3 + 10 - 1$$
$$= 13 - 1$$
$$= 12$$

There are no Brackets, Indices or Divide, so start with Multiply, then Add, then Subtract.

Example 18   Work out $(10 + 2)^2 - 5 \times 3^2$

$$(10 + 2)^2 - 5 \times 3^2 = 12^2 - 5 \times 3^2$$
$$= 144 - 5 \times 9$$
$$= 144 - 45$$
$$= 99$$

Brackets first, then Indices, Multiply, and finally Subtract.

Exercise 1H

D

1 Work out
  a $5 \times (2 + 3)$ b $5 \times 2 + 3$ c $20 \div 4 + 1$ d $20 \div (4 + 1)$
  e $(6 + 4) \div -2$ f $6 + 4 \div 2$ g $24 \div (6 - 2)$ h $24 \div 6 - 2$
  i $7 - (4 + 2)$ j $7 - 4 + 2$ k $5 \times 4 - 2 \times 3$ l $28 - 4 \times -6$
  m $14 + 3 \times 6$ n $6 + 3 \times 5 - 12 \div 2$ o $25 - 5 \times 4 + 3$ p $(15 - 5) \times (4 + 3)$

2 Work out
  a $(3 + 4)^2$ b $3^2 + 4^2$ c $3 \times (4 + 5)^2$ d $3 \times 4^2 + 3 \times 5^2$
  e $2 \times (4 + 2)^2$ f $3 \times \sqrt{25} + 2 \times 3^3$ g $\dfrac{(2 + 5)^2}{3^2 - 2}$ h $\dfrac{5^2 - 2^2}{-3}$

B

3 Work out
  a $(2 + 3)^3 \div \sqrt{25}$ b $((15 - 5) \times 4) \div ((2 + 3) \times 2)$
  c $2^3 + 6^2 \div \sqrt{9} - 4 \times 3$ d $(\sqrt[3]{-27} - 2)^2 + \sqrt{3^2 \times 2^2}$

1.8 You understand the index laws

Key Points

◉ The n in a^n is called a power or an index. It tells you how many times the given number must be multiplied by itself.

◉ The laws of indices are:

$a^m \times a^n = a^{m+n}$　　To multiply two powers of the same number add the indices.

$a^m \div a^n = a^{m-n}$　　To divide two powers of the same number subtract the indices.

$(a^m)^n = a^{m \times n}$　　To raise a power to a further power multiply the indices together.

Example 19　Work out　**a** 3^4　**b** 2^6

a $3^4 = 3 \times 3 \times 3 \times 3 = 81$
b $2^6 = 2 \times 2 \times 2 \times 2 \times 2 \times 2 = 64$

Results Plus
Watch Out!

Remember that 3^4 means $3 \times 3 \times 3 \times 3$.
It does not mean 3×4.

Example 20　Write each expression as a power of 5.　**a** $5^6 \times 5^4$　**b** $5^{12} \div 5^4$　**c** $(5^3)^2$

a $5^6 \times 5^4 = 5^{4+6} = 5^{10}$ ←　　　Use the index law　$a^m \times a^n = a^{m+n}$

b $5^{12} \div 5^4 = 5^{12-4} = 5^8$ ←　　　Use the index law　$a^m \div a^n = a^{m-n}$

c $(5^3)^2 = 5^{3 \times 2} = 5^6$ ←　　　Use the index law　$(a^m)^n = a^{m \times n}$

Example 21　Work out $\dfrac{4^7 \times 4}{4^5}$

$\dfrac{4^7 \times 4}{4^5} = \dfrac{4^7 \times 4^1}{4^5}$

Simplify the top of the fraction, add 7 and 1.

$= \dfrac{4^8}{4^5}$

$= 4^3$

$= 4 \times 4 \times 4 = 64$

As the question asks you to 'Work out', the final answer must be a number.

Results Plus
Watch Out!

Remember that 4 is the same as 4^1.

Exercise 1I

1 Write as a power of a single number

　a $6^5 \times 6^7$　　**b** $4^7 \div 4^2$　　**c** $(7^2)^3$　　**d** $5^9 \div 5^3$　　**e** $3^8 \times 3^2$

　f $\dfrac{3^3 \times 3^5}{3^4}$　**g** $\dfrac{5^6 \times 5^7}{5^4}$　**h** $\dfrac{2^8 \times 2^5}{2^7}$　**i** $\dfrac{6^{15}}{6 \times 6^9}$　**j** $\dfrac{4^2 \times 4^7}{4^3 \times 4^4}$

2 Work out

　a $10^2 \times 10^3$　**b** $5^7 \div 5^4$　　**c** $(2^3)^2$　　**d** $3^4 \div 3^2$　　**e** 4×4^2

　f $\dfrac{3^3 \times 3^5}{3^6}$　**g** $\dfrac{2^6 \times 2^2}{2^4}$　**h** $\dfrac{4^7}{4 \times 4^4}$　**i** $\dfrac{10^5 \times 10^6}{10^7}$　**j** $\dfrac{7^8 \times 7}{7^3 \times 7^4}$

3 Find out the value of n in the following.

　a $3^n \div 3^2 = 3^3$　**b** $8^5 \div 8^n = 8^2$　**c** $2^5 \times 2^n = 2^{10}$　**d** $3^n \times 3^5 = 3^9$　**e** $2^6 \times 2^3 = 2^n$

　f $40 = 5 \times 2^n$　**g** $32 = 2^n$　**h** $20 = 2^n \times 5$　**i** $48 = 3 \times 2^n$　**j** $54 = 2 \times 3^n$

C

B

1.9 You can understand and use numbers written in standard form

Key Points

- Standard form is used to represent very large (or very small) numbers.
  A number is in standard form when it is in the form $a \times 10^n$ where $1 \leqslant a < 10$ and n is a whole number. For large numbers n is positive. For small numbers n is negative.

- A number in standard form looks like this.

$$6.7 \times 10^4$$

This part is written as a number between 1 and 10.

This part is written as a power of 10.

- These numbers are all in standard form: 4.5×10^2, 9×10^{-8}, 1.2657×10^6.

- These numbers are not in standard form because the first number is not between 1 and 10: 67×10^9, 0.087×10^3.

- It is often easier to multiply and divide very large or very small numbers, or estimate a calculation, if the numbers are written in standard form.

- To input numbers in standard form into your calculator, use the $\boxed{10^x}$ or $\boxed{\text{EXP}}$ key.
  To enter 4.5×10^7 press the keys $\boxed{4}$ $\boxed{\cdot}$ $\boxed{5}$ $\boxed{\times}$ $\boxed{10^x}$ $\boxed{7}$.

Example 22 Write these numbers in standard form.

    a 50 000   **b** 34 600 000   **c** 682.5

a $50\,000 = 5 \times 10\,000$
$\qquad\quad = 5 \times 10^4$

b $34\,600\,000 = 3.46 \times 10\,000\,000$ ← Use 3.46 not 34.6 or 346 as 3.46 is between 1 and 10.
$\qquad\qquad\quad = 3.46 \times 10^7$

c $682.5 = 6.825 \times 100$
$\qquad\quad = 6.825 \times 10^2$

ResultsPlus
Exam Tip

Remember for large numbers the power of 10 is positive.

Example 23 Write as an ordinary number

    a 8.1×10^5 **b** 6×10^8

a $8.1 \times 10^5 = 8.1 \times 100\,000$ ← Multiply 8.1 by 10 five times.
$\qquad\qquad\; = 810\,000$

b $6 \times 10^8 = 6 \times 100\,000\,000$ ← Multiply 6 by 10 eight times.
$\qquad\qquad = 600\,000\,000$

B

Exercise 1J

1. Write these numbers in standard form.
   a 700 000   b 600   c 2000   d 900 000 000   e 80 000
   f 43 000   g 561 000   h 56   i 34.7   j 60

2. Write these as ordinary numbers.
   a 6×10^5 b 1×10^4 c 8×10^5 d 3×10^8 e 7×10^1
   f 3.96×10^4 g 6.8×10^7 h 8.02×10^3 i 5.7×10^1 j 9.23×10^0

3. In 2008 there were approximately 7 000 000 000 people in the world. Write this number in standard form.

Example 24   Write these in standard form.
a 0.000 000 006   b 0.000 56

a $0.000\,000\,006 = 6 \div 10^9$ Dividing by 10 nine times gives 0.000 000 006.
$= 6 \times 10^{-9}$ Dividing by 10^9 is equivalent to multiplying by 10^{-9}.

b $0.000\,56 = 5.6 \div 10^4$ Use 5.6 rather than 56 as 5.6 is between 1 and 10.
$= 5.6 \times 10^{-4}$

Example 25   Write these as ordinary numbers.
a 3×10^{-6} b 1.5×10^{-3}

a $3 \times 10^{-6} = 3 \div 10^6$ b $1.5 \times 10^{-3} = 1.5 \div 10^3$
$= 0.000\,003$ $= 0.0015$

Exercise 1K

1. Write these numbers in standard form.
   a 0.005   b 0.04   c 0.000 007   d 0.9   e 0.0008
   f 0.0047   g 0.987   h 0.000 803 4   i 0.000 15   j 0.601

2. Write these as ordinary numbers.
   a 6×10^{-5} b 8×10^{-2} c 5×10^{-7} d 3×10^{-1} e 1×10^{-8}
   f 8.43×10^{-5} g 2.01×10^{-2} h 4.2×10^{-7} i 7.854×10^{-1} j 9.4×10^{-4}

3. Write these numbers in standard form.
   a 457 000   b 0.0023   c 0.0003   d 2 356 000   e 0.782

4. Write these as ordinary numbers.
   a 4.12×10^{-4} b 3×10^3 c 2.065×10^7 d 4×10^{-6} e 3.27×10^8

5. A particle of sand has a diameter of 0.0625 mm. Write this number in standard form.

B

Example 26 Write in standard form
a 40×10^2 b 0.008×10^{-2}

a $40 \times 10^2 = 4 \times 10^1 \times 10^2$
$\qquad = 4 \times 10^{1+2}$
$\qquad = 4 \times 10^3$

Write 40 in standard form.
Use the rule $a^m \times a^n = a^{m+n}$.

b $0.008 \times 10^{-2} = 8 \times 10^{-3} \times 10^{-2}$
$\qquad = 8 \times 10^{-3+-2}$
$\qquad = 8 \times 10^{-5}$

Write 0.008 in standard form.
Use $a^m \times a^n = a^{m+n}$.

ResultsPlus
Exam Tip
The power of 10 tells you how many 0s there are.
$10^2 = 100$ 2 zeros
$10^{-2} = 0.01$ 2 zeros

Example 27 Use a calculator to work out
a $(3.4 \times 10^6) \times (7.1 \times 10^4)$
b $(4.56 \times 10^8) \div (3.2 \times 10^{-3})$

a $(3.4 \times 10^6) \times (7.1 \times 10^4)$
$\qquad = 2.414 \times 10^{11}$

Use the EXP or 10^x button on your calculator.

b $(4.56 \times 10^8) \div (3.2 \times 10^{-3})$
$\qquad = 1.425 \times 10^{11}$

ResultsPlus
Exam Tip
Include brackets here to ensure that the answer from the calculation on the top of the fraction is divided by the answer to the calculation on the bottom of the fraction.

Exercise 1L

1 Write these in standard form.
a 45×10^3 b 980×10^{-3} c 3400×10^{-2} d 186×10^{10}

2 Write these in standard form.
a 0.009×10^5 b 0.045×10^6 c 0.3708×10^{-12} d 0.006×10^{-7}

3 Some of these numbers are not in standard form. State if a number is in standard form. If a number is not in standard form then rewrite it so that it is in standard form.
a 7.8×10^4 b 890×10^6 c 13.2×10^{-5} d 0.56×10^9
e $60\,000 \times 10^{-8}$ f 8.901×10^{-7} g $0.040\,05 \times 10^{-10}$ h 9080×10^{15}

4 Write these numbers in order of size. Start with the smallest number.
6.3×10^6, 0.637×10^7, $6\,290\,000$, 63.4×10^5

5 Evaluate these expressions. Give your answers in standard form correct to 3 significant figures.
a $(3.5 \times 10^{11}) \div (6.5 \times 10^6)$ b $(1.33 \times 10^{10}) \times (4.66 \times 10^4)$
c $(3.5 \times 10^{11}) \div (6.5 \times 10^{-6})$ d $(1.33 \times 10^{-10}) \times (4.66 \times 10^4)$

B

A

Exam review

Self-assessment checklist

I can:

- add, subtract, multiply and divide with negative numbers [p. 2]
- multiply and divide with decimal numbers [p. 3]
- write a number as a product of its prime factors [p. 4]
- find the highest common factor (HCF) of two or more numbers [p. 4]
- find the lowest common multiple (LCM) of two or more numbers [p. 4]
- round a number to a given number of decimal places [p. 6]
- round a number to a given number of significant figures [p. 6]
- estimate the answer to a calculation by first rounding each number to 1 significant figure [p. 8]
- use the answer from one calculation to find the answer to a second calculation [p. 9]
- work out the value of numerical expressions by using the correct order of operations (BIDMAS) [p. 10]
- use the laws of indices to simplify and evaluate numerical expressions involving powers [p. 11]
- convert between ordinary numbers and numbers in standard index form [p. 12]
- calculate with numbers in standard index form. [p. 12]

Exam practice

1 a The temperature during an Autumn morning went up from −3°C to 6°C.
      By how many degrees did the temperature rise?
   b During the afternoon the temperature fell by 11°C from 6°C.
      What was the temperature at the end of the afternoon?

2 Work out
   a $3 - 7$ b $-3 + 5$ c $-11 - 4$ d $4 - (-6)$ e $(-5) + (+3)$

3 Work out
   a $+3 \times -7$ b -4×-5 c $16 \div -2$ d $-15 \div -3$ e $-28 \div +4$

4

City	Temperature
Cardiff	−2°C
Edinburgh	−4°C
Leeds	2°C
London	−1°C
Plymouth	5°C

The table gives information about the temperatures at midnight in five cities.
   a Write down the lowest temperature.
   b Work out the difference in temperature between Cardiff and Plymouth.
   c Which city has a temperature halfway between London and Plymouth?   *May 2009*

5 Jill says
   'If you multiply any two prime numbers together, the answer will always be an odd number'.
   Write down an example to show that Jill is wrong.   *June 2006*

F

A02

A03

6 Work out
   a 2.34×5
   b 0.24×6
   c 0.3×0.4
   d 25.6×1.6
   e $15.3 \div 3$
   f $81.4 \div 4$

7 Paul drives 175 miles to a meeting.
   His company pays him 37p for each mile.
   Work out how much the company pays Paul.
   Nov 2010

8 At midnight the temperature was $-9°C$.
   By 10 am, the temperature had risen by $8°C$.
   a Work out the temperature at 10 am.

   At midday the temperature was $5°C$.
   b Work out the difference between the temperature at midnight and the temperature at midday.

   On another day the temperature at midnight was $-7°C$, the temperature at 10 am was $-1°C$ and the temperature at midday was $3°C$.
   Jenny says that, on this day, the temperature at 10 am is halfway between the temperatures at midnight and at midday.
   c Is Jenny correct?
   You must give a reason for your answer.
   Nov 2010

9 A car travels 17.2 kilometres on 1 litre of fuel. How far will it travel on 8.5 litres of fuel?

10 Angela has £15.76.
   She buys as many bottles of drink costing £1.20 each as she can.
   How many does she buy and how much money does she have left?

11 Work out
   a $51.3 \div 0.9$
   b $0.0412 \div 0.4$
   c $30 \div 0.05$

12 Round these numbers to 1 decimal place.
   a 23.48
   b 1.7502
   c 0.3479
   d 150.03

13 Round these numbers to the number of decimal places given in brackets.
   a 7.263 (2)
   b 73.0448 (2)
   c 0.041 68 (3)
   d 0.7208 (3)

14 Round these numbers to the number of significant figures given in brackets.
   a 8317 (2)
   b 20 056 (3)
   c 0.546 72 (1)
   d 20.873 (3)

15 Work out an estimate for the total cost of 36 books costing £7.97 each.

16 A packet of 18 slices of bacon costs £5.80.
   Work out an estimate for the cost of each slice of bacon.

17 Ethan has a '5p off per litre' voucher for use at a local petrol station.
   He fills up his tank with 43 litres of petrol normally costing 104.9p per litre.
   How much does he pay?

18 Cans of drink are put into packs of 24. How many packs can be filled from 750 cans of drink?

19 Plain tiles cost 28p each.
Patterned tiles cost £9.51 each.
Julie buys 450 plain tiles and 15 patterned tiles.
Work out the total cost of the tiles.

Nov 2007

* **20** Yusuf is planning a disco party at his Youth Club.
Here are his costs.

Mobile Disco	£230
Hire of room	£150
Other costs	£30
Food	£12 per person

Yusuf charges £16 per ticket.
He sells 100 tickets.
Is there enough money from the ticket sales for Yusuf to pay all his costs?
You must show your working.

March 2011

21 A buzzer buzzes every 4 seconds and a bell rings every 6 seconds. The buzzer and the bell start at the same time. How many times in the first minute will they make a sound at the same instant?

22 Find the missing numbers in each case.
a $? \times 3 = -12$ **b** $(-20) \div (-5) = ?$ **c** $(-6) + ? = (28)$
d $(-5) \times ? = (-20)$ **e** $6 - ? = 8$

23 For each of these calculations, work out an estimated answer.
a $\dfrac{823 \times 4872}{3261}$ **b** $\dfrac{3.6 \times 4.5}{9.8}$ **c** $\dfrac{2.4 \times 7.9}{3.9 \times 2.3}$

24 Using the information that $4.8 \times 34 = 163.2$ write down the value of
a 48×34 **b** 4.8×3.4 **c** $163.2 \div 48$ *June 2008*

25 Use the information that $322 \times 48 = 15\,456$ to find the value of
a 3.22×4.8 **b** 0.322×0.48 **c** $15\,456 \div 4.8$

26 Comp Parts and Z Parts both sell memory sticks.

COMP PARTS
Memory Sticks £4 Each
1 free stick for every 10 sticks bought

Z PARTS
Memory Sticks
£55 for a box of 10 sticks

There are 150 students in Year 10 in a school.
A teacher needs to buy a memory stick for each student.
At which of the shops should he buy the memory sticks?
You must show all your working.

March 2011

27 Find the Lowest Common Multiple (LCM) of 8 and 12.   *Nov 2010*

28 a Express 108 as the product of its prime factors.
   b Find the highest common factor of 108 and 24.

29 a Express the following numbers as products of their prime factors.
      i 60   ii 96
   b Find the highest common factor of 60 and 96.
   c Work out the lowest common multiple of 60 and 96.

A02 A03

30 Doughnuts are sold in packs of 8. Cakes are sold in packets of 6.
   What is the smallest number of packs of doughnuts and the smallest number of packets of cakes that can be bought so that the number of doughnuts is equal to the number of cakes?

31 Simplify $5^5 \div 5^2$
   Write your answer as a power of 5.   *Nov 2009*

ResultsPlus
Achieving Full Marks

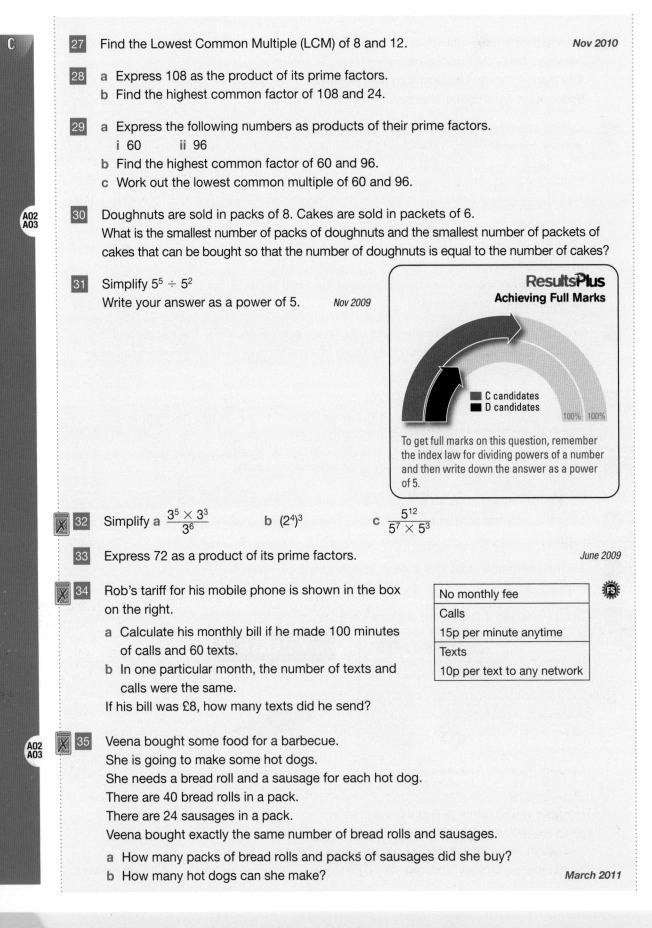

■ C candidates
■ D candidates
100% 100%

To get full marks on this question, remember the index law for dividing powers of a number and then write down the answer as a power of 5.

32 Simplify a $\dfrac{3^5 \times 3^3}{3^6}$ b $(2^4)^3$ c $\dfrac{5^{12}}{5^7 \times 5^3}$

33 Express 72 as a product of its prime factors.   *June 2009*

34 Rob's tariff for his mobile phone is shown in the box on the right.

   a Calculate his monthly bill if he made 100 minutes of calls and 60 texts.
   b In one particular month, the number of texts and calls were the same.
   If his bill was £8, how many texts did he send?

| No monthly fee |
| Calls |
| 15p per minute anytime |
| Texts |
| 10p per text to any network |

35 Veena bought some food for a barbecue.
   She is going to make some hot dogs.
   She needs a bread roll and a sausage for each hot dog.
   There are 40 bread rolls in a pack.
   There are 24 sausages in a pack.
   Veena bought exactly the same number of bread rolls and sausages.

   a How many packs of bread rolls and packs of sausages did she buy?
   b How many hot dogs can she make?   *March 2011*

36 James thinks of two numbers.

He says 'The highest common factor (HCF) of my two numbers is 3.

The lowest common multiple (LCM) of my two numbers is 45'.

Write down the two numbers James could be thinking of. *June 2008*

37 Jon and Alice are planning a holiday.

They are going to stay at a hotel.

The table shows information about prices at the hotel.

	Price per person per night (£)		
	Double room	**Single room**	**per person per day**
01 Nov – 29 April	59.75	118.00	31.75
30 April – 08 July	74.25	147.00	31.00
09 July – 29 Aug	81.75	161.75	31.00
30 Aug – 31 Oct	74.25	147.00	31.00
Saver Prices 5 nights for the price of 4 nights from 1st May to 4th July. 3 nights for the price of 2 nights in November.			

Jon and Alice will stay in a double room.

They will eat dinner at the hotel every day.

They can stay at the hotel for 3 nights in June or 4 nights in November.

Which of these holidays is cheaper? *March 2011*

38 Work out an estimate for the value of each of these. In each case state whether your answer is an overestimate or an underestimate.

a $\dfrac{5.4 \times 3.2}{0.187}$ b $\dfrac{0.32}{0.00195}$ c $\dfrac{0.88 \times 0.37}{0.131}$ d $\dfrac{59 \times 36}{0.415}$

39 Work out an estimate for $\dfrac{3870}{236 \times 4.85}$ *Nov 2010*

40 a Write 56 as a product of its prime factors.

b Find the Highest Common Factor (HCF) of 56 and 42. *Nov 2010*

41 a i Write 7900 in standard form   ii Write 0.000 35 in standard form.

b Work out $\dfrac{4 \times 10^3}{8 \times 10^{-5}}$ Give your answer in standard form.

42 In 2003 the population of Great Britain was 6.0×10^7.

In 2003 the population of India was 9.9×10^8.

Work out the difference between the population of India and the population of Great Britain in 2003.

Give your answer in standard form. *June 2007*

43 Write whether each of the following statements is true or false. If the statement is false give an example to show it is false.

a The sum of two prime numbers is always a prime number.

b The difference between consecutive prime numbers is never 2.

c The product of two prime numbers is always a prime number.

A02
A03

A02

A03

19

2 FRACTIONS

2.1 You can order fractions and convert between improper fractions and mixed numbers

Key Points

- You can find an equivalent fraction by multiplying or dividing both numerator (top number) and denominator (bottom number) by the same whole number.
- You can write a fraction in its simplest form by dividing numerator and denominator by the same whole number.
- Fractions can be ordered by writing them with the same common denominator.
- A fraction with a numerator that is larger than the denominator is called an improper fraction.
- An improper fraction can be written as a mixed number with a whole number part and a proper fraction part.

Example 1 Write the fraction $\frac{18}{24}$ in its simplest form.

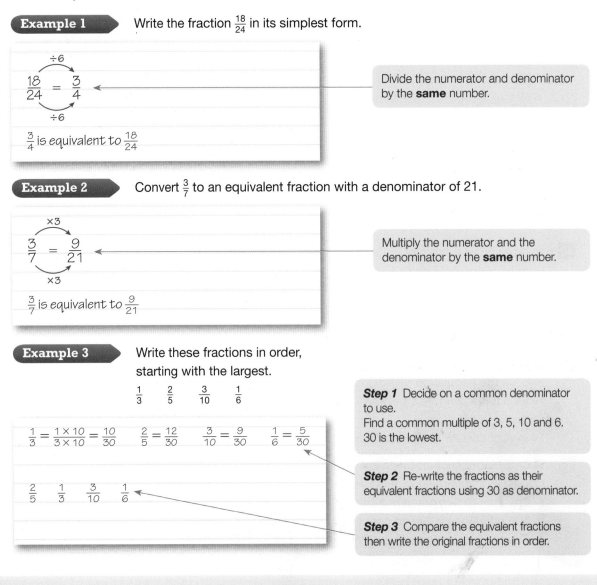

$$\frac{18}{24} = \frac{3}{4}$$

Divide the numerator and denominator by the **same** number.

$\frac{3}{4}$ is equivalent to $\frac{18}{24}$

Example 2 Convert $\frac{3}{7}$ to an equivalent fraction with a denominator of 21.

$$\frac{3}{7} = \frac{9}{21}$$

Multiply the numerator and the denominator by the **same** number.

$\frac{3}{7}$ is equivalent to $\frac{9}{21}$

Example 3 Write these fractions in order, starting with the largest.

$$\frac{1}{3} \quad \frac{2}{5} \quad \frac{3}{10} \quad \frac{1}{6}$$

Step 1 Decide on a common denominator to use.
Find a common multiple of 3, 5, 10 and 6. 30 is the lowest.

$$\frac{1}{3} = \frac{1 \times 10}{3 \times 10} = \frac{10}{30} \qquad \frac{2}{5} = \frac{12}{30} \qquad \frac{3}{10} = \frac{9}{30} \qquad \frac{1}{6} = \frac{5}{30}$$

Step 2 Re-write the fractions as their equivalent fractions using 30 as denominator.

$$\frac{2}{5} \quad \frac{1}{3} \quad \frac{3}{10} \quad \frac{1}{6}$$

Step 3 Compare the equivalent fractions then write the original fractions in order.

Exercise 2A

Questions in this chapter are targeted at the grades indicated.

1 Copy and complete these equivalent fractions.

a $\frac{1}{6} = \frac{\square}{18}$

b $\frac{3}{7} = \frac{\square}{14}$

c $\frac{3}{8} = \frac{\square}{48}$

d $\frac{4}{7} = \frac{\square}{21}$

e $\frac{5}{6} = \frac{\square}{36}$

f $\frac{2}{3} = \frac{6}{\square}$

g $\frac{4}{9} = \frac{24}{\square}$

h $\frac{5}{7} = \frac{\square}{56}$

i $\frac{9}{10} = \frac{90}{\square}$

j $\frac{7}{12} = \frac{84}{\square}$

k $\frac{7}{8} = \frac{49}{\square}$

l $\frac{2}{9} = \frac{\square}{81}$

2 By writing equivalent fractions, find the smaller fraction in each pair.

a $\frac{2}{5}$ or $\frac{1}{4}$

b $\frac{2}{4}$ or $\frac{4}{5}$

c $\frac{2}{3}$ or $\frac{3}{4}$

d $\frac{3}{5}$ or $\frac{7}{10}$

3 Write these fractions in order of size. Put the smallest one first.

a $\frac{1}{2}, \frac{3}{4}, \frac{2}{3}$

b $\frac{4}{5}, \frac{5}{6}, \frac{7}{15}$

c $\frac{3}{4}, \frac{4}{5}, \frac{1}{2}$

d $\frac{3}{7}, \frac{5}{14}, \frac{1}{2}, \frac{4}{7}$

Hint: Find the equivalent fractions with the same common denominator.

Example 4 Write $\frac{23}{7}$ as a mixed number.

$23 \div 7 = 3 \text{ remainder } 2$

$= 3\frac{2}{7}$

ResultsPlus
Exam Tip

A fraction is how something is divided up or shared out.

Step 1 Do the division.

Step 2 As this is 3 whole ones with 2 left over, the mixed number is $3\frac{2}{7}$

Example 5 Write $5\frac{3}{4}$ as an improper fraction.

$5\frac{3}{4} = \frac{20}{4} + \frac{3}{4} = \frac{23}{4}$

Each whole number is the same as $\frac{4}{4}$ (4 quarters).
So, the whole number 5 is $5 \times \frac{4}{4} = \frac{20}{4}$ (20 quarters).

Exercise 2B

1 Write these improper fractions as mixed numbers.

a $\frac{5}{2}$

b $\frac{7}{4}$

c $\frac{9}{7}$

d $\frac{11}{8}$

e $\frac{9}{8}$

f $\frac{16}{5}$

g $\frac{23}{10}$

h $\frac{24}{5}$

i $\frac{16}{7}$

j $\frac{12}{5}$

k $\frac{20}{3}$

l $\frac{16}{9}$

m $\frac{39}{4}$

n $\frac{27}{5}$

o $\frac{26}{9}$

p $\frac{17}{10}$

2 Write these mixed numbers as improper fractions.

a $1\frac{1}{2}$

b $5\frac{1}{2}$

c $2\frac{3}{4}$

d $1\frac{2}{3}$

e $3\frac{1}{4}$

f $4\frac{2}{5}$

g $3\frac{7}{10}$

h $5\frac{1}{5}$

i $7\frac{3}{4}$

j $2\frac{1}{4}$

k $1\frac{9}{10}$

l $9\frac{1}{3}$

m $2\frac{5}{6}$

n $5\frac{3}{8}$

o $3\frac{5}{8}$

p $1\frac{9}{100}$

2.2 You can add and subtract fractions

> ### Key Points
> ● Fractions can be added or subtracted when they have the same common denominator.
> ● To add or subtract fractions that have different denominators you need to find equivalent fractions that have the same common denominator.

Example 6   Work out $\frac{5}{8} + \frac{3}{7}$

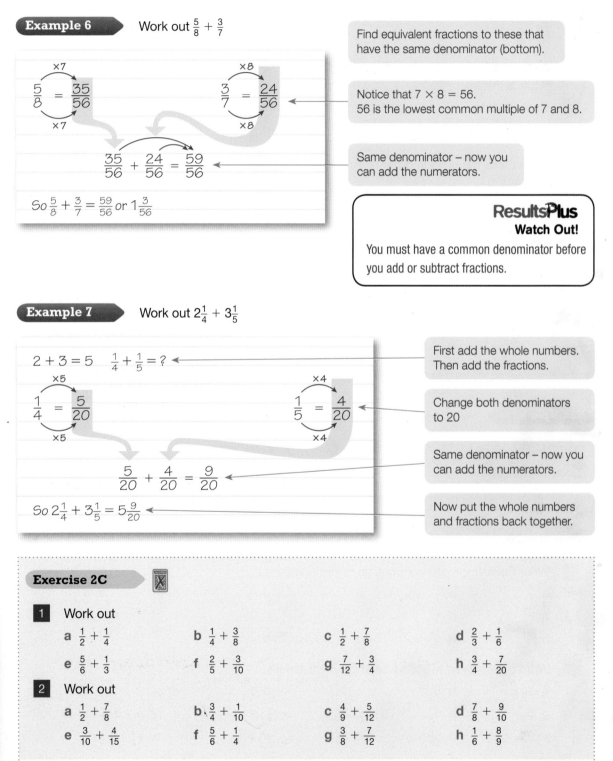

Find equivalent fractions to these that have the same denominator (bottom).

Notice that $7 \times 8 = 56$.
56 is the lowest common multiple of 7 and 8.

Same denominator – now you can add the numerators.

$$\frac{35}{56} + \frac{24}{56} = \frac{59}{56}$$

So $\frac{5}{8} + \frac{3}{7} = \frac{59}{56}$ or $1\frac{3}{56}$

ResultsPlus
Watch Out!
You must have a common denominator before you add or subtract fractions.

Example 7   Work out $2\frac{1}{4} + 3\frac{1}{5}$

$2 + 3 = 5 \quad \frac{1}{4} + \frac{1}{5} = ?$

First add the whole numbers.
Then add the fractions.

$$\frac{1}{4} = \frac{5}{20} \qquad \frac{1}{5} = \frac{4}{20}$$

Change both denominators to 20

$$\frac{5}{20} + \frac{4}{20} = \frac{9}{20}$$

Same denominator – now you can add the numerators.

So $2\frac{1}{4} + 3\frac{1}{5} = 5\frac{9}{20}$

Now put the whole numbers and fractions back together.

Exercise 2C

1 Work out

   a $\frac{1}{2} + \frac{1}{4}$ **b** $\frac{1}{4} + \frac{3}{8}$ **c** $\frac{1}{2} + \frac{7}{8}$ **d** $\frac{2}{3} + \frac{1}{6}$

   e $\frac{5}{6} + \frac{1}{3}$ **f** $\frac{2}{5} + \frac{3}{10}$ **g** $\frac{7}{12} + \frac{3}{4}$ **h** $\frac{3}{4} + \frac{7}{20}$

2 Work out

   a $\frac{1}{2} + \frac{7}{8}$ **b** $\frac{3}{4} + \frac{1}{10}$ **c** $\frac{4}{9} + \frac{5}{12}$ **d** $\frac{7}{8} + \frac{9}{10}$

   e $\frac{3}{10} + \frac{4}{15}$ **f** $\frac{5}{6} + \frac{1}{4}$ **g** $\frac{3}{8} + \frac{7}{12}$ **h** $\frac{1}{6} + \frac{8}{9}$

D

3 Work out

a $\frac{1}{2} + \frac{1}{3}$ b $\frac{2}{5} + \frac{1}{6}$ c $\frac{5}{8} + \frac{1}{5}$ d $\frac{3}{4} + \frac{1}{9}$

e $\frac{5}{6} + \frac{3}{7}$ f $\frac{9}{10} + \frac{2}{7}$ g $\frac{2}{3} + \frac{7}{10}$ h $\frac{3}{5} + \frac{2}{7}$

4 Work out

a $1\frac{1}{2} + 2\frac{1}{8}$ b $2\frac{3}{4} + 3\frac{7}{8}$ c $1\frac{3}{4} + 2\frac{5}{16}$ d $\frac{3}{4} + 3\frac{5}{8}$

e $2\frac{9}{16} + 1\frac{5}{8}$ f $1\frac{3}{10} + 1\frac{2}{3}$ g $3\frac{1}{6} + \frac{2}{7}$ h $2\frac{5}{6} + 1\frac{1}{7}$

5 Jo cycled $2\frac{3}{4}$ miles to one village and then a further $4\frac{1}{3}$ miles to her home.
What is the total distance Jo cycled?

Example 8   Work out $\frac{1}{3} - \frac{5}{24}$

$\frac{1}{3} - \frac{5}{24} = \frac{8}{24} - \frac{5}{24}$ ←   24 is used as a common denominator.

$= \frac{3}{24}$ or $\frac{1}{8}$ ← $\frac{3}{24}$ can be simplified (cancelled) to $\frac{1}{8}$

Example 9   Work out $4\frac{2}{5} - 1\frac{1}{2}$

$4\frac{2}{5} - 1\frac{1}{2} = \frac{22}{5} - \frac{3}{2}$

$= \frac{44}{10} - \frac{15}{10}$

$= \frac{29}{10}$ or $2\frac{9}{10}$

Step 1 Change each mixed number to an improper fraction.

Step 2 Convert the fractions so they have a common denominator.

Step 3 Subtract the numerators and change to a mixed number.

Exercise 2D

Hint: Write these fractions with the same common denominator first, then subtract the numerators.

1 Work out

a $\frac{1}{2} - \frac{1}{4}$ b $\frac{7}{8} - \frac{3}{4}$ c $\frac{5}{8} - \frac{1}{2}$ d $\frac{3}{4} - \frac{1}{8}$

e $\frac{5}{6} - \frac{1}{3}$ f $\frac{7}{12} - \frac{1}{3}$ g $\frac{9}{10} - \frac{2}{5}$ h $\frac{1}{4} - \frac{1}{20}$

2 Work out

a $\frac{2}{3} - \frac{1}{2}$ b $\frac{5}{8} - \frac{1}{3}$ c $\frac{1}{5} - \frac{1}{6}$ d $\frac{3}{5} - \frac{1}{6}$

e $\frac{4}{5} - \frac{2}{3}$ f $\frac{3}{4} - \frac{3}{5}$ g $\frac{7}{10} - \frac{1}{3}$ h $\frac{9}{10} - \frac{3}{4}$

3 In a school, $\frac{7}{16}$ of the students are girls. What fraction of the students are boys?

4 Work out

a $4\frac{5}{8} - 2\frac{1}{4}$ b $6\frac{1}{2} - 5\frac{1}{4}$ c $9\frac{1}{2} - 7\frac{3}{10}$ d $4 - 1\frac{3}{10}$

e $4\frac{4}{5} - 3\frac{9}{10}$ f $1\frac{2}{3} - \frac{11}{12}$ g $5\frac{3}{4} - 2\frac{19}{20}$ h $4\frac{7}{8} - 1\frac{2}{3}$

2.3 You can multiply and divide fractions

Key Points

- To multiply two fractions, multiply the numerators together and multiply the denominators together.
- To find a fraction of a quantity, multiply the fraction by the quantity. For example, $\frac{3}{4}$ of $60 = \frac{3}{4} \times 60$.
- To divide fractions, turn the dividing fraction upside down and multiply the fractions.

Example 10 Work out

a $\frac{3}{5} \times \frac{2}{3}$ b $\frac{4}{7} \times 3$ c $2\frac{3}{5} \times 1\frac{1}{4}$

Step 1 Write any mixed numbers as improper fractions.
Step 2 Multiply numerators together and denominators together.
Step 3 Simplify if possible.

a $\frac{3}{5} \times \frac{2}{3} = \frac{3 \times 2}{5 \times 3} = \frac{6}{15} = \frac{2}{5}$

                  Divide top and bottom by 3.

b $\frac{4}{7} \times 3$

                  First, write the whole number 3 as $\frac{3}{1}$

$= \frac{4}{7} \times \frac{3}{1}$

$= \frac{4 \times 3}{7 \times 1} = \frac{12}{7}$

                  Divide top and bottom by 5.

c $2\frac{3}{5} \times 1\frac{1}{4} = \left(\frac{10}{5} + \frac{3}{5} \right) \times \left(\frac{4}{4} + \frac{1}{4} \right) = \frac{13}{5} \times \frac{5}{4}$

       $= \frac{13 \times 5}{5 \times 4} = \frac{65}{20} = \frac{13}{4}$

ResultsPlus
Watch Out!

Many students forget to convert mixed numbers to improper fractions before multiplying or dividing e.g. $2\frac{3}{5} = \frac{13}{5}$.

Exercise 2E

1. Work out

   a $\frac{1}{2} \times \frac{3}{4}$ b $\frac{3}{8} \times \frac{1}{4}$ c $\frac{2}{5} \times \frac{4}{5}$ d $\frac{3}{8} \times \frac{3}{4}$

   e $\frac{5}{12} \times \frac{1}{3}$ f $\frac{7}{10} \times \frac{3}{4}$ g $\frac{3}{10} \times \frac{3}{5}$ h $\frac{2}{3} \times \frac{2}{3}$

2. Work out

   a $\frac{1}{2} \times \frac{4}{5}$ b $\frac{3}{4} \times \frac{4}{5}$ c $\frac{5}{6} \times \frac{3}{5}$ d $\frac{4}{5} \times \frac{3}{10}$

   e $\frac{5}{6} \times \frac{3}{4}$ f $\frac{7}{12} \times \frac{3}{14}$ g $\frac{8}{9} \times \frac{3}{10}$ h $\frac{3}{4} \times \frac{16}{21}$

3. Work out

   a $\frac{1}{2} \times 7$ b $\frac{2}{3} \times 5$ c $6 \times \frac{4}{5}$ d $8 \times \frac{3}{4}$

   e $\frac{7}{10} \times 20$ f $9 \times \frac{2}{3}$ g $10 \times \frac{2}{5}$ h $\frac{5}{6} \times 12$

4. Work out

   a $\frac{1}{2}$ of 8   b $\frac{1}{5}$ of 25   c $\frac{1}{3}$ of 21   d $\frac{1}{6}$ of 54

   e $\frac{1}{4}$ of 28   f $\frac{3}{4}$ of 28   g $\frac{1}{10}$ of 440   h $\frac{3}{5}$ of 30

D

5 Work out

a $\frac{2}{3} \times 1\frac{1}{3}$　　　　b $\frac{2}{5} \times 2\frac{1}{3}$　　　　c $1\frac{1}{2} \times \frac{1}{4}$　　　　d $1\frac{1}{2} \times 2\frac{1}{2}$

e $3\frac{1}{4} \times \frac{1}{2}$　　　　f $\frac{2}{3} \times 4\frac{1}{4}$　　　　g $\frac{5}{6} \times 1\frac{1}{3}$　　　　h $2\frac{1}{2} \times \frac{7}{10}$

6 A machine takes $5\frac{1}{2}$ minutes to produce a special type of container.

How long would the machine take to produce 15 containers at the same rate?

Example 11 Work out

a $\frac{1}{4} \div \frac{3}{5}$　　　b $\frac{15}{16} \div 5$　　　c $3\frac{1}{2} \div 4\frac{3}{4}$

a $\frac{1}{4} \div \frac{3}{5} = \frac{1}{4} \times \frac{5}{3}$

　$= \frac{1 \times 5}{4 \times 3} = \frac{5}{12}$

Turn the second fraction upside down and multiply.

b $\frac{15}{16} \div 5 = \frac{15}{16} \div \frac{5}{1}$

　$= \frac{15}{16} \times \frac{1}{5}$

　$= \frac{15}{80}$

　$= \frac{3}{16}$

ResultsPlus
Watch Out!

When dividing, make sure you turn the second fraction upside down, not the first fraction.

Divide top and bottom by 5.

c $3\frac{1}{2} \div 4\frac{3}{4} = \frac{7}{2} \div \frac{19}{4}$

　$= \frac{7}{2} \times \frac{4}{19}$

　$= \frac{28}{38}$

　$= \frac{14}{19}$

Change mixed numbers to improper fractions.

Turn the second fraction upside down and multiply.

Simplify the answer.

Exercise 2F

Hint: You need to write any whole numbers as fractions with the denominator 1.

E

1 Work out

a $\frac{1}{3} \div \frac{1}{4}$　　　　b $\frac{1}{4} \div \frac{1}{3}$　　　　c $\frac{3}{4} \div \frac{1}{2}$　　　　d $\frac{1}{2} \div \frac{7}{10}$

e $\frac{2}{3} \div \frac{1}{5}$　　　　f $\frac{5}{8} \div \frac{1}{3}$　　　　g $\frac{5}{6} \div \frac{3}{4}$　　　　h $\frac{7}{10} \div \frac{4}{5}$

2 Work out

a $8 \div \frac{1}{2}$　　　　b $12 \div \frac{3}{4}$　　　　c $6 \div \frac{3}{5}$　　　　d $8 \div \frac{7}{8}$

e $4 \div \frac{4}{5}$　　　　f $1 \div \frac{7}{12}$　　　　g $5 \div \frac{1}{3}$　　　　h $6 \div \frac{1}{4}$

3 Work out

a $2\frac{1}{2} \div \frac{1}{2}$　　　　b $3\frac{1}{4} \div 2\frac{1}{2}$　　　　c $3\frac{3}{4} \div 2\frac{1}{4}$　　　　d $1\frac{5}{8} \div 3\frac{1}{6}$

e $3\frac{2}{3} \div 7\frac{1}{3}$　　　　f $5\frac{1}{2} \div 2\frac{3}{4}$　　　　g $1\frac{7}{10} \div 2\frac{7}{10}$　　　　h $\frac{7}{8} \div 1\frac{2}{3}$

C

4 Work out

a $\frac{3}{4} \div 8$　　　　b $\frac{5}{6} \div 2$　　　　c $\frac{3}{5} \div 6$　　　　d $\frac{4}{5} \div 5$

e $1\frac{1}{3} \div 4$　　　　f $3\frac{1}{4} \div 6$　　　　g $2\frac{5}{6} \div 10$　　　　h $2\frac{1}{2} \div 15$

2.4 You can solve problems using fractions

Key Points

◉ You can use your knowledge of fractions to solve problems from real life.
◉ You can find a fraction of a quantity by using multiplication of fractions.

Example 12   Find $\frac{3}{8}$ of £96

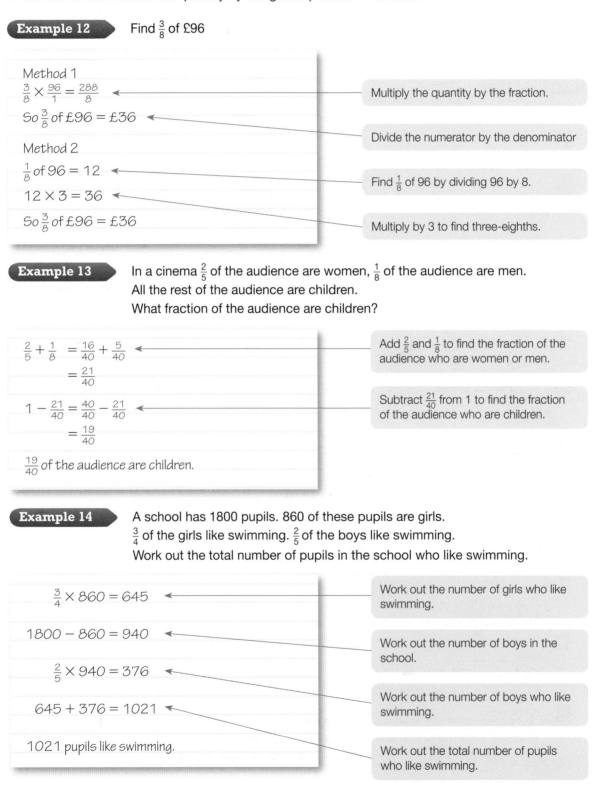

Method 1
$\frac{3}{8} \times \frac{96}{1} = \frac{288}{8}$

So $\frac{3}{8}$ of £96 = £36

Multiply the quantity by the fraction.

Divide the numerator by the denominator

Method 2
$\frac{1}{8}$ of 96 = 12

12 × 3 = 36

So $\frac{3}{8}$ of £96 = £36

Find $\frac{1}{8}$ of 96 by dividing 96 by 8.

Multiply by 3 to find three-eighths.

Example 13   In a cinema $\frac{2}{5}$ of the audience are women, $\frac{1}{8}$ of the audience are men.
All the rest of the audience are children.
What fraction of the audience are children?

$\frac{2}{5} + \frac{1}{8} = \frac{16}{40} + \frac{5}{40}$

$= \frac{21}{40}$

Add $\frac{2}{5}$ and $\frac{1}{8}$ to find the fraction of the audience who are women or men.

$1 - \frac{21}{40} = \frac{40}{40} - \frac{21}{40}$

$= \frac{19}{40}$

Subtract $\frac{21}{40}$ from 1 to find the fraction of the audience who are children.

$\frac{19}{40}$ of the audience are children.

Example 14   A school has 1800 pupils. 860 of these pupils are girls.
$\frac{3}{4}$ of the girls like swimming. $\frac{2}{5}$ of the boys like swimming.
Work out the total number of pupils in the school who like swimming.

$\frac{3}{4} \times 860 = 645$

Work out the number of girls who like swimming.

$1800 - 860 = 940$

Work out the number of boys in the school.

$\frac{2}{5} \times 940 = 376$

Work out the number of boys who like swimming.

$645 + 376 = 1021$

Work out the total number of pupils who like swimming.

1021 pupils like swimming.

Exercise 2G

1 Work out

    a $\frac{1}{6}$ of 30   **b** $\frac{3}{4}$ of 56   **c** $\frac{2}{3}$ of 144   **d** $\frac{5}{9}$ of 81

    e $\frac{2}{5}$ of £35   **f** $\frac{7}{10}$ of £120   **g** $\frac{7}{8}$ of £6.40   **h** $\frac{3}{16}$ of £32

2 In a survey carried out to find out whether 150 local people were in favour of a new sports centre being built, $\frac{1}{5}$ were against the project, $\frac{7}{10}$ were in favour and the rest did not give an opinion.

    a How many people were in favour of the project?

    b How many people did not give an opinion?

3 Out of 98 workers in a company, $\frac{5}{7}$ are female.
How many of the workers are male?

> **ResultsPlus**
> **Exam Tip**
> Remember to give your answer as a whole number, not a fraction, of the male workers.

4 Simon spends $\frac{1}{2}$ of his money on rent and $\frac{1}{3}$ of his money on transport.

    a What fraction of his money does he spend on rent and transport altogether?

    b What fraction of his money is left?

5 $\frac{8}{9}$ of an iceberg lies below the surface of the water. The total volume of an iceberg is 990 m³.
What volume of this iceberg is below the surface?

6 DVDs are sold for £14 each. $\frac{2}{5}$ of the £14 goes to the DVD company.
How much of the £14 goes to the DVD company?

7 An MP3 player usually costs £130. In a sale all prices are reduced by $\frac{2}{5}$.
Work out the sale price of the MP3 player.

8 A factory has 1710 workers. 650 of the workers are female.
$\frac{2}{5}$ of the female workers and $\frac{1}{4}$ of the male workers are under the age of 30.
How many workers in total are aged under 30?

9 Tammy watches two films. The first film is $1\frac{3}{4}$ hours long and the second one is $2\frac{1}{3}$ hours long.
Work out the total length of the two films.

10 $\frac{2}{3}$ of a square is shaded. $\frac{3}{4}$ of the shaded part is shaded blue.
What fraction of the whole square is shaded blue?

11 Alison, Becky and Carol take part in a charity relay race.
The race is over a total distance of $2\frac{5}{8}$ km.
Each girl runs an equal distance. Work out how far each girl runs.

12 In a book, $\frac{3}{8}$ of the pages have pictures on them.
Given that 72 pages have a picture on, work out the number of pages in the book.

13 Alex spent $\frac{2}{7}$ of his pocket money on a computer game.
He spent $\frac{1}{4}$ of his pocket money on sweets. He saved the rest.
Given that Alex saved £4.50, work out how much pocket money he got.

D

A02
A03

A02

A02
A03

C

A02
A03

A02
A03

Exam review

Self-assessment checklist

I can:

- find equivalent fractions by multiplying (or dividing) both numerator and denominator [p.20]
- simplify fractions by dividing the numerator and denominator by the same whole number [p.20]
- order fractions by using equivalent fractions [p.20]
- convert between improper fractions and mixed numbers [p.20]
- add and subtract fractions by using common denominators [p.22]
- multiply fractions by multiplying the numerators together and multiplying the denominators [p.24]
- divide fractions by turning the second fraction upside down and multiplying [p.24]
- find a fraction of a quantity by multiplying the quantity by the fraction [p.24]
- solve problems involving fractions. [p.26]

Exam practice

1 In each case, write down which fraction is larger. You must show your working.

    a $\frac{2}{3}$ or $\frac{3}{5}$ **b** $\frac{3}{4}$ or $\frac{5}{6}$ **c** $\frac{7}{10}$ or $\frac{3}{4}$ **d** $\frac{4}{9}$ or $\frac{11}{25}$

2 Here are the fractions $\frac{3}{4}$ and $\frac{4}{5}$.
Which is the larger fraction? You must show working to explain your answer.
You may copy and use the grids to help with your explanation.

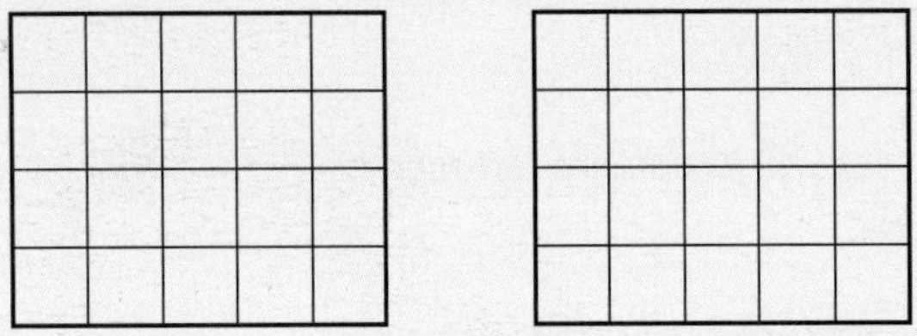

June 2007

3 Put these fractions in order of size. Start with the largest.

    $\frac{3}{10}$ $\frac{1}{3}$ $\frac{4}{15}$ $\frac{29}{100}$

4 Work out

    a $\frac{3}{5} \times \frac{2}{9}$ **b** $\frac{7}{15} \times \frac{5}{21}$ **c** $\frac{9}{16} \div \frac{3}{4}$

5 Work out

    a $\frac{5}{12} + \frac{1}{4}$ **b** $\frac{7}{15} + \frac{4}{45}$ **c** $\frac{3}{5} + \frac{3}{8}$ **d** $\frac{7}{12} + \frac{4}{9}$ **e** $\frac{7}{9} - \frac{1}{3}$

6 The diagram shows a rectangle.
Work out the distance all the way around the rectangle.

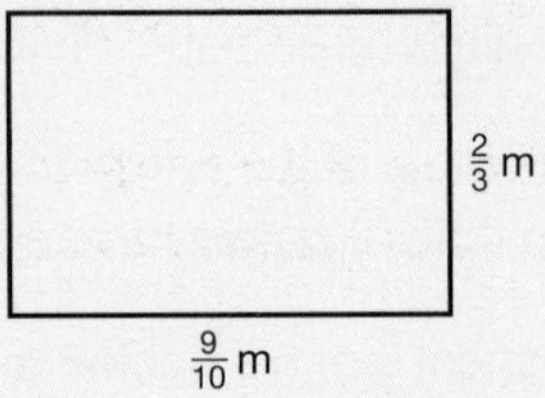

    $\frac{2}{3}$ m

    $\frac{9}{10}$ m

7 Work out $\frac{17}{20} - \frac{2}{5}$

Nov 2010

8 A club has some members who are adults and some who are children.

$\frac{2}{3}$ of the members are children.

$\frac{1}{4}$ of the adults are men.

$\frac{1}{2}$ of the children are boys.

What fraction of the members of the club are female?

9 Work out   **a** $2\frac{1}{2} \times 3\frac{2}{5}$ **b** $3\frac{3}{8} \div 2\frac{4}{7}$ **c** $1\frac{2}{5} \div 1\frac{11}{14}$

10 Work out $2\frac{2}{3} \times 1\frac{1}{4}$

Give your answer in its simplest form.   *June 2007*

11 Work out

a $1\frac{3}{4} - \frac{7}{16}$ **b** $2\frac{1}{4} - \frac{1}{2}$ **c** $4\frac{3}{8} - 1\frac{1}{2}$ **d** $5\frac{1}{5} - 2\frac{7}{15}$

12 All 480 students in a school studied either French, German or Spanish.

$\frac{2}{3}$ of the students studied French.

$\frac{1}{4}$ of the students studied German.

Gemma said that at least $\frac{1}{10}$ of the students studied Spanish.

Explain why Gemma is wrong.

13 36 students each went to one revision class.

$\frac{1}{6}$ of the students went to the physics revision class.

$\frac{2}{9}$ of the students went to the biology revision class.

All of the other students went to the chemistry revision class.

How many students went to the chemistry revision class?

June 2009

ResultsPlus
Achieving Full Marks

■ C candidates
■ D candidates   100% 100%

To get full marks on this question you need to show how you get your answer. One way to do this is to work out $\frac{1}{6}$ of 36 and $\frac{2}{9}$ of 36 and compare.

14 The diagram represents a part of a machine.

In order to fit the machine, the part must be between $6\frac{1}{16}$ cm and $6\frac{3}{16}$ cm long.

Will the part fit the machine?

You must explain your answer.

Diagram **NOT** accurately drawn

⟵ $2\frac{1}{2}$ cm ⟶ ⟵ $3\frac{5}{8}$ cm ⟶

15 A full glass of water holds $\frac{1}{6}$ of a bottle of water.

How many glasses of water can be filled from $2\frac{1}{2}$ bottles of water?   *June 2007*

3 USING A CALCULATOR

3.1 You can use a calculator effectively and efficiently

Key Points

- You need to take care when writing down the answer from a calculator display.
  If you are working in pounds, the calculator display 3.4 means £3.40.
- You must make sure that your answer makes sense in the context of the question.
  Sometimes the answer to a problem must be a whole number and if the calculator display shows a decimal you will need to think carefully about whether to round it up or round it down.
- With a scientific calculator you can work out squares using the x^2 key.
  Some calculators have an x^3 key for working out cubes.
- Scientific calculators have a power (or index) key. It can be shown by x^y or y^x or $x^\blacksquare$ or $\wedge$.
- To work out square or cube roots on a calculator use the $\sqrt{}$ or $\sqrt[3]{}$ key.
- The reciprocal of a number is 1 divided by the number.
  For a fraction this is the same as turning it upside down.

  The reciprocal of 2 is $\frac{1}{2}$ (or 0.5). The reciprocal of $\frac{1}{3}$ is $\frac{3}{1}$ (or 3). The reciprocal of $\frac{3}{4}$ is $\frac{4}{3}$ (or $1.\dot{3}$).
- To work out reciprocals you can use the reciprocal key on a calculator. It is usually shown by $1/x$ or x^{-1}.

Example 1   It takes 22 minutes to fill a water tank.
How many tanks can be filled completely in 10 hours?

10 hours = 10 × 60 = 600 minutes   ← Convert the hours into minutes so that both measurements are in minutes.

$\boxed{6}\boxed{0}\boxed{0}\boxed{÷}\boxed{2}\boxed{2}\boxed{=}$

27.2727...
So 27 tanks can be completely filled.

ResultsPlus
Exam Tip

Always write down the calculation that you are doing.

Example 2   Use a calculator to work out $1.2^3 + 6.25$.

Method 1

$\boxed{1}\boxed{.}\boxed{2}\boxed{x^3}\boxed{=}$ ← Or you could key in 1.2 × 1.2 × 1.2 =

The result is 1.728.
1.728 + 6.25 =   ← Add the result to 6.25.
The answer is 7.978.

Method 2

$\boxed{1}\boxed{.}\boxed{2}\boxed{x^3}\boxed{+}\boxed{6}\boxed{.}\boxed{2}\boxed{5}\boxed{=}$

The answer is 7.978.

Key in the whole calculation.

Example 3   Use a calculator to work out $\sqrt{14.44}$.

$$\boxed{\sqrt{}}\boxed{1}\boxed{4}\boxed{.}\boxed{4}\boxed{4}\boxed{=}$$

On some calculators you first key in 14.44 and then press the square root key.

$\sqrt{14.44} = 3.8$

Example 4   Find the reciprocal of 20.

Method 1

The reciprocal of 20 is $\frac{1}{20}$.

You could give the answer as a fraction

$$\boxed{1}\boxed{\div}\boxed{2}\boxed{0}\boxed{=}$$

The reciprocal of 20 is 0.05.   or as a decimal.

Method 2

$$\boxed{2}\boxed{0}\boxed{1/x}\boxed{=}$$

Use the reciprocal key on your calculator.

The reciprocal of 20 is 0.05.

Exercise 3A   Questions in this chapter are targeted at the grades indicated.

1. The total cost of five adult cinema tickets is £44.50.
   Work out the cost of one adult cinema ticket.

2. Tom's company pays him 45p for each mile that he drives his car.
   Work out how much money Tom's company pays him when he drives 126 miles.

3. Colin needs 160 tiles for a room.
   Tiles are sold in boxes. There are 12 tiles in each box.
   Work out the least number of boxes of tiles that Colin needs.

   Hint: Round up your answer so that Colin has enough tiles.

4. The battery life of a calculator is 420 hours. Work out the battery life in days and hours.

5. Work out
   a 2.5^2 b 47^2 c 6^3 d 2^5 e 11^4

6. Work out
   a $17^2 + 10$ b $2.7^2 + 5.42$ c $2.1^3 + 1.96$ d $1.4^3 - 1.544$

7. Work out
   a $\sqrt{625}$ b $\sqrt{2.56}$ c $\sqrt{22.09}$ d $\sqrt[3]{729}$

8. Work these out, giving your answers correct to three significant figures.
   a $\sqrt{150}$ b $\sqrt{80}$
   c $\sqrt[3]{30}$ d $\sqrt[3]{425}$

   ResultsPlus
   Exam Tip
   Write down all the figures on your calculator display before you round your answer to three significant figures. (See Section 1.4 on Rounding.)

9. Work out
   a $\sqrt{51.84} + 4.8$ b $\sqrt{841} - 21.3$ c $\sqrt[3]{9.261} - 1.9$ d $\sqrt[3]{1.728} + 1.8$

10. Find the reciprocals of these numbers.
    a 10   b 4   c 8

11. Use your calculator to find the reciprocals of these numbers.
    a 2.5   b 50   c 16   d 0.2   e 0.125

3.2 You can use a calculator to work out complex calculations

Key Points

- All scientific calculators carry out mathematical operations in the same order. You need to know about BIDMAS in order to use a scientific calculator properly (see Section 1.7).
- On most scientific calculators you can key in calculations in the order in which they are written down, although you may need to use brackets in some calculations.
- When you are doing a division calculation you must remember to divide by ALL of the denominator.
- Most scientific calculators have the negative sign. This button can be keyed in before a number to enter negative numbers. It usually looks like this $\boxed{(-)}$.

Example 5   Work out the value of $\dfrac{16.3 + 7.82}{7.2 - 4.7}$.

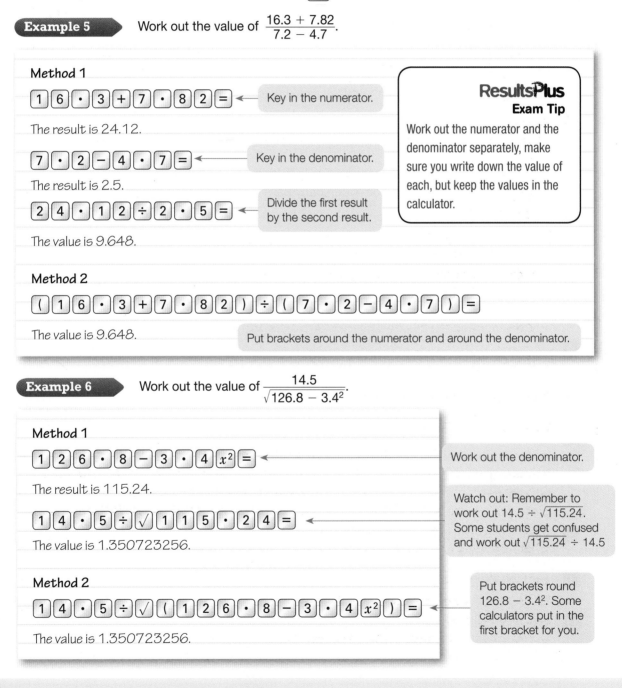

Method 1

$\boxed{1}\boxed{6}\boxed{\cdot}\boxed{3}\boxed{+}\boxed{7}\boxed{\cdot}\boxed{8}\boxed{2}\boxed{=}$ ← Key in the numerator.

The result is 24.12.

$\boxed{7}\boxed{\cdot}\boxed{2}\boxed{-}\boxed{4}\boxed{\cdot}\boxed{7}\boxed{=}$ ← Key in the denominator.

The result is 2.5.

$\boxed{2}\boxed{4}\boxed{\cdot}\boxed{1}\boxed{2}\boxed{÷}\boxed{2}\boxed{\cdot}\boxed{5}\boxed{=}$ ← Divide the first result by the second result.

The value is 9.648.

ResultsPlus
Exam Tip

Work out the numerator and the denominator separately, make sure you write down the value of each, but keep the values in the calculator.

Method 2

$\boxed{(}\boxed{1}\boxed{6}\boxed{\cdot}\boxed{3}\boxed{+}\boxed{7}\boxed{\cdot}\boxed{8}\boxed{2}\boxed{)}\boxed{÷}\boxed{(}\boxed{7}\boxed{\cdot}\boxed{2}\boxed{-}\boxed{4}\boxed{\cdot}\boxed{7}\boxed{)}\boxed{=}$

The value is 9.648.

Put brackets around the numerator and around the denominator.

Example 6   Work out the value of $\dfrac{14.5}{\sqrt{126.8 - 3.4^2}}$.

Method 1

$\boxed{1}\boxed{2}\boxed{6}\boxed{\cdot}\boxed{8}\boxed{-}\boxed{3}\boxed{\cdot}\boxed{4}\boxed{x^2}\boxed{=}$ ← Work out the denominator.

The result is 115.24.

$\boxed{1}\boxed{4}\boxed{\cdot}\boxed{5}\boxed{÷}\boxed{\sqrt{}}\boxed{1}\boxed{1}\boxed{5}\boxed{\cdot}\boxed{2}\boxed{4}\boxed{=}$

The value is 1.350723256.

Watch out: Remember to work out 14.5 ÷ √115.24. Some students get confused and work out √115.24 ÷ 14.5

Method 2

$\boxed{1}\boxed{4}\boxed{\cdot}\boxed{5}\boxed{÷}\boxed{\sqrt{}}\boxed{(}\boxed{1}\boxed{2}\boxed{6}\boxed{\cdot}\boxed{8}\boxed{-}\boxed{3}\boxed{\cdot}\boxed{4}\boxed{x^2}\boxed{)}\boxed{=}$

The value is 1.350723256.

Put brackets round $126.8 - 3.4^2$. Some calculators put in the first bracket for you.

Exercise 3B

1 Work out

   a $(5.2 + 2.7)^2$ **b** $(12.4 - 9.71)^2$ **c** $(2.43 + 1.87)^3$ **d** $(5.1 - 3.7)^3$

2 Work out

   a $12^2 + 13^2$ **b** $34^2 + 6^3$ **c** $12^3 - 23^2$ **d** $38^2 - 18^2$

3 Work out

   a $\sqrt{17.8 + 13.56}$ **b** $\sqrt{415 - 159}$ **c** $\sqrt[3]{129 - 65}$ **d** $\sqrt[3]{1.85 + 1.525}$

4 Work out the value of each of these.
Write down all the figures on your calculator display.

   a $\dfrac{4.78 - 1.42}{0.84}$ **b** $\dfrac{48.88}{3.62 + 5.78}$

   c $\dfrac{12.24 \times 2.5}{6.8}$ **d** $\dfrac{35.36}{12.6 - 5.8}$

> **ResultsPlus**
> **Exam Tip**
>
> If you want to work these out in one stage on your calculator, put brackets round the numerator and brackets round the denominator when there is a calculation to do.

5 Work out the value of each of these.
Write down all the figures on your calculator display.

   a $\dfrac{13.2 - 6.84}{2.8 + 3.41}$ **b** $\dfrac{5.6 \times 8.1}{12.5 - 3.9}$ **c** $\dfrac{1}{2.5} + \dfrac{1}{4.5}$

   d $\dfrac{4.37 \times 6.52}{2.8 + 7.19}$ **e** $\dfrac{17.6 + 9.82}{23.6 - 5.94}$ **f** $\dfrac{4.5}{8} - \dfrac{3.5}{7}$

6 **a** Work out $\sqrt{\dfrac{7.5^2}{2.6 + 5.87}}$

      Write down all the numbers on your calculator display.

   b Work out $\dfrac{(7.62 - 3.85)^3}{(6.05 + 1.8)^2}$

      Write down all the numbers on your calculator display.

7 Work out $\dfrac{4.5 \times 10^8}{5.625 \times 10^5}$

*8 Some students were given this task to do:

   Work out $\dfrac{8.8 - \sqrt{(8.8^2 - 4 \times 3.8 \times 4.4)}}{2 \times 4.4}$

   Jim's working was $(8.8 - \sqrt{10.56}) \div 8.8$ to get the answer 0.631 correct to 2 d.p.
   Inewara's working was $(8.8 - \sqrt{10.56}) \div 2 \times 4.4$ to get the answer 12.21 correct to 2 d.p.
   Gemma's working was $8.8 - \sqrt{10.56} \div (2 \times 4.4)$ to get the answer 8.43 correct to 2 d.p.
   Bill's working was $(8.8 - \sqrt{10.56}) \div 2 \times 4.4$ to get the answer 1.65 correct to 2 d.p.
   Which student, if any, got the correct answer?
   What mistakes did the other students make?

9 $4.8 \times 6.4^2 + 6.4 \times 4.8^2$
   Ben says that by putting one pair of brackets in this expression he can make the answer bigger than 5000.
   Is Ben correct? You must explain your answer.

Exam review

Self-assessment checklist

I can:

- interpret a calculator display, for example, when working with money [p. 30]
- decide whether to round up or down where the answer to a question should be a whole number [p. 30]
- use the keys for working out squares, square roots, powers and reciprocals on a calculator [p. 30]
- find the values of the reciprocal of a number by working out 1 divided by the number [p. 30]
- find the reciprocal of a fraction by turning it upside down [p. 30]
- carry out mathematical operations in the correct order by using BIDMAS [p. 32]
- carry out complex calculations involving division in fractions by making sure the values of the numerator and denominator are found before dividing. [p. 32]

Exam practice

E

1. Christine buys a calculator costing £3.99, a pencil case costing £1.65 and two rulers costing 28p each. She pays with a £10 note. How much change should she get from her £10 note?

2. Shares in a company cost £6.23 each. Tauqeer has £500.
   He buys as many shares as he can.
   Work out how many shares Tauqeer can buy.

3. Work out
   a 2.9^2
   b 12^3
   c $\sqrt{51.84}$
   d $\sqrt[3]{15.625}$

4. Work these out, giving your answers correct to one decimal place.
   a $2.8^2 + \sqrt{34}$
   b $\sqrt{56} - 2.3^2$
   c $4.7^2 - \sqrt{28}$
   d $3.8^2 - \sqrt{50}$

5. Which of the following fractions will be recurring when written as decimals?
   $\frac{3}{4}$ $\frac{5}{6}$ $\frac{2}{5}$ $\frac{1}{7}$ $\frac{15}{24}$

   > **Hint:** To convert a fraction to a decimal, divide the numerator by the denominator.

D

6. Use a calculator to work out
   $(-2.7)^2 + (-3.5^2)$

   > **Hint:** Remember to use the $(-)$ key on the calculator.

   Nov 2008

7. Work out
   a $(3.7 + 2.64)^2$
   b $\sqrt{17 + 25.25}$
   c $(2.1 + 2.8)^2 \times 1.2$

8. Work out the value of each of these.
   Write down all the figures on your calculator display.
   a $\dfrac{5.68 - 1.52^2}{0.83}$
   b $\dfrac{1}{3.58^2 - 2.87}$
   c $\dfrac{8.7 + 5.92}{16.3 - 4.56}$

9. a Work out the value of $(2.5 + 0.9)^2 \div 4.2$
   Write down all the figures on your calculator display.
   b Write down your answer to part **a** correct to 1 significant figure.

   March 2007

10 Work out $\dfrac{4.6 + 3.85}{3.2^2 - 6.51}$

Write down all the numbers on your calculator display.

June 2009

ResultsPlus
Achieving Full Marks

■ C candidates
■ D candidates
100% 100%

To get full marks on this question, either put brackets round the numerator and round the denominator, or work each one out separately, before you divide the numerator by the denominator.

11 To work out a person's daily calorie requirement you can use one of these rules.

Gender	Daily calorie requirement
Female	655 + (9.6 × weight in kg) + (1.8 × height in cm) − (4.7 × age in years)
Male	66 + (13.7 × weight in kg) + (5 × height in cm) − (6.8 × age in years)

The table below shows some information about four people.

Name	Gender	Age (years)	Weight (kg)	Height (cm)
Sophie	F	32	68	165
Chelsea	F	47	55	175
Kenny	M	27	98	191
Hassan	M	38	117	182

Work out the recommended daily calorie intake for each person.
Which person has the greatest daily calorie requirement?
Which person has the smallest daily calorie requirement?

12 Find the reciprocal of   **a** $\frac{5}{8}$ **b** 2.5   **c** $\frac{1}{4}$

13 Use your calculator to work out $\dfrac{22.4 \times 14.5}{8.5 \times 3.2}$

Write down all the figures on your calculator display.

June 2007

*14 A large tub of popcorn costs £3.80 and holds 200 g.
A regular tub of popcorn costs £3.50 and holds 175 g.
Rob says that the 200 g large tub is the better value for money. Linda says that the 175 g regular tub is the better value for money. Who is correct?
Explain the reasons for your answer.
You must show all your working.

£3.80

£3.50

200 g
Large

175 g
Regular

June 2006

15 **a** Use your calculator to work out $\dfrac{4.7}{9.4 - 3.5}$

Write down all the figures on your calculator display.

b Write these numbers in order of size.
Start with the smallest number.

0.82 $\frac{4}{5}$ 85% $\frac{2}{3}$ $\frac{7}{8}$

Hint: Change each number to a decimal.

June 2007 adapted

D

A03

A03

4 PERCENTAGES

4.1 You can find a percentage of a quantity

Key Points

- 'Percentage' means 'out of a hundred'. Percentages can be written as fractions or decimals.
- You should know these percentages and their fraction and decimal equivalents.

Percentage	1%	10%	25%	50%	75%
Decimal	0.01	0.1	0.25	0.5	0.75
Fraction	$\frac{1}{100}$	$\frac{1}{10}$	$\frac{1}{4}$	$\frac{1}{2}$	$\frac{3}{4}$

- If a percentage can be written as a simple fraction it is easy to work out a percentage of a quantity without using a calculator. For example:
  - to work out 50% of a quantity you work out $\frac{1}{2}$ of it
  - to work out 25% of a quantity you work out $\frac{1}{4}$ of it.
- To work out a percentage of a quantity using fractions you should:
  - write the percentage as a fraction, and then
  - multiply the fraction by the quantity.
- To work out a percentage of a quantity using decimals you should:
  - write the percentage as a decimal, and then
  - multiply the decimal by the quantity.

Example 1   Work out 30% of 50. Do not use a calculator.

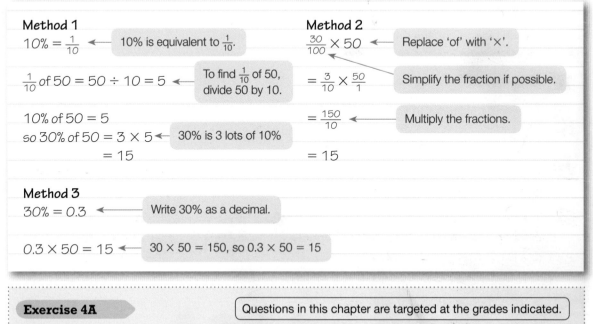

Method 1

$10\% = \frac{1}{10}$ ← 10% is equivalent to $\frac{1}{10}$.

$\frac{1}{10}$ of 50 = 50 ÷ 10 = 5 ← To find $\frac{1}{10}$ of 50, divide 50 by 10.

10% of 50 = 5

so 30% of 50 = 3 × 5 ← 30% is 3 lots of 10%

= 15

Method 2

$\frac{30}{100} \times 50$ ← Replace 'of' with '×'.

$= \frac{3}{10} \times \frac{50}{1}$ ← Simplify the fraction if possible.

$= \frac{150}{10}$ ← Multiply the fractions.

= 15

Method 3

$30\% = 0.3$ ← Write 30% as a decimal.

$0.3 \times 50 = 15$ ← 30 × 50 = 150, so 0.3 × 50 = 15

Exercise 4A   Questions in this chapter are targeted at the grades indicated.

F

1   Work out
   a   50% of £24
   b   50% of 80 kg
   c   25% of 32 m
   d   75% of 76p
   e   10% of £60
   f   20% of 70 km
   g   15% of 20 kg
   h   35% of £40

2 Simon's salary last year was £35 400. He saved 10% of his salary.
Simon wants to buy a car costing £3650. Has he saved enough?

3 Jamal earns £28 000 in one year. He gets £1000 tax free. On the remainder
he pays income tax at 20%. Work out how much income tax he pays in that year.

4 The price of a new sofa is £480. Leah pays a deposit of 15% of the price.
Work out the deposit she pays.

5 The normal cost of a suit is £120. In a sale the cost of the suit is reduced by 35%.
Work out how much the cost of the suit is reduced by in the sale.

6 Rahma pays income tax. She pays 20% on the first £37 400 of her income and
40% on income over £37 400. Rahma's income last year was £59 400.
Work out how much income tax she paid last year.

Example 2

The normal price of a television is £375.
Harry is given a discount of 24%.
Work out the discount that Harry is given.

ResultsPlus
Exam Tip

Learn how to use your calculator
for problems which contain less
common percentages.

To work out 24% of 375 it is quicker to use a calculator.

$24\% = \frac{24}{100}$ ← Change the percentage to a fraction or decimal.

$\frac{24}{100} \times 375 = 90$ ← Key in $\boxed{2}\boxed{4}\boxed{\div}\boxed{1}\boxed{0}\boxed{0}\boxed{\times}\boxed{3}\boxed{7}\boxed{5}\boxed{=}$
or $\boxed{0}\boxed{\cdot}\boxed{2}\boxed{4}\boxed{\times}\boxed{3}\boxed{7}\boxed{5}\boxed{=}$

Harry is given a discount of £90.

Exercise 4B

1 Work out
a 12% of £40   b 86% of 45 kg   c 54% of £370   d 5% of 640 km

2 There are 250 boats in a harbour. 46% of the boats are yachts.
How many yachts are there in the harbour?

3 Alan invested £1200 in a savings account. At the end of the year he received 4% interest.
Work out how much interest he received.   *Hint:* 4% written as a decimal is 0.04

4 In a restaurant a service charge of 12.5% is added to the cost of the meal.
Work out the service charge when the cost of the meal is £60.   *Hint:* 12.5% written as a decimal is 0.125

5 VAT is charged at the rate of $17\frac{1}{2}\%$.
Work out the VAT charged on a ladder costing £84

6 Roger bought 50 pineapples at 80p each.
He sold all the pineapples.
On each of the first 36 pineapples he made a 35% profit.
On each of the remaining pineapples he made a 40% loss.
Work out the overall profit or loss that Roger made.

4.2 You can use percentages to solve problems

Key Points

- To increase a quantity by a percentage, work out the increase and add this to the original quantity.
- To decrease a quantity by a percentage, work out the decrease and subtract this from the original quantity.
- An alternative method is to work out the multiplier for an increase or decrease and then multiply the original amount by the multiplier to find the new amount.

Example 3

A packet contains 500 g of cereal plus 18% extra cereal free.
Work out the weight of cereal in the packet.

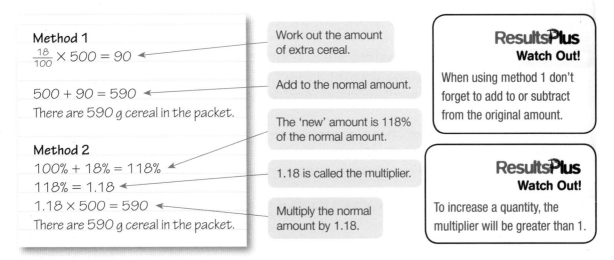

Method 1

$\frac{18}{100} \times 500 = 90$ ← Work out the amount of extra cereal.

$500 + 90 = 590$ ← Add to the normal amount.
There are 590 g cereal in the packet.

The 'new' amount is 118% of the normal amount.

Method 2

$100\% + 18\% = 118\%$

$118\% = 1.18$ ← 1.18 is called the multiplier.

$1.18 \times 500 = 590$ ← Multiply the normal amount by 1.18.
There are 590 g cereal in the packet.

ResultsPlus
Watch Out!

When using method 1 don't forget to add to or subtract from the original amount.

ResultsPlus
Watch Out!

To increase a quantity, the multiplier will be greater than 1.

Example 4

In a sale all normal prices are reduced by 12%.
The normal price of a suit is £125.
Work out the sale price of the suit.

Method 1

$\frac{12}{100} \times 125 = 15$ ← Work out the reduction.

$125 - 15 = 110$ ← Subtract to work out the sale price.
The sale price is £110.

Method 2

$100\% - 12\% = 88\%$ ← The sale price is 88% of the normal price.

$88\% = 0.88$ ← 0.88 is the multiplier.

$0.88 \times 125 = 110$ ← Multiply the normal price by 0.88.
The sale price is £110.

ResultsPlus
Exam Tip

To decrease a quantity, the multiplier will be less than 1.

Exercise 4C

1. The price of rail fares increased by 11%.
   Before the increase the price of a ticket was £87.
   Work out the price of the ticket after the increase.

2. Karen's salary is £26 500. Her salary is increased by 3%. Work out her new salary.

3. A travel company reduced the prices of its holidays by 12%.
   What is the new price of a holiday which was originally priced at £695?

4. A car tyre costs £48 plus VAT at 20%. Work out the total cost of the car tyre.

5. Katie invests £3600. The interest rate is 3.5% per year.
   How much will Katie have in her account at the end of one year?

6. Raja bought a car for £8000. In one year the value of the car depreciated by 10%.
   Work out the value of the car one year after he bought it.

7. The normal price of a pack of croissants is £1.96.
   The normal price is reduced by 25%.
   Work out the price after the reduction.

8. A store reduced all normal prices by 15% in a two-day sale.
   Work out the sale price of:
   a a drill with a normal price of £70
   b a lawnmower with a normal price of £180
   c a tin of paint with a normal price of £14.

9. In a super-sale a shop reduces its sale prices by a further 10%.

   SALE $\frac{1}{2}$ **off** normal prices **PLUS** an extra 10% off sale prices

   In the super-sale, Steve buys a camera with a normal price of £240.
   How much does he pay?

10. In a sale all prices are reduced by 15%.
    Work out the sale price of each of the following:
    a a television set that normally costs £300
    b a CD player that normally costs £40
    c a computer that normally costs £1200.

11. Alan weighs 82 kg before going on a diet. He sets himself a target of losing 5% of his original weight.
    What is his target weight?

4.3 You can work out compound interest

Key Points

- Banks and building societies pay compound interest on savings.
- At the end of the first year, interest is paid on the money in an account. This interest is then added to the account. At the end of the second year, interest is paid on the total amount in the account, that is, the original amount of money plus the interest earned in the first year.
- At the end of each year, interest is paid on the total amount in the account at the start of that year. For example, if £200 is invested in a bank account and interest is paid at a rate of 5% then

Year	Amount at start of year	Amount plus interest	Total amount at year end
1	£200	200×1.05	£210
2	£210	$210 \times 1.05 = 200 \times 1.05^2$	£220.50
3	£220.50	$220.50 \times 1.05 = 200 \times 1.05^3$	£231.52
4	£231.52	$231.52 \times 1.05 = 200 \times 1.05^4$	£243.10
5	£243.10	$243.10 \times 1.05 = 200 \times 1.05^5$	£255.26
6	£255.26	$255.26 \times 1.05 = 200 \times 1.05^6$	£268.02

- To calculate compound interest, find and use the multiplier:
  - Total amount after n years = original amount $\times$ multiplier^n
- Depreciation is the loss in value of an object, such as a car, over a period of time.

Example 5

£4000 is invested for 2 years at 5% per annum compound interest.
Work out the **total interest** earned over the 2 years.

Method 1

$$100\% + 5\% = 105\%$$

Work out the multiplier for an increase of 5%.

$$105\% = 1.05$$

$$4000 \times 1.05^2 = 4410$$

Multiply the original amount by 1.05^2 to find the amount in the account after 2 years.

$$4410 - 4000 = 410$$

The total interest earned over the 2 years is £410.

Subtract the original amount to find the interest.

Method 2

$$\frac{5}{100} \times 4000 = 200$$

Work out the interest in the first year.

$$4000 + 200 = 4200$$

Add the interest to the original amount.

$$\frac{5}{100} \times 4200 = 210$$

Work out the interest in the second year.

$$200 + 210 = 410$$

Find the total interest.

The total interest earned over the 2 years is £410.

ResultsPlus
Watch Out!

Read this type of question carefully to determine whether you need to work out just the interest or the final amount in the account including the interest.

Example 6 The value of a machine when new is £8000.
The value of the machine depreciates by 10% each year.
Work out its value after 3 years.

$100\% - 10\% = 90\%$ ◄──────────── Work out the multiplier for a decrease of 10%.
$90\% = 0.9$

$8000 \times 0.9 \times 0.9 \times 0.9 = £5832$ ◄──── Multiply the value when new by 0.9^3 to find the value after 3 years.

The value of the machine after 3 years is £5832.

Exercise 4D

1 £1000 is invested for 2 years at 5% per annum compound interest.
Work out the total amount in the account after 2 years.

2 £6500 is invested in a bank account for 4 years.
Compound interest is paid at a rate of 3%.
Calculate the total amount of interest paid over the 4 years.

Hint: Remember to add interest before working out the next year's compound interest.

3 A house cost £200 000. Its value increases by 12% each year.
How much is the house worth after 2 years?

4 A car cost £12 000. Its value depreciates at a rate of 15% per year.
What is the car worth after 2 years?

5 Mrs Bell buys a house for £60 000. In the first year, the value of the house increases by 16%.
In the second year, the value of the house decreases by 4% of its value at the beginning
of that year.
   a Write down the single number, as a decimal, that the original value of the house can be
   multiplied by to find its value after 2 years.
   b Work out the value of the house after the 2 years.

6 Ben says that an increase of 40% followed by an increase of 20% is the same as an
increase of 60%.
Is Ben correct? You must give a reason for your answer.

7 Jeremy deposits £3000 in a bank account.
Compound interest is paid at a rate of 4% per annum.
Jeremy wants to leave the money in the account until there is at least £4000 in
the account.
Calculate the least number of years Jeremy must leave his money in the bank account.

C

B

A02
A03

A03

4.4 You can work out one quantity as a percentage of another

Key Points

- To write one quantity as a percentage of another quantity:
  - write down the first quantity as a fraction of the second quantity
  - convert the fraction to a percentage.
- To work out percentage profit or percentage loss use:
  - percentage profit (or increase) $= \dfrac{\text{profit (or increase)}}{\text{original amount}} \times 100\%$
  - percentage loss (or decrease) $= \dfrac{\text{loss (or decrease)}}{\text{original amount}} \times 100\%$

Example 7
  a Convert 11 out of 20 to a percentage.
  b Convert 23 cm out of 4 m to a percentage.

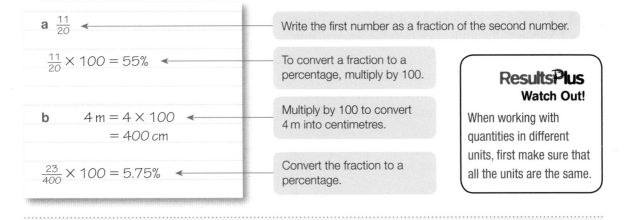

a $\dfrac{11}{20}$ ← Write the first number as a fraction of the second number.

$\dfrac{11}{20} \times 100 = 55\%$ ← To convert a fraction to a percentage, multiply by 100.

b $4\,\text{m} = 4 \times 100$ ← Multiply by 100 to convert 4 m into centimetres.
$= 400\,\text{cm}$

$\dfrac{23}{400} \times 100 = 5.75\%$ ← Convert the fraction to a percentage.

ResultsPlus
Watch Out!

When working with quantities in different units, first make sure that all the units are the same.

Exercise 4E

1 The table gives information about Year 10 at Mathstown School. Work out the percentage of students in Year 10 who are girls.

	Number of girls	Number of boys
Year 10	108	132

2 Write:
  a £3 as a percentage of £6
  b 2 kg as a percentage of 8 kg
  c 4p as a percentage of 10p
  d 8 cm as a percentage of 40 cm
  e 60p as a percentage of £2.40
  f 15 mm as a percentage of 6 cm
  g 36 minutes as a percentage of 1 hour
  h 50 cm as a percentage of 4 m.

3 Janet scored 36 out of 40 in a German test. Work out her score as a percentage.

4 Jerry took 60 bottles to a bottle bank. 27 of the bottles were green.
What percentage of the bottles were green?

5 A 40 g serving of cereal contains 8 g of protein, 24 g of carbohydrates, 4.5 g of fat and 3.5 g of fibre.
What percentage of the serving is:
  a protein
  b carbohydrates
  c fat
  d fibre?

Example 8

Karen bought a car for £1200.
One year later, she sold it for £840.
Work out her percentage loss.

$1200 - 840 = 360$ ← Subtract the selling price from the original price to find her loss.

$\frac{360}{1200}$ ← Write down the fraction $\frac{\text{loss}}{\text{original price}}$

$\frac{360}{1200} \times 100 = 30\%$ ← Multiply $\frac{360}{1200}$ by 100 to change it to a percentage.

Her percentage loss is 30%.

ResultsPlus
Watch Out!

Some students get confused about which number to use as the denominator. Remember to use the original value.

Example 9

Tony bought a box of 24 oranges for £4.
He sold all the oranges for 21p each.
Work out his percentage profit.

$24 \times 21 = 504p$ ← Work out the total amount, in pence, Tony received from selling all the oranges.

$504 - 400 = 104p$ profit ← Subtract the original price from the selling price to find his profit in pence.

$\frac{104}{400}$ ← Write down the fraction $\frac{\text{profit}}{\text{original price}}$

$\frac{104}{400} \times 100 = 26\%$ ← Multiply $\frac{104}{400}$ by 100 to change it to a percentage.

Percentage profit = 26%.

Exercise 4F

1. Calculate the percentage increase or decrease to the nearest 1%:
   a £24 to £36   b 12.5 kg to 20 kg   c 45 cm to 39.5 cm
   d 2 minutes to 110 seconds.

2. In a sale, the price of a clock is reduced from £32 to £27.20. Work out the percentage reduction.

3. Rob bought a crate of 40 melons for £30. He sold all the melons for £1.05 each. Work out his percentage profit.

*4. David owns three shops selling DVDs.
He tells the staff in each of the shops that some of them will receive a bonus. He will give the bonus to the staff who work in the shop that has the biggest

	DVDs sold Jan–Jun	DVDs sold Jul–Dec
Shop A	12 893	13 562
Shop B	9 875	10 346
Shop C	11 235	11 853

percentage increase in the number of DVDs sold from the first half to the second half of the year.
Which shop should receive the bonus? You must show how you decided on your answer.

C

A02
A03

A03

Exam review

Self-assessment checklist

I can:

- convert between percentages, decimals and fractions   [p. 36]
- work out a simple percentage of a quantity without using a calculator   [p. 36]
- work out any percentage of a quantity by using a calculator   [p. 36]
- increase or decrease a quantity by a percentage   [p. 38]
- calculate compound interest   [p. 40]
- write one quantity as a percentage of another   [p. 42]
- work out percentage profit or percentage loss.   [p. 42]

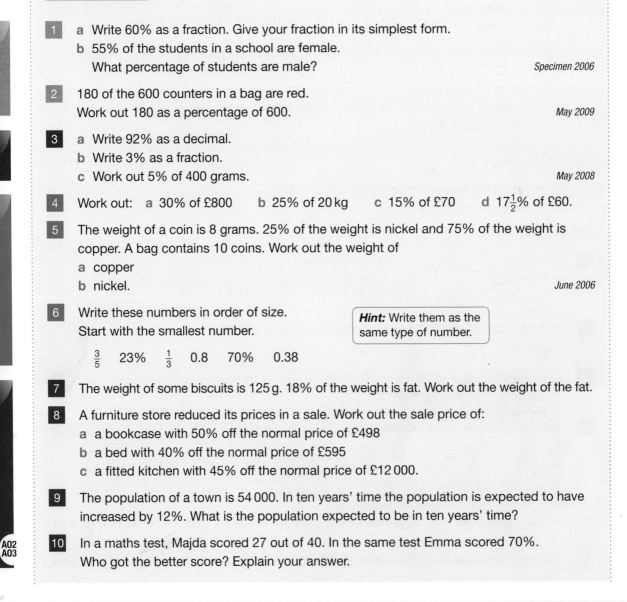

Exam practice

1   a   Write 60% as a fraction. Give your fraction in its simplest form.

     b   55% of the students in a school are female.

       What percentage of students are male?   *Specimen 2006*

2   180 of the 600 counters in a bag are red.

     Work out 180 as a percentage of 600.   *May 2009*

3   a   Write 92% as a decimal.

     b   Write 3% as a fraction.

     c   Work out 5% of 400 grams.   *May 2008*

4   Work out: a   30% of £800   b   25% of 20 kg   c   15% of £70   d $17\frac{1}{2}$% of £60.

5   The weight of a coin is 8 grams. 25% of the weight is nickel and 75% of the weight is copper. A bag contains 10 coins. Work out the weight of

     a   copper

     b   nickel.   *June 2006*

6   Write these numbers in order of size.

     Start with the smallest number.   **Hint:** Write them as the same type of number.

        $\frac{3}{5}$ 23% $\frac{1}{3}$ 0.8   70%   0.38

7   The weight of some biscuits is 125 g. 18% of the weight is fat. Work out the weight of the fat.

8   A furniture store reduced its prices in a sale. Work out the sale price of:

     a   a bookcase with 50% off the normal price of £498

     b   a bed with 40% off the normal price of £595

     c   a fitted kitchen with 45% off the normal price of £12 000.

9   The population of a town is 54 000. In ten years' time the population is expected to have increased by 12%. What is the population expected to be in ten years' time?

10   In a maths test, Majda scored 27 out of 40. In the same test Emma scored 70%.

      Who got the better score? Explain your answer.

* **11** Jack wants to buy a new shed. There are three shops that sell the shed he wants.

Sheds For U	**Garden World**	**Ed's Sheds**
25% off	£210	$\frac{1}{3}$ off
normal price of	plus VAT	usual price of
£320	at $17\frac{1}{2}$%	£345

Jack wants to pay as little as possible. From which of these three shops should Jack buy his shed?

12 A computer costs £360 plus $17\frac{1}{2}$ % VAT.
Calculate the total cost of the computer. *Nov 2009*

ResultsPlus
Achieving Full Marks

■ C candidates
■ D candidates
100% 100%

To get full marks on question 12, show all your working clearly and remember to add the VAT to the £360 to find the *total* cost.

13 The normal price of a cat basket is £20.
In a sale, the manager reduces the price of the cat basket by 15%.
Work out the price of the cat basket in the sale. *Nov 2008*

14 The normal price of a computer game is £21.30.
The normal price is reduced by 20%.
What is its reduced price?

15 Students went to London or to York on a school trip.
The table shows the some information about the children.

	London	York
Boys	27	13
Girls	18	22

a What percentage of all the girls went to York?
b What percentage of all those who went to London were boys?
c What percentage of all the children went to London?

* **16** Rachael is a sales manager.
Last year, Rachael had a 10% pay rise. This year, she had a 5% pay rise.
Ziggy says, 'Rachael has had a 15% pay rise over the two years.'
Is Ziggy correct? Explain your answer.

17 Lizzie bought a van.
The total cost of the van was £6000 plus VAT at $17\frac{1}{2}$%.
Lizzie paid £3000 when she got the van.
She paid the rest of the total cost of the van in 10 equal monthly payments.
Work out the amount of each monthly payment. *Nov 2010*

18 Toby invested £4500 for 2 years in a savings account.
He was paid 4% per annum compound interest.
How much did Toby have in his savings account after 2 years? *June 2009*

19 The value of a car depreciates by 35% each year.
At the end of 2007, the value of the car was £5460.
Work out the value of the car at the end of 2006. *Nov 2008*

D
A03

C
A02

A03

A02

B

5 RATIO AND PROPORTION

5.1 You can understand and use ratio

Key Points

- Ratios are used to compare quantities.

The ratio of green triangles to white triangles is $4:2$.
The ratio of white triangles to green triangles is $2:4$.

- They can be simplified like fractions.
- Ratios can also be used to write down a fraction.
- It is sometimes useful to write ratios in the form $1:n$, where n can be a whole number or a decimal. This form is often used for scales in maps and scale drawings (see section 11.8).

Example 1

A box contains 12 milk chocolates and 8 dark chocolates.
What fraction of these chocolates are dark?

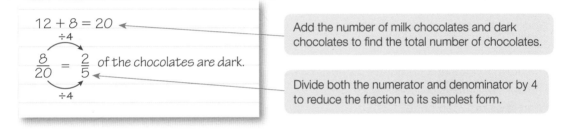

$12 + 8 = 20$

$\dfrac{8}{20} = \dfrac{2}{5}$ of the chocolates are dark.

$\div 4$

Add the number of milk chocolates and dark chocolates to find the total number of chocolates.

Divide both the numerator and denominator by 4 to reduce the fraction to its simplest form.

Example 2

Write the ratio 40 minutes : 3 hours in its simplest form.

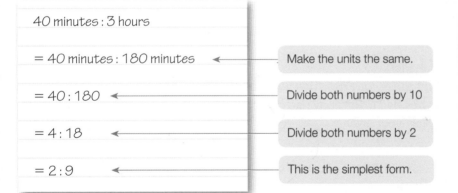

40 minutes : 3 hours

$= 40$ minutes : 180 minutes

$= 40 : 180$

$= 4 : 18$

$= 2 : 9$

Make the units the same.

Divide both numbers by 10

Divide both numbers by 2

This is the simplest form.

ResultsPlus
Exam Tip

A question will often ask you to write your ratio in its simplest form. Remember to do this by cancelling down!

Example 3

Write the ratio 6 : 9 in the form $1 : n$.

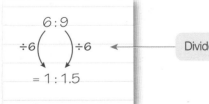

$6 : 9$

$\div 6 \qquad \div 6$

$= 1 : 1.5$

Divide by 6 to make the first number into 1.

Exercise 5A

Questions in this chapter are targeted at the grades indicated.

E

1 There are 200 boys and 150 girls in a school.
Write down the ratio of the number of boys to the number of girls.
Give your ratio in its simplest form.

2 In a bird aviary there are 20 finches, 36 canaries and 24 budgies.
Write down the ratio of the number of finches to the number of canaries to the number of budgies.
Give your ratio in its simplest form.

3 Write these ratios in their simplest form.
a 20 minutes : 1 hour   b 40p : £1   c 75 cm : 3 m   d 600 g : 2 kg

4 A table has a length of 1.2 m and a width of 40 cm.
a Find, in its simplest form, the ratio of the length of the table to the width of the table.
b Find, in its simplest form, the ratio of the width of the table to the length of the table.

5 A box contains blue pens, red pens and black pens in the ratio 7 : 1 : 2.
a What fraction of these pens are red?
b What fraction of these pens are blue?

D

6 On the farm, $\frac{1}{3}$ of the pigs are female.
What is the ratio of female pigs to male pigs on this farm?

7 Write these ratios in the form 1 : n.
a 2 : 5   b 5 : 12   c 10 : 3   d 200 : 250

8 In a school there are 120 teachers and 1740 students. The headteacher wants to display on his website the ratio of the number of teachers to the number of students in the form 1 : n. Work out this ratio.

9 An art gallery issues this guidance to schools planning to visit the gallery.

A03

> The recommended adult/pupil ratio is:
>
> For Years 1 to 3, a minimum of 1 adult to every 5 pupils
> For Years 4 to 9, a minimum of 1 adult to 10 pupils
> For Years 10 onwards, a minimum of 1 adult to 15 pupils

A primary school is planning a visit to the art gallery.
The table shows information about the pupils going on the visit.
Work out the minimum number of adults that need to go on the visit.

Year	Number of pupils
2	7
3	13
4	12
5	14

10 In a cinema, there are 160 children and 200 adults.
a What fraction of the audience are children?
b Write down the ratio of the number of children to the number of adults.
Give your ratio in its simplest form.
c Write your answer to part b in the form 1 : n.

5.2 You can solve problems involving ratio

Key Points

- If you know the ratio of two quantities and you know one of the quantities then the other quantity can be found by using equivalent ratios.
- Maps, scale drawings and models have a scale to tell us how a distance on the map, drawing or model relates to the real distance.
  For example, a scale of 1 : 12 means that every 1 cm on a drawing or model represents 12 cm in real life.
- Sometimes we want to divide a quantity in a certain ratio.
  Suppose Sam and Hannah buy a box of chocolates costing £3.00.
  If Sam paid £2.00 and Hannah paid £1.00 they might decide to share the chocolates in the ratio 2 : 1.

Example 4

To make concrete, 2 parts of cement is used to every 5 parts of sand.
- **a** Write down the ratio of cement to sand.
- **b** 4 buckets of cement are used. How many buckets of sand will be needed?
- **c** 20 buckets of sand are used. How many buckets of cement will be needed?

a 2 : 5

b $4 \div 2 = 2$ ← The amount of cement has been multiplied by 2.

cement : sand

$$\times 2 \binom{2 \quad : \quad 5}{4 \quad : \quad 10} \times 2$$ ← Multiply 5 by 2.

10 buckets of sand will be needed.

c $20 \div 5 = 4$ ← The amount of sand has been multiplied by 4.

cement : sand

$$\times 4 \binom{2 \quad : \quad 5}{8 \quad : \quad 20} \times 4$$ ← Multiply 2 by 4.

8 buckets of cement will be needed.

Example 5

The scale of a map is 1 : 20 000.
Work out the real distance, in kilometres, that 9 cm on the map represents.

1 : 20 000 ← 1 cm on the map represents a real distance of 20 000 cm.

$9 \times 20\,000 = 180\,000$ ← Multiply the length on the map by 20 000.

The real distance is 180 000 cm.

$180\,000 \div 100 = 1800$ m ← Change 180 000 cm to kilometres.

$1800 \div 1000 = 1.8$ km

9 cm on the map represents a real distance of 1.8 km.

Example 6   Heidi and Kirsty share £75 in the ratio 2 : 3.
Work out how much money each girl receives.

2 + 3 = 5   ← Work out the total number of shares.

75 ÷ 5 = 15   ← Work out the size of one share.

15 × 2 = 30   ← Heidi receives 2 shares.

15 × 3 = 45   ← Kirsty receives 3 shares.

Heidi gets £30 and Kirsty gets £45.

ResultsPlus
Watch Out!

Some students divide the total amount by the numbers in the ratio. Make sure you work out the number of shares first.

Exercise 5B

1 Margaret makes porridge by mixing oats and water in the ratio 1 : 2.
Work out the number of cups of water she uses for:
    a 2 cups of oats   b 3 cups of oats   c 10 cups of oats.

2 Sidra is making a fruit drink.
She mixes orange juice, pineapple juice and syrup in the ratio 3 : 4 : 1.
    a If she uses 600 ml of orange juice, how much syrup will she need?
    b If she uses 1 l of pineapple juice, how much orange juice will she need?

3 Paul makes green paint by mixing 2 parts of yellow paint with 3 parts of blue paint.
Paul has 500 ml of yellow paint and 1 litre of blue paint.
What is the maximum amount of green paint that Paul can make?

4 Alex uses a scale of 1 : 50 to draw a plan of his bedroom.
On the plan the length of the bedroom is 8 cm.
Work out the real length of the bedroom.

5 Shannon makes a scale model of a house. She uses a scale of 1 : 12.
The height of the model house is 60 cm.
Work out the height of the real house.

6 The scale of a map is 1 : 100 000.
On the map the distance between two towns is 6 cm.
Work out the real distance between the two towns.

7 The ratio of boys to girls in a class is 4 : 5.
There are 27 students in the class. Work out the number of girls in the class.

8 Three boys shared £30 in the ratio 5 : 3 : 2.
William received the smallest amount. Work out how much William received.

9 Masud made some compost. He mixed soil, manure and leaf mould in the ratio 3 : 2 : 1.
Masud made 120 litres of compost. Work out how much manure he used.

5.3 You can solve problems involving direct proportion and inverse proportion

Key Points

- If two quantities increase or decrease at the same rate they are in direct proportion.
- There are two methods that can be used to solve problems that involve direct proportion.
  - The first method is called the unitary method because it finds the cost of one item first (see Example 7).
  - The second method (the ratio method) is particularly useful for recipe questions (see Example 8).
- Two quantities are said to be in inverse proportion if one quantity increases at the same rate as the other quantity decreases (see Example 10).

Example 7

Seven bricks weigh 21 kg.
Work out the weight of 10 of these bricks.

$21 \div 7 = 3$ ← First work out the weight of one brick.

$3 \times 10 = 30$ ← First work out the weight of one brick.

10 bricks weigh 30 kg.

Example 8

This is a list of ingredients needed to make fruit crumble for 4 people.

350 g fruit   100 g flour   50 g margarine   50 g sugar

Work out the amount of margarine needed to make fruit crumble for 12 people.

$12 \div 4 = 3$ ← 3 times as much of each ingredient is needed.

$50 \times 3 = 150$ ← $\div 4$ then $\times 12$ is the same as $\times 3$.

150 g of margarine is needed. ← Multiply the amount of margarine by 3.

Example 9

a   Martin went to Spain. He changed £400 into euros.
    The exchange rate was £1 = 1.08 euros. How many euros did he receive?

b   When Martin came home he changed 63 euros into pounds.
    The new exchange rate was £1 = 1.05 euros. How many pounds did he receive?

a $400 \times 1.08 = 432$ ← Multiply the number of pounds by 1.08.
    Martin received 432 euros.

b $63 \div 1.05 = 60$ ←
    Martin received £60.   Divide the number of euros by 1.05.

Example 10

It takes 3 men 2 days to build a wall.

Work out how long it will take 2 men to build the wall.

$3 \times 2 = 6$ ← 1 man would take 6 days to build the wall.

$6 \div 2 = 3$ ← There are now 2 men so divide by 2.

2 men will take 3 days. ← Check: $3 \times 2 = 6$ and $2 \times 3 = 6$.

ResultsPlus
Exam Tip

Think about the problem. If there are fewer men then the work should take more time.

Exercise 5C

1 Five pens cost 75p. Work out the cost of eight of these pens.

2 Three 2.5 litre tins of paint cost £44.94. Work out the cost of five of the 2.5 litre tins of paint.

3 This is a list of ingredients needed to make 50 cheese straws.

   100 g flour   50 g margarine   75 g cheese

   Connor wants to make 100 cheese straws. Work out the amount of each ingredient Connor needs.

4 This is a list of ingredients needed to make 20 almond biscuits.

   175 g flour   50 g ground almonds   75 g caster sugar   150 g margarine

   a Work out the amount of flour needed to make 60 almond biscuits.
   b Work out the amount of margarine needed to make 10 almond biscuits.
   c Work out the amount of ground almonds needed to make 30 almond biscuits.

5 Hannah went on holiday to France. She changed £200 into euros.
   The exchange rate was £1 = 1.08 euros. Work out how many euros Hannah received.

6 Suha is going to the USA. The exchange rate is £1 = $1.42
   a Convert £300 into dollars.   b Convert $355 into pounds.

7 Danny paid 74 francs for a meal in Switzerland. The exchange rate was £1 = 1.85 francs.
   Work out the cost of the meal in pounds.

*8 Sian is going on holiday to America. In January she notices that the exchange rate is £1 = $1.74.
   When she exchanges £450 for dollars in July the exchange rate has dropped to £1 = $1.61.
   How many more dollars would Sian have received if she had exchanged her money in January?

9 It takes 10 men 2 days to cut a hedge.
   Work out how long it will take to cut the hedge if there are: a 5 men   b 4 men.

10 5 computers process a certain amount of information in 10 hours.
   Work out how long it will take 25 computers to process the same amount of information.

11 A document will fit onto exactly 32 pages if there are 500 words on a page.
   If the number of words on each page is reduced to 400, how many more pages will there be in the document?

D

A03

A03 B

A02
A03

A02
A03

Exam review

Self-assessment checklist

I can:

- write ratios as fractions [p. 46]
- write ratios in their simplest form [p. 46]
- write ratios in the form $1 : n$ [p. 46]
- solve problems by using equivalent ratios [p. 48]
- divide a quantity in a given ratio [p. 48]
- solve problems that involve direct proportion by using the unitary method [p. 50]
- solve problems that involve direct proportion by using the ratio method [p. 50]
- solve problems that involve inverse proportion. [p. 50]

Exam practice

1 The distance from Ailing to Beeford is 2 km.
The distance from Ceetown to Deeton is 800 metres.
Write as a ratio
Distance from Ailing to Beeford: Distance from Ceetown to Deeton.
Give your answer in its simplest form.

2 There are some oranges and apples in a box.
The total number of oranges and apples is 54.
The ratio of the number of oranges to the
number of apples is 1 : 5.
Work out the number of apples in the
box. *June 2009*

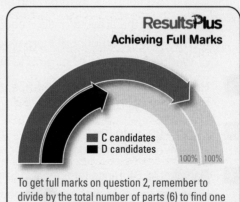

ResultsPlus
Achieving Full Marks

■ C candidates
■ D candidates
100% 100%

To get full marks on question 2, remember to
divide by the total number of parts (6) to find one
part, then calculate the number of apples (5 parts).

3 A garage sells British cars and foreign cars.
The ratio of the number of British cars sold to
the number of foreign cars sold is 2 : 7.
The garage sells 45 cars in one week.
Work out the number of British cars the garage sold that week. *June 2008*

4 Alice builds a model of a house. She uses a scale of 1 : 20.
The height of the real house is 10 metres.
a Work out the height of the model.
The width of the model is 80 cm.
b Work out the width of the real house.

5 There are 600 counters in a bag.
90 of the 600 are yellow. 180 of the 600 are red.
The rest of the counters in the bag are blue or green.
There are twice as many blue counters as green counters.
Work out the number of green counters in the bag. *May 2009*

6   Here is a list of ingredients for making fudge for 6 people.
Work out how much of each ingredient is needed to make fudge for 9 people.

> **Fudge**
> Ingredients for 6 people
> *600 g of sugar*
> *12 g of butter*
> *480 g of condensed milk*
> *90 ml of milk*

Nov 2006

7   Ron went to Spain.
He changed £200 into euros (€).
The exchange rate was £1 = €1.40.
a How many euros did he get?
When he came home he changed €10.64 back into pounds.
The exchange rate was now £1 = €1.33.
b How many pounds did he receive?

June 2006

8   Bob lays 200 bricks in one hour.
He always works at the same speed. He starts work at 9 am.
Bob takes 15 minutes for morning break and 30 minutes for lunch break.
Bob has to lay 960 bricks.
Work out the time at which he will finish laying bricks.

June 2006 adapted

A03

9   The exchange rate between pounds (£) and euros (€) is £1 = €1.08 in London and €1 = 88p in Paris.
Will has £1200 to change into euros. Should he do it in London or Paris?

A02

10   In August 2008, Eddie hired a car in Italy.
The cost of hiring the car was £620.
The exchange rate was £1 = €1.25.
a Work out the cost of hiring the car in euros (€).
Eddie bought some perfume in Italy.
The cost of the perfume in Italy was €50.
The cost of the same perfume in London was £42.
The exchange rate was still £1 = €1.25.
b Work out the difference between the cost of the perfume in Italy and the cost of the perfume in London. Give your answer in pounds (£).

June 2010

A02

11   Mr Brown makes some compost.
He mixes soil, manure and leaf mould in the ratio 3 : 1 : 1.
Mr Brown makes 75 litres of compost.
How many litres of soil does he use?

Nov 2006

12   A large ball of wool is used to knit a scarf.
The scarf is 40 stitches wide and 120 cm long. If the same size ball of wool is used to knit a scarf 25 stitches wide, work out the length of the new scarf.

A03

13   Grace and Jack share £140 in the ratio 3 : 4.
Work out the amount of money that Jack gets.

Nov 2010

6 ALGEBRA

6.1 You can collect like terms

Key Points

- A variable is something that can change, e.g. speed, and is shown using a letter, e.g. a, b or c.
- A term is a multiple of a letter that denotes a variable, e.g. $5a$, $6b$, c, $3de$, $4f^2$.
- Terms that use the same variable or arrangement of letters are called like terms.
- You can add or subtract like terms to simplify expressions.
  a is the same as $1a$, so $a + a + a = 3a$ and $2b - b = 2b - 1b = b$.
- It is also possible to have negative values when you collect like terms.

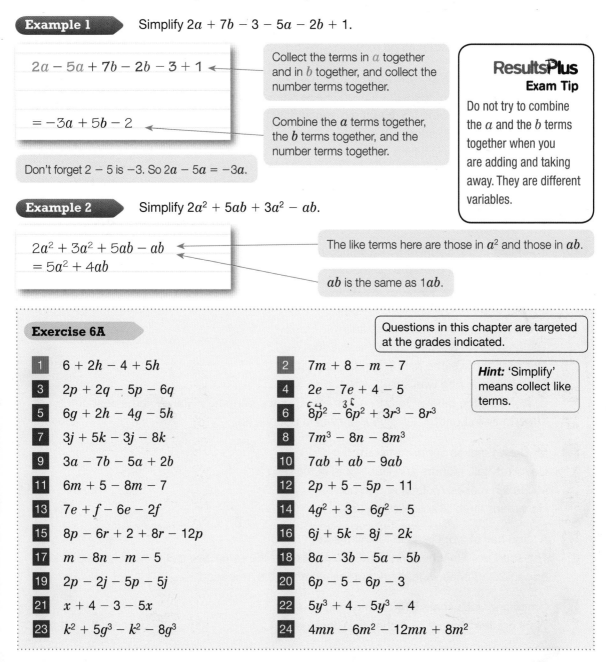

Example 1   Simplify $2a + 7b - 3 - 5a - 2b + 1$.

$$2a - 5a + 7b - 2b - 3 + 1$$

Collect the terms in a together and in b together, and collect the number terms together.

$$= -3a + 5b - 2$$

Combine the a terms together, the b terms together, and the number terms together.

Don't forget $2 - 5$ is -3. So $2a - 5a = -3a$.

ResultsPlus
Exam Tip

Do not try to combine the a and the b terms together when you are adding and taking away. They are different variables.

Example 2   Simplify $2a^2 + 5ab + 3a^2 - ab$.

$$2a^2 + 3a^2 + 5ab - ab$$
$$= 5a^2 + 4ab$$

The like terms here are those in a^2 and those in ab.

ab is the same as $1ab$.

Exercise 6A

Questions in this chapter are targeted at the grades indicated.

1. $6 + 2h - 4 + 5h$
2. $7m + 8 - m - 7$

Hint: 'Simplify' means collect like terms.

3. $2p + 2q - 5p - 6q$
4. $2e - 7e + 4 - 5$
5. $6g + 2h - 4g - 5h$
6. $8p^2 - 6p^2 + 3r^3 - 8r^3$
7. $3j + 5k - 3j - 8k$
8. $7m^3 - 8n - 8m^3$
9. $3a - 7b - 5a + 2b$
10. $7ab + ab - 9ab$
11. $6m + 5 - 8m - 7$
12. $2p + 5 - 5p - 11$
13. $7e + f - 6e - 2f$
14. $4g^2 + 3 - 6g^2 - 5$
15. $8p - 6r + 2 + 8r - 12p$
16. $6j + 5k - 8j - 2k$
17. $m - 8n - m - 5$
18. $8a - 3b - 5a - 5b$
19. $2p - 2j - 5p - 5j$
20. $6p - 5 - 6p - 3$
21. $x + 4 - 3 - 5x$
22. $5y^3 + 4 - 5y^3 - 4$
23. $k^2 + 5g^3 - k^2 - 8g^3$
24. $4mn - 6m^2 - 12mn + 8m^2$

6.2 You can multiply and divide with numbers and letters

Key Points

⊙ When you multiply terms and variables in algebra you can combine them by writing them next to each other.

So $\quad p \times q \quad$ is written as $\quad pq$

and $\quad a \times a \quad$ is written as $\quad aa \quad$ or $\quad a^2 \quad$ (a squared)

while $\quad a \times a \times a$ is written as $\quad aaa \quad$ or $\quad a^3 \quad$ (a cubed).

⊙ Dividing algebraic expressions is like cancelling fractions.

So $10a \div 2 = 5a$, and $\dfrac{b^3}{b} = b^2$

Example 3 Simplify **a** $2a \times 3a \times 4b$ **b** $\dfrac{20ab}{5b}$

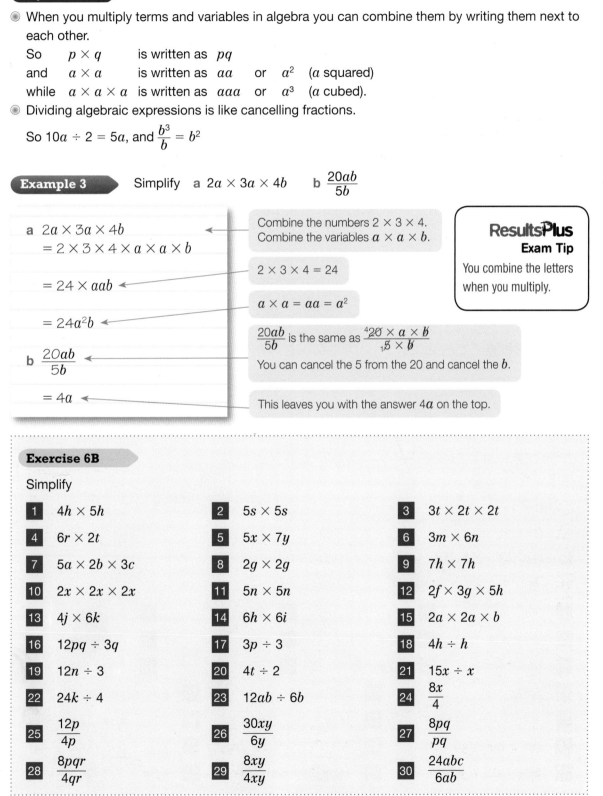

a $2a \times 3a \times 4b$

$= 2 \times 3 \times 4 \times a \times a \times b$

$= 24 \times aab$

$= 24a^2b$

b $\dfrac{20ab}{5b}$

$= 4a$

Combine the numbers $2 \times 3 \times 4$.
Combine the variables $a \times a \times b$.

$2 \times 3 \times 4 = 24$

$a \times a = aa = a^2$

$\dfrac{20ab}{5b}$ is the same as $\dfrac{^4 \cancel{20} \times a \times \cancel{b}}{_1 \cancel{5} \times \cancel{b}}$

You can cancel the 5 from the 20 and cancel the b.

This leaves you with the answer $4a$ on the top.

ResultsPlus
Exam Tip

You combine the letters when you multiply.

Exercise 6B

Simplify

1 $4h \times 5h$

2 $5s \times 5s$

3 $3t \times 2t \times 2t$

4 $6r \times 2t$

5 $5x \times 7y$

6 $3m \times 6n$

7 $5a \times 2b \times 3c$

8 $2g \times 2g$

9 $7h \times 7h$

10 $2x \times 2x \times 2x$

11 $5n \times 5n$

12 $2f \times 3g \times 5h$

13 $4j \times 6k$

14 $6h \times 6i$

15 $2a \times 2a \times b$

16 $12pq \div 3q$

17 $3p \div 3$

18 $4h \div h$

19 $12n \div 3$

20 $4t \div 2$

21 $15x \div x$

22 $24k \div 4$

23 $12ab \div 6b$

24 $\dfrac{8x}{4}$

25 $\dfrac{12p}{4p}$

26 $\dfrac{30xy}{6y}$

27 $\dfrac{8pq}{pq}$

28 $\dfrac{8pqr}{4qr}$

29 $\dfrac{8xy}{4xy}$

30 $\dfrac{24abc}{6ab}$

D

6.3 You can expand single brackets

Key Points

● To expand a bracket, multiply everything inside the bracket by what is outside.
● To simplify an expression with brackets, expand the brackets and collect like terms.

Example 4

a Expand $2(3a + 6)$ b Expand $a(2a + 5)$
c Simplify $8(2x + 3) - 3(x - 2)$

a $2(3a + 6)$
$= 2 \times (3a + 6)$ $2(3a + 6)$ means $2 \times (3a + 6)$

$= 2 \times 3a + 2 \times 6$ You multiply everything inside the bracket by the 2.

$= 6a + 12$ You multiply the $3a$ by the 2 and the 6 by the 2.
$2 \times 3a + 2 \times 6$
The + sign follows down.

b $a \times (2a + 5)$

$= a \times 2a + a \times 5$ $a(2a + 5)$ means $a \times (2a + 5)$.
You multiply everything inside the bracket by the a.

$= 2aa + 5a$ You multiply the $2a$ by the a and the 5 by the a.

$= 2a^2 + 5a$ $2a \times a + a \times 5$

Don't forget $a \times a = aa = a^2$
The + sign follows down.

c $8(2x + 3) - 3(x - 2)$

$= 8 \times 2x + 8 \times 3 - 3 \times x - 3 \times -2$ Multiply each term in the second bracket by -3.

$= 16x + 24 - 3x + 6$ $-3 \times -2 = +6$

$= 13x + 30$ Collect the like terms.

Exercise 6C

Expand

1	$5(a - 4)$	2	$6(n + 2)$	3	$5(4 - h)$	4	$3(7 - w)$
5	$3(2a - 5)$	6	$6(2n + 7)$	7	$5(4 - 3h)$	8	$3(7 - 4w)$
9	$a(a + 4)$	10	$y(2y - 2)$	11	$g(5 + g)$	12	$h(4 - 5h)$
13	$5p(2p + 3)$	14	$5x(3x - y)$	15	$3(x + 2) + 2(x + 4)$
16	$4(2x - 1) + 3(4x + 7)$	17	$5(3x + 2) + 4(2x + 1)$	18	$7(3 - 2x) + 3(2x - 3)$
19	$6(4 - 2x) - 3(5 + 3x)$	20	$4(3 - 2x) + 3(1 - 5x)$	21	$2(3x - 5y) + 3(2x - 4y)$
22	$5(6y + 2x) - 4(3x + 2y)$	23	$x(x + 3) + 5(x - 2)$	24	$y(2y + 3) - 2(y - 4)$

D

C

6.4 You can factorise expressions

Key Points

⦿ Putting in a bracket is called factorising.
⦿ Factorising is the reverse process to expanding brackets.

Example 5

a Factorise $2a + 10$.
b Factorise completely $10a^2 - 15ab$.

'Factorise' means take out the common factor of the terms in the expression, i.e. factors that are in both terms.

a $2a + 10$
$= 2 \times a + 2 \times 5$

$2a = 2 \times a$ 2 and a are factors of $2a$.
$10 = 2 \times 5$ 2 and 5 are factors of 10.

$= 2(a + 5)$

You take the 2 and put it outside the bracket. That leaves the a and the $+ 5$ inside the bracket.

ResultsPlus
Exam Tip

When you see the word 'factorise' it means you put the bracket back in.

b $10a^2 - 15ab$
$= 5a(2a - 3b)$

The common factor may be both a number and a letter.
Take $5a$ outside the bracket. It is a common factor of both $10a^2$ and $15ab$.

Exercise 6D

Hint: Always check your answer by expanding.

Factorise each of the expressions in questions 1–6.

1 a $2x + 6$ b $6y + 2$ c $15b - 5$
   d $3x + 5xy$ e $12x + 8y$ f $12x - 16$

2 a $3x^2 + 4x$ b $5y^2 - 3y$ c $5b^2 - 2b$
   d $7c - 3c^2$ e $6m^2 - m$ f $4xy + 3x$

3 a $8x^2 + 4x$ b $6p^2 + 3p$ c $6x^2 - 3x$
   d $3b^2 - 9b$ e $12a + 3a^2$ f $15c - 10c^2$

4 a $ax^2 + ax$ b $pr^2 - pr$ c $ab^2 - ab$
   d $qr^2 + q^2$ e $a^2x + ax^2$ f $6a^3 - 9a^2$

5 a $12a^2b + 18ab^2$ b $4x^2y - 2xy^2$ c $4a^2b + 8ab^2 + 12ab$
   d $4x^2y + 6xy^2 - 2xy$ e $12ax^2 + 6a^2x - 3ax$ f $a^2bc + ab^2c + abc^2$

6 a $5x + 20$ b $12y - 10$ c $3x^2 + 5x$
   d $4y - 3y^2$ e $8a + 6a^2$ f $12b^2 - 8b$
   g $cy^2 + cy$ h $3dx^2 - 6dx$ i $9c^2d + 15cd^2$

7 a Factorise $ax + ay$.
   b Work out $13 \times 2883 + 13 \times 117$.

Hint: Think of 13 as a and the other numbers as x and y.

6.5 You can replace letters with numbers

Key Point

◉ You can substitute values into an algebraic expression to work out the value of the expression.

Example 6

$a = 4$ and $b = 5$
Work out the value of

    a $3a - b$ **b** $3ab$ **c** $a^2 + 2b$ **d** $6(a + b)$

a $3a - b = 3 \times 4 - 5$

        $= 12 - 5$

        $= 7$

> The numbers replace the letters so $3a = 3 \times 4$ and $b = 5$.
>
> Remember: multiplication before subtraction.

b $3ab = 3 \times 4 \times 5 = 60$

> $3ab = 3 \times a \times b$

c $a^2 + 2b = 4 \times 4 + 2 \times 5$

          $= 16 + 10$

          $= 26$

> $a^2 = a \times a = 4 \times 4$

d $6(a + b) = 6(4 + 5)$

           $= 6(9) = 54$

> First work out the bracket and then multiply by 6.

Exercise 6E

Find the value of these expressions when $a = 2$, $b = 5$ and $c = 3$.

1 $b + b + b$	**2** $b - a$	**3** $5c$	**4** $3b + c$
5 $2b - a$	**6** $5c + 2a$	**7** $2b - c$	**8** $4b - 5a$
9 $6a + 3b$	**10** $a + b + c$	**11** $2a + 4b - 8c$	**12** $5c - 4c$
13 $3(a + 2b)$	**14** $5(a + 2c)$	**15** $4(c - b)$	**16** $5(2a - b)$
17 $5(c + 2a)$	**18** $2(2b - 3c)$	**19** $4(5b - 3a)$	**20** $4(2b - 3c)$
21 $6(a + 3b)$	**22** $2(a + b + c)$	**23** $2(a - 4b)$	**24** $5(c - a - b)$

25 $p = 3$, $q = 2$, $r = 5$ and $s = 0$

Work out the value of the following expressions.

    a $p + r$ **b** $5p - 2r$ **c** pqr

    d $pr - pq$ **e** $4(p + 7)$ **f** $p(q + 4)$

    g $p(r - q)$ **h** $r^2 + 1$ **i** $(p + r)^2$

F

D

Example 7 $p = 2$, $q = -3$ and $r = -5$
Work out the value of

   a $q - r$ b qr c $p(q + r)$ d $r^2 + 6r$

a $q - r = -3 - (-5)$
   $= -3 + 5$
   $= 2$

Subtracting a negative number is the same as adding a positive number.

b $qr = -3 \times -5$
   $= 15$

When you multiply two numbers which have the same sign the answer is positive.

c $p(q + r) = 2 \times (-3 + -5)$
   $= 2(-8)$
   $= -16$

A bracket means times.
Work out the value of the bracket first.

d $r^2 + 6r = (-5)^2 + 6 \times -5$
   $= (-5 \times -5) - 30$
   $= 25 - 30$
   $= -5$

Square and multiply before adding.

Exercise 6F

In this exercise $a = -5$, $b = 6$, $c = -2$, $d = \frac{1}{2}$ and $e = 1$.

Work out the value of the following expressions.

1 $b(c - a)$ 2 $c(a + b)$ 3 $3bc$

4 $bd - 1$ 5 $ab - bc$ 6 $2ab + 3ac$

7 $3ac - 2bc$ 8 $abcd$ 9 $3d(a + 1)$

10 $5(c - 1)$ 11 $a(b + c)$ 12 a^2

13 $3c^2d$ 14 $4a^2 - 3$ 15 $5c^2 + 3c$

16 $2a^2 - 3a$ 17 $(a + 1)^2$ 18 $(c + 3)^2$

19 $(a + b)^2$ 20 $(a + c)^2$ 21 $(c - a)^2$

22 $2b^3$ 23 $3a^3$ 24 $6c^3$

25 $2(b + c)^2$ 26 $a^2 - b^2$ 27 $(a - c)^3$

28 Tilly says that when $g = 4$, the value of $2g^2$ is 64.
    Meg says that when $g = 4$, the value of $2g^2$ is 32.
    Which girl is correct? You must explain your answer.

E

D

A03

6.6 You can use powers in algebra to simplify expressions

Key Points

- In the expression x^n, the number n is called the power or index.
- $x^m \times x^n = x^{m+n}$
- $x^m \div x^n = x^{m-n}$
- $(x^m)^n = x^{m \times n}$
- Any variable raised to the power of 1 is equal to the variable itself, e.g. $x^1 = x$.
- Any variable raised to the power 0 is equal to 1, e.g. $x^0 = 1$.

Example 8 Simplify **a** $x^5 \times x^3$ **b** $y^7 \div y^4$ **c** $a^3 \times a \times a^5$ **d** $(x^3)^2$
e $3x^2 \times 4x^3$ **f** $10x^6 \div 5x^3$ **g** $(3a^2)^4$

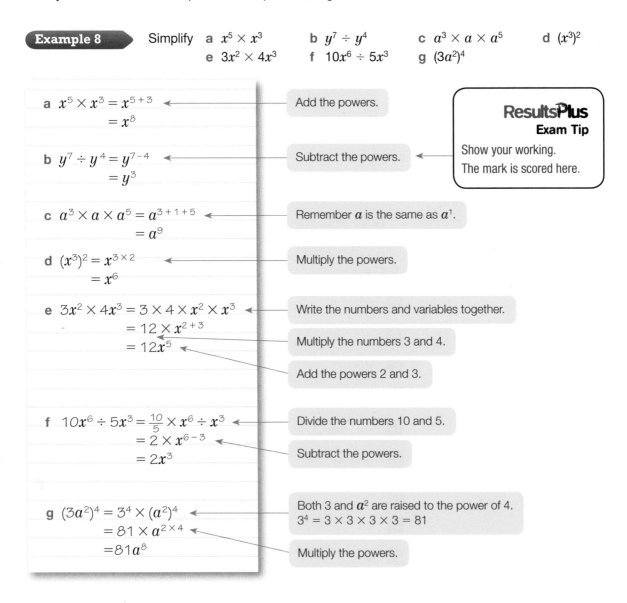

a $x^5 \times x^3 = x^{5+3}$ ← Add the powers.
$= x^8$

ResultsPlus
Exam Tip
Show your working.
The mark is scored here.

b $y^7 \div y^4 = y^{7-4}$ ← Subtract the powers.
$= y^3$

c $a^3 \times a \times a^5 = a^{3+1+5}$ ← Remember a is the same as a^1.
$= a^9$

d $(x^3)^2 = x^{3 \times 2}$ ← Multiply the powers.
$= x^6$

e $3x^2 \times 4x^3 = 3 \times 4 \times x^2 \times x^3$ ← Write the numbers and variables together.
$= 12 \times x^{2+3}$ ← Multiply the numbers 3 and 4.
$= 12x^5$ ← Add the powers 2 and 3.

f $10x^6 \div 5x^3 = \frac{10}{5} \times x^6 \div x^3$ ← Divide the numbers 10 and 5.
$= 2 \times x^{6-3}$ ← Subtract the powers.
$= 2x^3$

g $(3a^2)^4 = 3^4 \times (a^2)^4$ ← Both 3 and a^2 are raised to the power of 4. $3^4 = 3 \times 3 \times 3 \times 3 = 81$
$= 81 \times a^{2 \times 4}$ ← Multiply the powers.
$= 81a^8$

Exercise 6G

Simplify the following.

1 **a** $x^8 \times x^2$ **b** $y^3 \times y^8$ **c** $x^9 \times x^5$

2 **a** $a^5 \times a^3$ **b** $b^3 \times b^3$ **c** $d^7 \times d^4$

3 **a** $p^5 \div p^2$ **b** $q^{12} \div q^2$ **c** $t^8 \div t^4$

4 **a** $j^9 \div j^3$ **b** $k^5 \div k^4$ **c** $n^{25} \div n^{23}$

5 **a** $x^5 \times x^2 \times x^2$ **b** $y^2 \times y^4 \times y^3$ **c** $z^3 \times z^5 \times z^2$

6 **a** $3x^2 \times 2x^3$ **b** $5y^9 \times 3y^{20}$ **c** $6z^8 \times 4z^2$

7 **a** $12p^8 \div 4p^3$ **b** $15q^5 \div 3q^3$ **c** $6r^5 \div 3r^2$

8 **a** $(d^3)^4$ **b** $(e^5)^2$ **c** $(f^3)^3$ **d** $(g^7)^9$

9 **a** $(g^6)^4$ **b** $(h^2)^2$ **c** $(k^4)^0$ **d** $(m^0)^{56}$

10 **a** $(3d^2)^7$ **b** $(4e)^3$ **c** $(3f^{129})^0$

11 **a** $a^4 \times \dfrac{a^5}{a^9}$ **b** $b^7 \times \dfrac{b}{b^4}$ **c** $c^3 \times \dfrac{c^4}{c^2} \times c^5$

12 **a** $4d^9 \times 2d$ **b** $8e^8 \div 4e^4$ **c** $(4f^2)^2$

13 **a** $\dfrac{x^5 \times x^6}{x^{10}}$ **b** $\dfrac{y \times y^8}{y^3}$ **c** $\dfrac{z^7 \times z^9}{z^3 \times z^5}$

14 **a** $\dfrac{7d^2 \times 8d^4}{2d^3}$ **b** $\dfrac{3e \times 4e^9}{6e^5}$ **c** $\dfrac{5f^6 \times 6f^5}{10f^4}$

15 **a** $(3g^5)^2$ **b** $(2h^2)^4$ **c** $(10i^8)^3$

16 Keith asks five friends to work out $(2x^4)^3$.
Amy says $6x^7$, Bob says $6x^{12}$, Con says $8x^7$, Davish says $8x^{12}$ and Ed says $8x^{64}$.
Who is correct? Explain why.

17 Simplify
  a $15a^5b^6 \div 3a^3b^2$ **b** $30p^3q^4 \div 6p^2q$ **c** $\dfrac{8c^4d^7}{2c^2d^3}$ **d** $\dfrac{6x^3 \times 2x^4}{4x^2}$
  e $\dfrac{5m^2n \times 4mn^2}{2mn^2}$

18 Simplify
  a $(2x^3y^2)^4$ **b** $(7e^5f^3)^2$ **c** $(5p^5q)^3$ **d** $\left(\dfrac{2x^4y^2}{3xy^4}\right)^3$

19 Simplify
  a a^{-1} **b** $(b^2)^{-1}$ **c** c^{-2} **d** $(d^3)^{-1}$

20 Simplify
  a $(e^3)^{-2}$ **b** $(f^2)^{-4}$ **c** $(x^{-1})^{-2}$ **d** $(y^{-1})^{-1}$

6.7 You can multiply out the product of two brackets

Key Points

- To multiply out the product of two brackets:
  - multiply each term in the first bracket by the second bracket
  - expand the brackets
  - simplify the resulting expression.
- An alternative method is the grid method (see Example 9).

Example 9   Expand and simplify $(x + 2)(x + 3)$.

Method 1

$$(x + 2)(x + 3) = x(x + 3) + 2(x + 3)$$
$$= x^2 + 3x + 2x + 6$$
$$= x^2 + 5x + 6$$

Take each term in the first bracket, in turn, and multiply it by the second bracket.

Expand the brackets.

Collect the like terms.

Method 2 – the grid method

	x	$+3$
x	x^2	$+3x$
$+2$	$+2x$	$+6$

Each term in the first bracket is multiplied by each term in the second bracket.

$$(x + 2)(x + 3) = x^2 + 3x + 2x + 6$$
$$= x^2 + 5x + 6$$

Add the four terms highlighted.

Collect like terms.

Example 10   Expand and simplify $(3t - 2)^2$.

$$(3t - 2)^2 = (3t - 2)(3t - 2)$$
$$= 3t(3t - 2) - 2(3t - 2)$$
$$= 9t^2 - 6t - 6t + 4$$
$$= 9t^2 - 12t + 4$$

Write out $(3t - 2)^2$ in full.

Check your signs are correct.

Exercise 6H

1   Expand and simplify

   a $(x + 3)(x + 4)$ **b** $(x + 1)(x + 2)$ **c** $(x + 2)(x - 5)$

   d $(y - 2)(y + 3)$ **e** $(y + 1)(y - 2)$ **f** $(x - 2)(x - 3)$

   g $(a - 4)(a - 5)$ **h** $(x + 2)^2$ **i** $(k - 7)^2$

2   Expand and simplify

   a $(x + 1)(2x + 1)$ **b** $(x - 1)(3x + 1)$ **c** $(y - 3)(3y + 1)$

   d $(2p + 1)(p + 3)$ **e** $(3s + 2)(2s + 5)$ **f** $(2x - 3)(2x + 5)$

   g $(2a - 1)(3a - 2)$ **h** $(3x + 2)^2$ **i** $(2k - 1)^2$

3   Expand and simplify

   a $(x + y)(x + 2y)$ **b** $(x - y)(x + 2y)$ **c** $(x - y)(x - 2y)$

   d $(3s - 2t)(2s - t)$ **e** $(2a + 3b)^2$ **f** $(2a - 3b)^2$

B

A

6.8 You can factorise simple quadratic expressions

Key Points

- Factorising is the reverse process to expanding brackets so, for example, factorising $x^2 + 5x + 6$ gives $(x + 2)(x + 3)$.

- To factorise the quadratic expression $x^2 + bx + c$
  - find two numbers, p and q, whose product is $+c$ and whose sum is $+b$
  - use these two numbers, p and q, to write down the factorised form $(x + p)(x + q)$.

- Any expression which may be written in the form $a^2 - b^2$, known as the difference of two squares, can be factorised using the result $a^2 - b^2 = (a + b)(a - b)$.

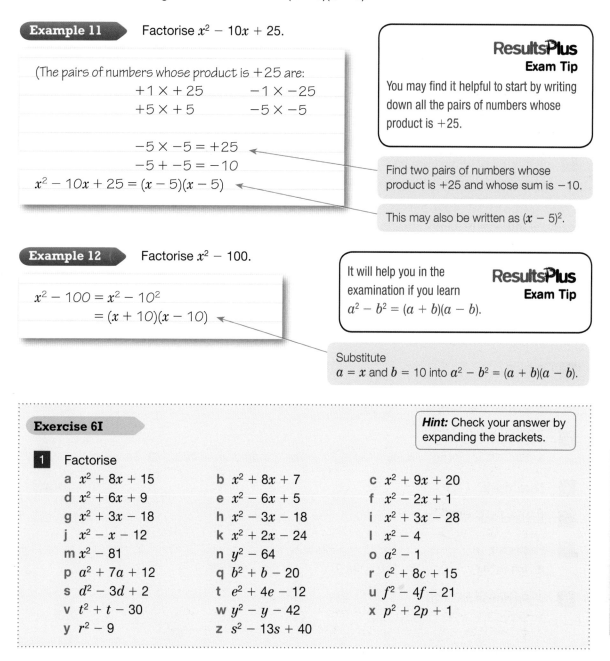

Example 11   Factorise $x^2 - 10x + 25$.

(The pairs of numbers whose product is $+25$ are:

$$+1 \times +25 \qquad -1 \times -25$$
$$+5 \times +5 \qquad -5 \times -5$$

$$-5 \times -5 = +25$$
$$-5 + -5 = -10$$
$$x^2 - 10x + 25 = (x - 5)(x - 5)$$

ResultsPlus
Exam Tip

You may find it helpful to start by writing down all the pairs of numbers whose product is $+25$.

Find two pairs of numbers whose product is $+25$ and whose sum is -10.

This may also be written as $(x - 5)^2$.

Example 12   Factorise $x^2 - 100$.

$$x^2 - 100 = x^2 - 10^2$$
$$= (x + 10)(x - 10)$$

It will help you in the examination if you learn $a^2 - b^2 = (a + b)(a - b)$.

ResultsPlus
Exam Tip

Substitute $a = x$ and $b = 10$ into $a^2 - b^2 = (a + b)(a - b)$.

Exercise 6I

Hint: Check your answer by expanding the brackets.

1 Factorise

  a $x^2 + 8x + 15$ **b** $x^2 + 8x + 7$ **c** $x^2 + 9x + 20$

  d $x^2 + 6x + 9$ **e** $x^2 - 6x + 5$ **f** $x^2 - 2x + 1$

  g $x^2 + 3x - 18$ **h** $x^2 - 3x - 18$ **i** $x^2 + 3x - 28$

  j $x^2 - x - 12$ **k** $x^2 + 2x - 24$ **l** $x^2 - 4$

  m $x^2 - 81$ **n** $y^2 - 64$ **o** $a^2 - 1$

  p $a^2 + 7a + 12$ **q** $b^2 + b - 20$ **r** $c^2 + 8c + 15$

  s $d^2 - 3d + 2$ **t** $e^2 + 4e - 12$ **u** $f^2 - 4f - 21$

  v $t^2 + t - 30$ **w** $y^2 - y - 42$ **x** $p^2 + 2p + 1$

  y $r^2 - 9$ **z** $s^2 - 13s + 40$

A

Exam review

Self-assessment checklist

I can:

- collect like terms and simplify the result [p. 54]
- multiply algebraic terms together to make a single term [p. 55]
- divide two algebraic terms to make a single term [p. 55]
- expand a single bracket [p. 56]
- factorise expressions by first taking out any common factors [p. 57]
- substitute values into an algebraic expression to work out the value of the expression [p. 58]
- use the rules for indices to simplify expressions involving indices [p. 60]
- multiply two brackets together and simplify the answer [p. 62]
- factorise an algebraic expression of the form $ax^2 + bx + c$ [p. 63]
- factorise an algebraic expression of the form $x^2 - a$ where a is a square number. [p. 63]

Exam practice

1 **a** Simplify $c + c + c$

    b Simplify $4x + 5y - 2x + y$

March 2011

2 In this set of rectangles, each expression in a rectangle is obtained by adding the two expressions immediately underneath.

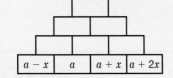

| $a - x$ | a | $a + x$ | $a + 2x$ |

What expression should go in the top square?

3 **a** Simplify $13x - 17y - 3x - 3y$.

    b Work out the value of $13 \times 99 - 17 \times 39 - 3 \times 99 - 3 \times 39$.

4 Simplify

    a $c + c + c$ **b** $e + f + e + f + e$ **c** $2a + 3a$

    d $2xy + 3xy - xy$ **e** $3a + 5b - a + 2b + 8$

June 2006

5 Simplify

    a $5bc + 2bc - 4bc$ **b** $4x + 3y - 2x + 2y$ **c** $m \times m \times m$ **d** $3n \times 2p$

Nov 2008

6 Factorise $x^2 + 4x$

June 2006

7 Expand $4(3a - 7)$

May 2008

8 Factorise

    a $5x + 15y$ **b** $15p - 9q$ **c** $cd + ce$

9 **a** Factorise $5p - 20$

    b Solve $3(x - 2) = x + 1$

March 2007

D

10 If $a = 1$, $b = 2$ and $c = -3$, find the value of

    a $\dfrac{c - ab}{c + ab}$ **b** $3(a + b)^2 - 2(b - c)^2$

11 $a = 4$, $b = \frac{1}{4}$, $c = -3$

    Work out

    a $\dfrac{5a}{b} + 7$ **b** $6a + \dfrac{2c}{3}$ **c** $3a - 6b + c$ **d** $a(a - 8b)$

12 $p = 2$

    Work out the value of $5p^2$.

13 $v = u + 10t$

    Work out the value of v when

    a $u = 10$ and $t = 7$

    b $u = -2.5$ and $t = 3.2$

14 **a** Work out the value of $2a + ay$ when $a = 5$ and $y = -3$.

    b Work out the value of $5t^2 - 7$ when $t = 4$.

15 Simplify

    a $x^6 \times x^3$ **b** $x^8 \div x^5$ **c** $(x^3)^5$ **d** $x^5 \div x^4$

    e $x \times x^4$ **f** $(x^6)^2$ **g** $x^8 \div x^8$ **h** $x^7 \div x$

    i $x^2 \times x^6 \times x^3$ **j** $x^8 \times x$ **k** $x^6 \times \dfrac{x^4}{x^7}$ **l** $x^3 \times \dfrac{x^7}{x^4} \times x^5$

16 Simplify

    a $4x^3 \times x^5$ **b** $3x^2 \times 5x^6$ **c** $7x \times 3x^4$ **d** $8x^9 \div 2x^5$

    e $24x^6 \div 3x$ **f** $36x^9 \div 4x^8$ **g** $(x^5)^2$ **h** $(x^3)^3$

17 Simplify

    a $a^3 \times a^4$ **b** $3x^2y \times 5xy^3$

18 Expand and simplify

    a $3a(b - 2a) + 2b(3a - 2b)$ **b** $4p(2q + 3p) + 3p(2p + q)$

    c $5c(3c + 2d) - 2c(c - d)$ **d** $a(a + b) + b(a + b)$

    e $3a(b + c) + 2b(a + c) - c(2a + 3b)$ **f** $2a(b - 2c) - 3b(2a + 3c)$

19 Factorise

    a $x^2 - 7x$ **b** $t^2 + at$ **c** $bx^2 - x$ **d** $3p^2 + py$ **e** $aq^2 - at$

20 **a** Factorise $x^2 - 5x$.

    b Work out the value of $105^2 - 5 \times 105$.   *Nov 2007 adapted*

21 $S = 2p + 3q$

    Work out the value of S when $p = -4$ and $q = 5$.

22 Expand and simplify $2(x - 4) + 3(x + 2)$ *June 2009*

23 **a** Factorise $5m + 10$ **b** Factorise $y^2 - 3y$ *Nov 2008*

C

A03

24 Expand and simplify $(x + 3)(x + 1)$ *Nov 2009*

ResultsPlus
Achieving Full Marks

■ C candidates
■ D candidates
100% 100%

To get both marks on this question, show all four terms in the expansion, before simplifying the expression.

25 **a** Expand and simplify $3(x + 5) + 2(5x - 6)$
  b Factorise **i** $5x + 10$ **ii** $x^2 - 7x$ *Nov 2010*

26 **a** Simplify **i** $c^5 \times c^6$ **ii** $e^{12} \div e^4$
  b Simplify fully $7x - 2(x - 3y) - 4y$ *Nov 2010*

27 Expand and simplify $(x + 4)(x - 3)$ *June 2009*

28 Expand **a** $(a + 2)^2$ **b** $(c - 3)^2$ **c** $(d + 1)^2$ **d** $(x + y)^2$

29 Expand and simplify
  a $(x + 5)(x + 10)$ **b** $(y + 9)^2$ **c** $(x - 4)(x + 2)$
  d $(x + 2)(x - 3)$ **e** $(t - 1)(t - 6)$ **f** $(x + 4)(2x + 3)$
  g $(3p - 1)(2p + 1)$ **h** $(2c + d)(2c - d)$ **i** $(4y - 1)^2$

30 Factorise
  a $t^2 + 11t + 30$ **b** $x^2 + 14x + 49$ **c** $p^2 + 2p - 15$
  d $y^2 - 12y + 36$ **e** $x^2 - 5x + 4$ **f** $s^2 - 64$

31 **a** Expand $3(x + 2)$
  b Factorise completely $12x^3y - 18xy^2$
  c Expand and simplify $(2x - 3)(x + 4)$
  d Simplify $5x^4y^3 \times 2x^3y^2$ *March 2011*

32 Expand and simplify $(2x + 4y)(4x - 5y)$ *Nov 2010*

33 **a** Factorise fully $20w^2y + 24wy^3$
  b Factorise $m^2 + 3m - 40$ *Nov 2010*

34 Simplify
  a $(a^5)^4$ **b** $(3b^4)^2$ **c** $(3e^5f)^3$

A03

35 The nth even number is $2n$.
Show algebraically that the sum of three consecutive even numbers is always a multiple of 6.
Nov 2008, adapted

A03

36 The expression $\dfrac{6x^2 y}{4y^3}$ can never take a negative value. Explain why.

37 Factorise
  a $x^2 - 400$ **b** $9t^2 - 4$ **c** $100 - y^2$ **d** $25 - 4p^2$

38 Use some of your answers to question 27 to work out the values of the following expressions without using a calculator.
  a $21^2 - 20^2$ **b** $10^2 - 9.9^2$ **c** $5^2 - 3^2$

7 SEQUENCES

7.1 You can continue and give the term-to-term rule for number patterns

Key Points

- A sequence is a pattern of numbers or shapes that follows a rule.
- Number patterns can be continued by adding, subtracting, multiplying and dividing.
- Patterns with pictures can be continued by finding the rule for continuing the pattern.
- The numbers in a number pattern are called terms.
- The term-to-term rule for a number pattern means you can say how you find a term from the one before it.

Example 1

a Write down the next two numbers in this number pattern.

2   6   10   14

b What is the rule you use to find the next number in the number pattern?

c Find the 10th number in this pattern.

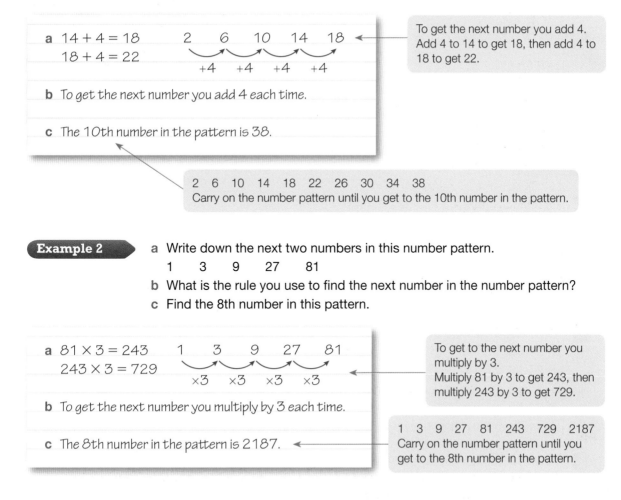

a $14 + 4 = 18$
$18 + 4 = 22$

To get the next number you add 4. Add 4 to 14 to get 18, then add 4 to 18 to get 22.

b To get the next number you add 4 each time.

c The 10th number in the pattern is 38.

2 6 10 14 18 22 26 30 34 38
Carry on the number pattern until you get to the 10th number in the pattern.

Example 2

a Write down the next two numbers in this number pattern.

1   3   9   27   81

b What is the rule you use to find the next number in the number pattern?

c Find the 8th number in this pattern.

a $81 \times 3 = 243$
$243 \times 3 = 729$

To get to the next number you multiply by 3.
Multiply 81 by 3 to get 243, then multiply 243 by 3 to get 729.

b To get the next number you multiply by 3 each time.

c The 8th number in the pattern is 2187.

1 3 9 27 81 243 729 2187
Carry on the number pattern until you get to the 8th number in the pattern.

Example 3

a Copy and complete the table for the number of matches used to make each member of the pattern.

Pattern number	1	2	3	4	5	6	7
Number of matches used	4	7	10				

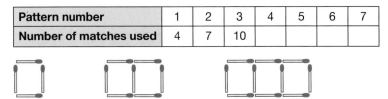

b Write down the rule to get the next number in the pattern.

c How many matches are there in pattern number 10?

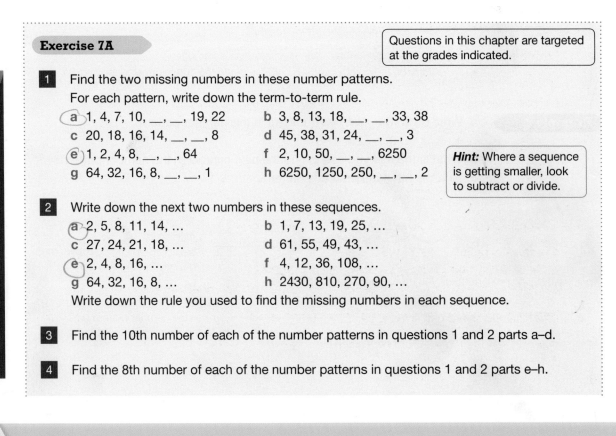

a

Pattern number	1	2	3	4	5	6	7
Number of matches used	4	7	10	13	16	19	22

Count the number of matches in each pattern and write down the number of matches used.

4   7   10

+3   +3   +3   +3

10 + 3 = 13   13 + 3 = 16
16 + 3 = 19   19 + 3 = 22

b Add 3 to the previous number.

c Pattern number 10 has 31 matches. ◄——— Continue the patterns.
22   25   28   31

Exercise 7A

Questions in this chapter are targeted at the grades indicated.

1 Find the two missing numbers in these number patterns.
For each pattern, write down the term-to-term rule.
   a 1, 4, 7, 10, __, __, 19, 22   b 3, 8, 13, 18, __, __, 33, 38
   c 20, 18, 16, 14, __, __, 8   d 45, 38, 31, 24, __, __, 3
   e 1, 2, 4, 8, __, __, 64   f 2, 10, 50, __, __, 6250
   g 64, 32, 16, 8, __, __, 1   h 6250, 1250, 250, __, __, 2

Hint: Where a sequence is getting smaller, look to subtract or divide.

2 Write down the next two numbers in these sequences.
   a 2, 5, 8, 11, 14, ...   b 1, 7, 13, 19, 25, ...
   c 27, 24, 21, 18, ...   d 61, 55, 49, 43, ...
   e 2, 4, 8, 16, ...   f 4, 12, 36, 108, ...
   g 64, 32, 16, 8, ...   h 2430, 810, 270, 90, ...
   Write down the rule you used to find the missing numbers in each sequence.

3 Find the 10th number of each of the number patterns in questions 1 and 2 parts a–d.

4 Find the 8th number of each of the number patterns in questions 1 and 2 parts e–h.

F

5 Abdul's mother gives him £20 each week to buy his lunch.
His lunch costs him £3 each day.
Here is the pattern of how he spends his money.

A03
E

Day	M	Tu	W	Th	F
Money left at end of day (£)	17	14			

How much money will Abdul have left at the end of the week?

6 Josie wants to buy her mum her favourite perfume as a birthday present.
The perfume costs £35.
Josie saves £3 the first week and then saves £2 each week.
The table should show the amount she has saved at the end of each week.

A02
A03

End of week	1	2	3	4
Total amount saved (£)	3	5	7	9

How long will it take Josie to save the full amount?

7 The number of rabbits in a particular colony doubled every month for 10 months.
The table shows the beginning of the pattern.

A02

Month	1	2	3	4	5
Number of rabbits	2	4	8		

a Copy and complete the table.
b How many rabbits were in the colony in month 10?

8 The number of radioactive atoms in a radioactive isotope halves every 10 years.
The table shows the beginning of the pattern.

A03

Years	0	10	20	30	40
Number of atoms	2560	1280	640		

a Copy and complete the table.
b How many radioactive atoms were in the isotope in year 100?

9 a Write down the number of matches in each of these patterns.

Pattern 1   Pattern 2   Pattern 3

b Draw the next two patterns.
c Write down the rule in words to continue the pattern.
d Use your rule to find the number of matches needed for pattern number 10.

10 Repeat question 9 with the triangular shape shown below.

7.2 You can find the *n*th term of a number pattern and can decide whether or not a number is in this number pattern

Key Points

⦿ The first difference can be used to find the *n*th term of a number pattern and then the *n*th term can be used to find any number in a sequence.

⦿ Number patterns or the *n*th term can be used to identify whether a number is in the pattern.

⦿ Sometimes you will be asked how you know if a number is part of a sequence. You would then have to explain why the number is in the sequence, or, why it is not in the sequence.

Example 4

Here is a number pattern 4, 7, 10, 13, 16, …

a Find the *n*th term in this number pattern.

b Find the 20th term in this number pattern

a

Term number	Term	Difference
1	4	+3
2	7	+3
3	10	+3
4	13	+3
5	16	
n	$3n + 1$	

b The 20th term is 61.

Step 1
Put the number pattern into a table of values.

Step 2
Find the difference between the terms in the number pattern. In this case it is +3.

Step 3
Multiply each term number by the difference to get a new pattern.
3, 6, 9, 12, 15 …

Step 4
Compare your new pattern with the original one and see what number you need to add or subtract to/from each term to get the original number pattern. In this case it is **+1**.
The *n*th term is $3n + 1$.
You replace the *n* by 20 in the *n*th term to find the 20th term. It is $3 \times 20 + 1 = 61$

Example 5

Here is a number pattern. 3 8 13 18 23

a Explain why 423 is in the pattern.   b Explain why 325 is not in the pattern.

a 423 is in the number pattern.
Every odd term ends in 3 and goes up
3, 13, 23, etc,
so 423 will be a member as it ends in a 3.

There are other ways of answering questions like these. For example, you could identify the *n*th term.
The *n*th term is $5n - 2$
$$\text{if } 5n - 2 = 423$$
$$5n = 425 \text{ so } n = 85$$
so 423 is the 85th term.

b 325 is not in the number pattern.
325 ends in a 5 and every member
of the pattern ends in either a 3 or
an 8 so 325 cannot be in the pattern.

The *n*th term is $5n - 2$ so if 325 is in the pattern.
$$5n - 2 = 325$$
$$5n = 327 \quad \text{so} \quad n = 65.4$$
If 325 is in the pattern *n* must be a whole number.
65.4 is not a whole number so 325 is not in the pattern.

Exercise 7B

A03

1. Write each pattern in a table and use the table to find the nth term of these number patterns. Use your nth term to find the 20th term in each of these number patterns.

   a 2, 5, 8, 11, 14, 17, ...   **b** 5, 8, 11, 14, 17, 20, ...

   c 1, 5, 9, 13, 17, 21, ...   **f** 2, 7, 12, 17, 22, 27, ...

   e 8, 13, 18, 23, 28, ...   **f** 40, 35, 30, 25, 20, ...

   g 35, 32, 29, 26, 23, ...   **h** 20, 18, 16, 14, 12, ...

   >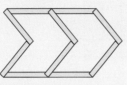
   > **Results**Plus
   > **Exam Tip**
   > To find the nth term of a sequence that gets smaller you subtract a multiple of n from a fixed number.
   > e.g. $15 - 2n$ is the nth term of 13, 11, 9, 7, ...

2. Here is a pattern made from sticks.

   Pattern number 1   Pattern number 2   Pattern number 3

   a Draw pattern number 4.

   b Copy and complete this table of values for the number of sticks used to make the patterns.

Pattern number	1	2	3	4	5	6
Number of sticks	6	10				

   c Write, in terms of n, the number of sticks needed for pattern number n.

   d How many sticks would be needed for pattern number 20?

3. For each of these number patterns, explain whether each of the numbers in brackets are members of the number pattern or not.

   a 1, 3, 5, 7, 9, 11, ...   (21, 34)   **b** 2, 5, 8, 11, 14, 17, ...   (50, 66)

   c 5, 8, 11, 14, 17, 20, ...   (50, 62)   **d** 2, 7, 12, 17, 22, 27, ...   (97, 120)

   e 40, 35, 30, 25, 20, ...   (85, 4)   **f** 3, 7, 11, 15, 19, 21, ...   (46, 79)

4. Here are the first four terms of an arithmetic sequence.

   A03

   3   7   11   15   ...

   Sandy claims that 201 is a term in this sequence.
   Is Sandy correct?

5. A gardener lays paving stones in the pattern shown here.

   A03

   Coloured paving stones cost £3 each and white paving stones cost £2 each.

   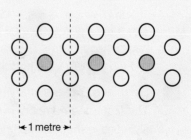

   ⟵ 1 metre ⟶

   The gardener wants to lay a path 16 metres long.

   a How much will the paving stones cost altogether?

   The gardener wants an algebraic expression for the cost of laying a path n metres long.

   b Find an expression, in terms of n for the cost in pounds of a path n metres long.

Exam review

Self-assessment checklist

I can:

- continue number patterns by adding or subtracting, or multiplying or dividing by a number [p. 67]
- give the term-to-term rule for number patterns [p. 67]
- find the nth term of a number pattern and use the nth term to find any number in a number pattern [p. 70]
- decide whether or not a number is in a number pattern. [p. 70]

Exam practice

1 Here are some patterns made of squares.

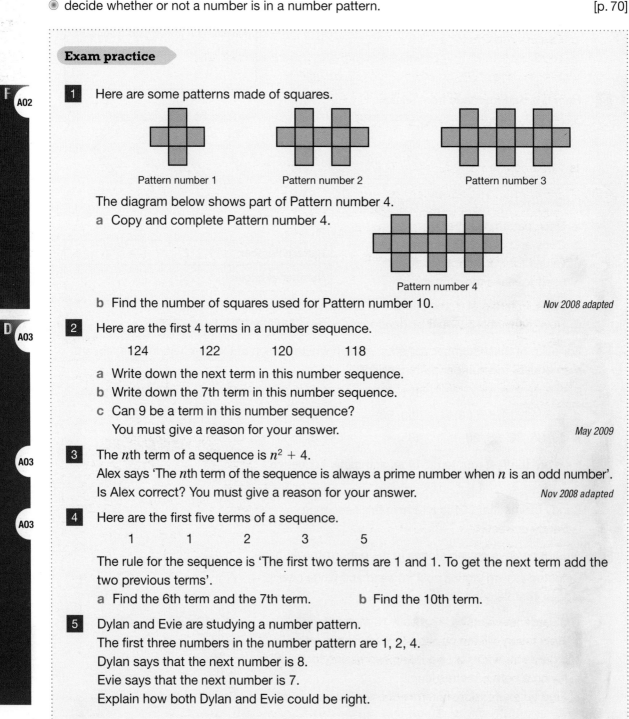

Pattern number 1   Pattern number 2   Pattern number 3

The diagram below shows part of Pattern number 4.

a Copy and complete Pattern number 4.

Pattern number 4

b Find the number of squares used for Pattern number 10. *Nov 2008 adapted*

2 Here are the first 4 terms in a number sequence.

124   122   120   118

a Write down the next term in this number sequence.
b Write down the 7th term in this number sequence.
c Can 9 be a term in this number sequence?
You must give a reason for your answer. *May 2009*

3 The nth term of a sequence is $n^2 + 4$.
Alex says 'The nth term of the sequence is always a prime number when n is an odd number'.
Is Alex correct? You must give a reason for your answer. *Nov 2008 adapted*

4 Here are the first five terms of a sequence.

1   1   2   3   5

The rule for the sequence is 'The first two terms are 1 and 1. To get the next term add the two previous terms'.

a Find the 6th term and the 7th term.   b Find the 10th term.

5 Dylan and Evie are studying a number pattern.
The first three numbers in the number pattern are 1, 2, 4.
Dylan says that the next number is 8.
Evie says that the next number is 7.
Explain how both Dylan and Evie could be right.

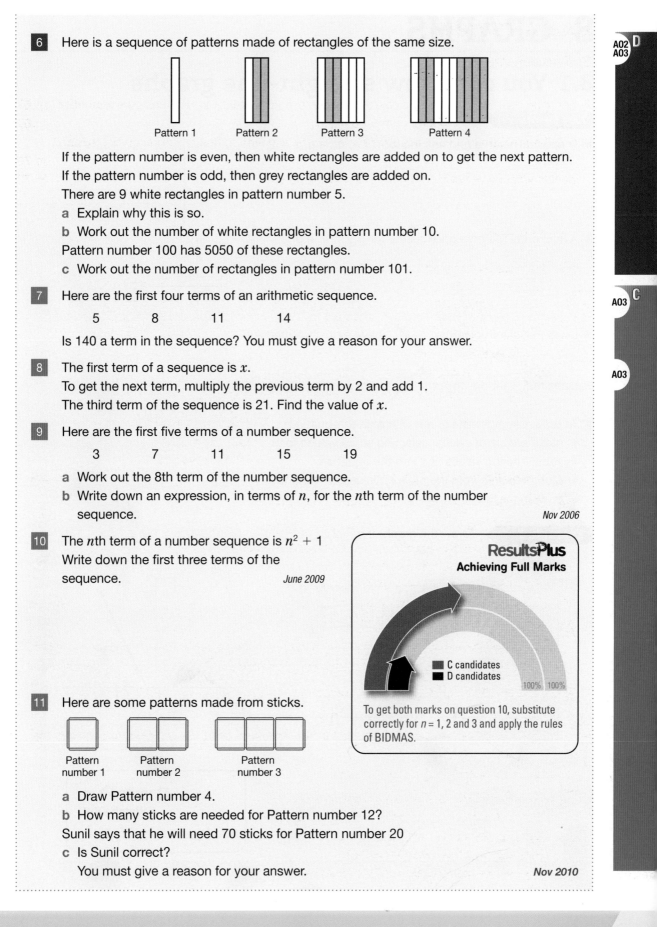

6   Here is a sequence of patterns made of rectangles of the same size.

Pattern 1   Pattern 2   Pattern 3   Pattern 4

If the pattern number is even, then white rectangles are added on to get the next pattern.
If the pattern number is odd, then grey rectangles are added on.
There are 9 white rectangles in pattern number 5.
a   Explain why this is so.
b   Work out the number of white rectangles in pattern number 10.
Pattern number 100 has 5050 of these rectangles.
c   Work out the number of rectangles in pattern number 101.

7   Here are the first four terms of an arithmetic sequence.

    5   8   11   14

Is 140 a term in the sequence? You must give a reason for your answer.

8   The first term of a sequence is x.
To get the next term, multiply the previous term by 2 and add 1.
The third term of the sequence is 21. Find the value of x.

9   Here are the first five terms of a number sequence.

    3   7   11   15   19

a   Work out the 8th term of the number sequence.
b   Write down an expression, in terms of n, for the nth term of the number
    sequence.   *Nov 2006*

10 The nth term of a number sequence is $n^2 + 1$
Write down the first three terms of the
sequence.   *June 2009*

ResultsPlus
Achieving Full Marks

■ C candidates
■ D candidates
100% 100%

To get both marks on question 10, substitute
correctly for $n = 1, 2$ and 3 and apply the rules
of BIDMAS.

11 Here are some patterns made from sticks.

Pattern   Pattern   Pattern
number 1   number 2   number 3

a   Draw Pattern number 4.
b   How many sticks are needed for Pattern number 12?
Sunil says that he will need 70 sticks for Pattern number 20
c   Is Sunil correct?
    You must give a reason for your answer.   *Nov 2010*

8 GRAPHS

8.1 You can draw straight-line graphs

Key Points

- A vertical line on a grid has the form $x = m$, e.g. $x = 2$

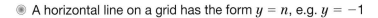

- A horizontal line on a grid has the form $y = n$, e.g. $y = -1$

- Lines that slant upwards ╱ have a positive gradient.

- Lines that slant downwards ╲ have a negative gradient.

- To draw a straight-line graph with a given equation:
  - make a table of values, selecting some values for x
  - substitute the values of x into the equation
  - plot the points from the table of values on the grid
  - draw in the line.

Example 1   Draw the graph of $y = 2x - 1$.

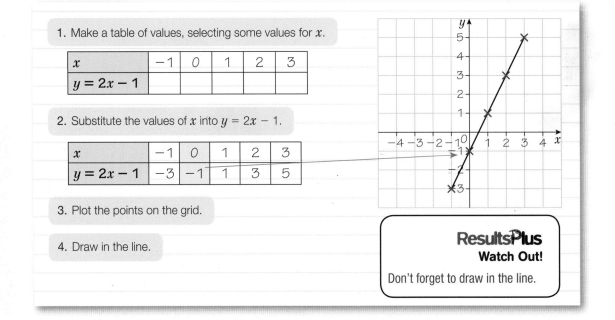

1. Make a table of values, selecting some values for x.

x	-1	0	1	2	3
$y = 2x - 1$					

2. Substitute the values of x into $y = 2x - 1$.

x	-1	0	1	2	3
$y = 2x - 1$	-3	-1	1	3	5

3. Plot the points on the grid.

4. Draw in the line.

ResultsPlus
Watch Out!
Don't forget to draw in the line.

Exercise 8A

Questions in this chapter are targeted at the grades indicated.

D

1 **a** Copy and complete the tables of values for the straight-line graphs below.

   b On a coordinate grid with the x-axis drawn from -3 to $+3$ and y-axis drawn from -10 to $+10$, draw the graphs of $y = x - 1$, $y = 2x - 4$, $y = 3x + 1$ and $y = x + 4$.

i

x	-3	-2	-1	0	1	2	3
$y = x - 1$		-3		-1	0	1	

ii

x	-3	-2	-1	0	1	2	3
$y = 2x - 4$		-8		-4		0	

iii

x	-3	-2	-1	0	1	2	3
$y = 3x + 1$	-8			1			10

iv

x	-3	-2	-1	0	1	2	3
$y = x + 4$			2		4		7

2 Draw the graphs of these straight lines on a coordinate grid with axes drawn from -4 to $+4$ on the x-axis and -10 to $+10$ on the y-axis.

   a $y = 2x + 1$ **b** $y = x - 3$ **c** $x = -3$ **d** $y = 3x + 2$

   e $y = \frac{1}{2}x + 3$ **f** $y = 2$ **g** $y = -3x$ **h** $y = x - 2$

Example 2   Draw the graph of $y = -2x - 1$.

1. Make a table of values, selecting some values for x.

x	-3	-2	-1	0	1
$y = -2x - 1$					

2. Substitute the values of x into $y = -2x - 1$.

x	-3	-2	-1	0	1
$y = -2x - 1$	5	3	1	-1	-3

3. Plot the points on the grid.

4. Draw in the line.

Exercise 8B

D

1 **a** Copy and complete the tables of values for the straight-line graphs below.

   b Draw the graphs of these straight lines on a coordinate grid with the x-axis drawn from -3 to $+3$ and y-axis drawn from -10 to $+10$.

i

x	-3	-2	-1	0	1	2	3
$y = -x - 1$		1		-1		-3	

ii

x	-3	-2	-1	0	1	2	3
$y = -2x - 4$			0		-4		-8

2 Draw the graphs of these straight lines on a coordinate grid with axes drawn from -4 to $+4$ on the x-axis and -10 to $+10$ on the y-axis.

   a $y = -2x + 1$ **b** $y = -x - 3$ **c** $y = -2$ **d** $y = 2 - 3x$

   e $y = -\frac{1}{2}x + 3$ **f** $x = 4$ **g** $y = -3x$ **h** $y = -x - 2$

8.2 You can draw and write the equations of straight-line graphs without a table of values

Key Points

- The equation of a straight-line graph can be written in the form $y = mx + c$.
  The number on its own (c) tells you where the straight line crosses the y-axis.
  The number (m) in front of the x tells you the gradient (steepness) of the line.
  - If m is positive the line will slope upwards from left to right.
  - If m is negative the line will slope downwards from left to right.
- To draw a straight line from the equation $y = mx + c$:
  - mark the point (c) where the line will cross the y-axis
  - find out the gradient – how many squares you go up (or down) each square you move to the right – from the number (m) in front of the x
  - join up the points with a straight line.
- When the line is in the form $x + y = c$ the c tells you where the graph cuts the x-axis and the y-axis.
- When you have a straight line for which you need to find the equation, you need to work out the gradient (the m in the equation) and look to see what the intercept on the y-axis is (the c in the equation). You then put these values in the equation $y = mx + c$ to find the equation of the line.

Example 3   On the grid, draw the graph of $y = 2x + 1$.

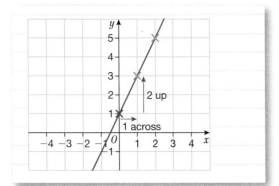

Step 1 Mark the point ✕ where the line will cross the y-axis.

Step 2 For each square you move to the right you then go up 2 because there is a 2 in front of the x.

Step 3 Join up the points with a straight line.

Example 4   On the grid, draw the graph of $x + y = 4$.

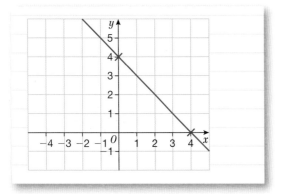

Step 1 Mark the value of the number on the x-axis and the y-axis.

Step 2 Join these points up with a straight line.

Exercise 8C

For each question, draw the graphs of all the straight lines on the same coordinate grid with the x-axis drawn from -3 to $+3$ and y-axis drawn from -10 to $+10$.

What do you notice about the set of graphs for each question?

1 **a** $y = x + 1$ **b** $y = x + 2$ **c** $y = x + 3$ **d** $y = x - 1$ **e** $y = x - 2$

2 **a** $y = -2x + 1$ **b** $y = -2x + 2$ **c** $y = -2x + 3$ **d** $y = -2x - 1$ **e** $y = -2x - 2$

3 **a** $y = 4x + 1$ **b** $y = 4x + 2$ **c** $y = 4x + 3$ **d** $y = 4x - 1$ **e** $y = 4x - 2$

4 **a** $x + y = 3$ **b** $x + y = 5$ **c** $x + y = 2$

5 Draw the graph of $y = 3x - 1$ for values of x from -2 to $+5$.

6 Draw the graph of $2x + y = 8$ for values of x from -1 to $+4$.

D

A02

A02

Example 5 Write down the equations of these straight lines.

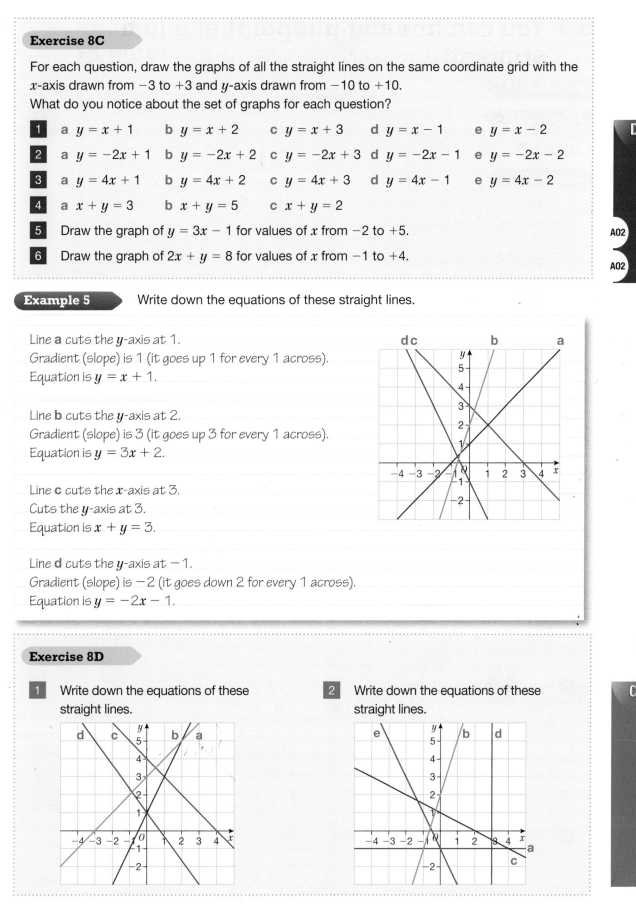

Line **a** cuts the y-axis at 1.
Gradient (slope) is 1 (it goes up 1 for every 1 across).
Equation is $y = x + 1$.

Line **b** cuts the y-axis at 2.
Gradient (slope) is 3 (it goes up 3 for every 1 across).
Equation is $y = 3x + 2$.

Line **c** cuts the x-axis at 3.
Cuts the y-axis at 3.
Equation is $x + y = 3$.

Line **d** cuts the y-axis at -1.
Gradient (slope) is -2 (it goes down 2 for every 1 across).
Equation is $y = -2x - 1$.

Exercise 8D

1 Write down the equations of these straight lines.

2 Write down the equations of these straight lines.

C

8.3 You can find the midpoint of a line segment

Key Points

- The midpoint of a line is halfway along the line.
- To find the midpoint you add the x-coordinates and divide by 2 and add the y-coordinates and divide by 2.

Example 6   Find the midpoint of RS.

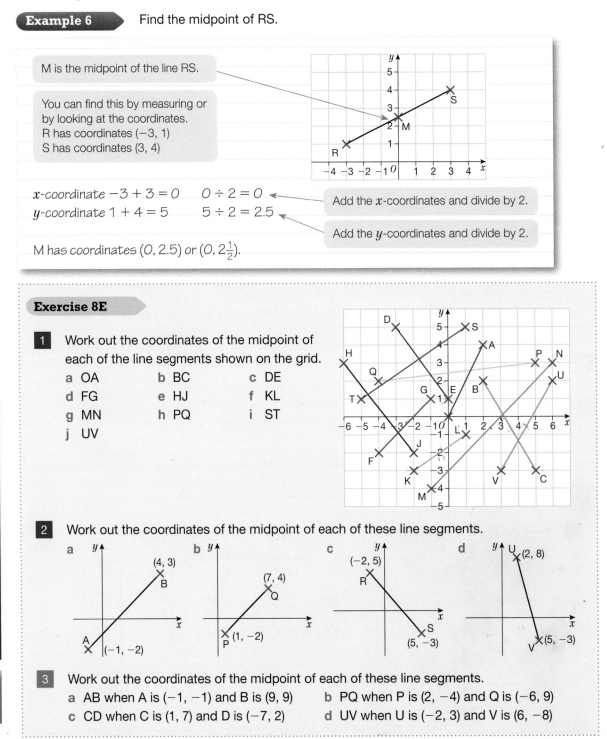

M is the midpoint of the line RS.

You can find this by measuring or by looking at the coordinates.
R has coordinates $(-3, 1)$
S has coordinates $(3, 4)$

x-coordinate $-3 + 3 = 0$ $0 \div 2 = 0$ Add the x-coordinates and divide by 2.
y-coordinate $1 + 4 = 5$ $5 \div 2 = 2.5$ Add the y-coordinates and divide by 2.

M has coordinates $(0, 2.5)$ or $(0, 2\frac{1}{2})$.

Exercise 8E

1 Work out the coordinates of the midpoint of each of the line segments shown on the grid.

  a OA   **b** BC   **c** DE
  d FG   **e** HJ   **f** KL
  g MN   **h** PQ   **i** ST
  j UV

2 Work out the coordinates of the midpoint of each of these line segments.

  a $(4, 3)$ B, A $(-1, -2)$
  b $(7, 4)$ Q, P $(1, -2)$
  c $(-2, 5)$ R, S $(5, -3)$
  d U $(2, 8)$, V $(5, -3)$

3 Work out the coordinates of the midpoint of each of these line segments.

  a AB when A is $(-1, -1)$ and B is $(9, 9)$ **b** PQ when P is $(2, -4)$ and Q is $(-6, 9)$
  c CD when C is $(1, 7)$ and D is $(-7, 2)$ **d** UV when U is $(-2, 3)$ and V is $(6, -8)$

D

C

8.4 You can interpret and draw graphs you meet in everyday life

Key Points

◉ Graphs can be used in real life to show the relationship between two variables, for example between the number of units of electricity used and what it costs to use them.

◉ A straight-line graph that goes through the origin means that the more items you buy the more it will cost you.

◉ A straight-line graph that does not cross the vertical axis at the origin means there is a basic charge and then the cost is related to the number of items you buy.

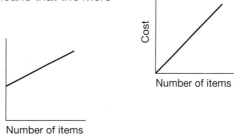

◉ Conversion graphs are used to convert measurements in one unit to measurements in a different unit. They can also be used to change between money systems in different countries.

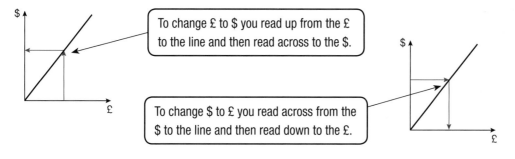

To change £ to $ you read up from the £ to the line and then read across to the $.

To change $ to £ you read across from the $ to the line and then read down to the £.

Example 7

Sam sells packets of crisps at 30p each.
He makes a table of values to help him remember what to charge people when they buy different numbers of packets of crisps.
Plot a graph to show this information.

This pattern goes up in 30s.

Number of packets	1	2	3	4	5	6
Cost in pence	30	60	90	120	150	180

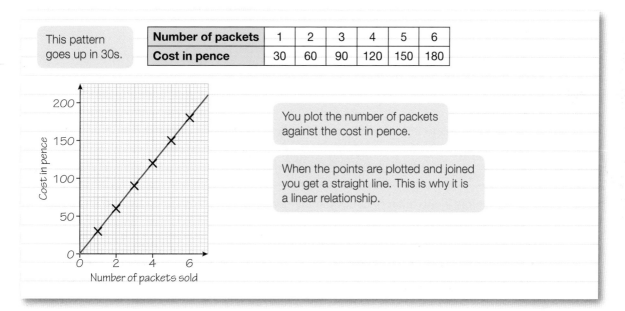

You plot the number of packets against the cost in pence.

When the points are plotted and joined you get a straight line. This is why it is a linear relationship.

Example 8

The conversion graph is used to convert between degrees Celsius (°C) and degrees Fahrenheit (°F).

a Use your conversion graph to convert **i** 60°C to °F   **ii** 80°F to °C

b Convert 160°C to °F.

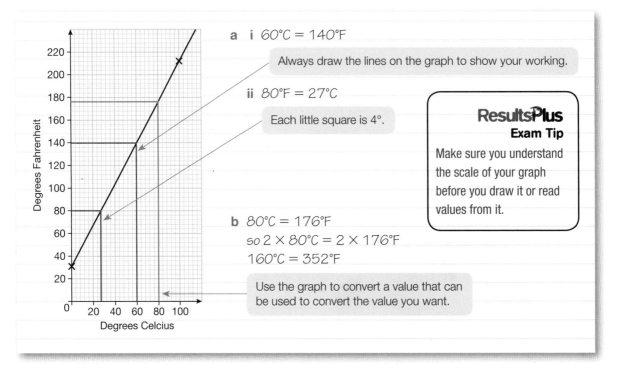

a i 60°C = 140°F

Always draw the lines on the graph to show your working.

ii 80°F = 27°C

Each little square is 4°.

ResultsPlus
Exam Tip

Make sure you understand the scale of your graph before you draw it or read values from it.

b 80°C = 176°F

so 2 × 80°C = 2 × 176°F

160°C = 352°F

Use the graph to convert a value that can be used to convert the value you want.

Exercise 8F

F

1 The table shows the cost of potatoes per kg.

Weight in kg	1	2	3	4	5
Cost in pence	30	60	90	120	150

a Draw a graph for this table.

b Work out how much 2.5 kg of potatoes would cost.

c Extend the graph to work out the cost of 6 kg of potatoes.

2 Bob has a contract phone. He pays £15 each month and then 10p for each minute he uses his phone.

a Copy and complete this table of values for the cost of using Bob's phone.

Minutes used	0	5	10	15	20	25	30	35	40	45	50
Cost in pounds	15		16								20

b Plot the points in the table on a coordinate grid and draw a graph to show the cost of using Bob's phone.

c Use your graph to find the cost of Bob using his phone for 32 minutes.

d One month Bob paid £17 to use his phone. For how many minutes did Bob use his phone that month?

3   The graph shows the cost of using
    a mobile phone for one month on
    three different tariffs.

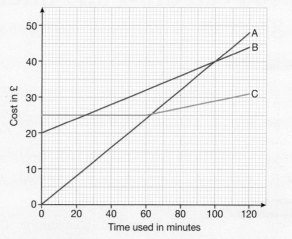

The three tariffs are

Tariff 1   Rental £20   every minute costs 20p
Tariff 2   Pay as you go   every minute costs 40p
Tariff 3   Rental £25   first 60 minutes free then each minute costs 10p

a Match each tariff with the letter of its graph.

Fiona uses her mobile phone for about 60 minutes each month.

b Explain which tariff would be the cheapest for her to use.
   You must give the reasons for your answer.

4

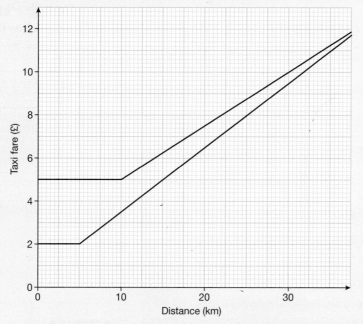

The graph shows the amount, in pounds, charged by two taxi firms.
Taxi firm A: charges £5 for up to 10 kilometres and then 25p for every extra kilometre.
Taxi firm B: charges £2 for up to 5 kilometres and then 30p for every extra kilometre.
a Copy the graphs and label with A and B to show which line represents each taxi firm.
b How much does taxi firm A charge for a 20 km journey?
c After how many kilometres does it become cheaper to use taxi firm A?
Taxi firm C charges £4 for the first 5 kilometres and then 20p for every extra kilometre.
James wants to travel 15 kilometres. He wants to pay as little as possible.
d Which taxi firm should James use? You must show how you obtained your answer.

8.5 You can draw and interpret distance–time graphs

Key Points

- On distance–time graphs:
  - time is always on the horizontal axis
  - distance is always on the vertical axis
  - a slanting line means movement is taking place
  - a horizontal line means no movement is taking place, the object is stationary.
- To work out speed you divide the distance travelled by the time taken.

Example 9

Mary travels to work by bus.
She walks the first 750 metres in 10 minutes, waits at the bus stop for 5 minutes, then travels the remaining 3000 metres by bus. She arrives at the work bus stop 21 minutes after she set off from home.
a Draw a distance–time graph of her journey.
b Work out the average speed of the bus in kilometres per hour.

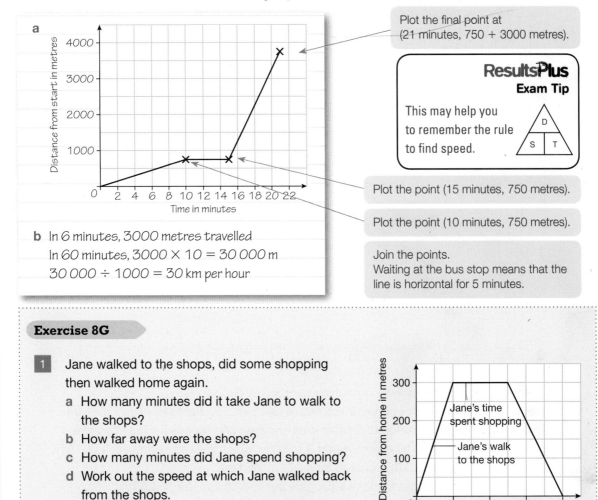

Plot the final point at (21 minutes, 750 + 3000 metres).

ResultsPlus
Exam Tip

This may help you to remember the rule to find speed.

Plot the point (15 minutes, 750 metres).

Plot the point (10 minutes, 750 metres).

Join the points.
Waiting at the bus stop means that the line is horizontal for 5 minutes.

b In 6 minutes, 3000 metres travelled
   In 60 minutes, 3000 × 10 = 30 000 m
   30 000 ÷ 1000 = 30 km per hour

Exercise 8G

C

1 Jane walked to the shops, did some shopping then walked home again.
   a How many minutes did it take Jane to walk to the shops?
   b How far away were the shops?
   c How many minutes did Jane spend shopping?
   d Work out the speed at which Jane walked back from the shops.
   First give your answer in metres per minute, then change it to km per hour.

* 2 Imran has a bath. The graph shows the depth of the bath water.

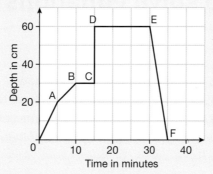

He starts at 0 by turning the hot and cold water taps on.

Between 0 and point A on the graph the depth of water goes up 20 cm in 5 minutes.

Explain what happens between points A and B, B and C, C and D, D and E, and E and F on the graph and how long each part of the process lasts.

3 Annabel travels to school. She walks 250 metres to the bus stop in 4 minutes, waits at the bus stop for about 5 minutes and then travels the remaining 1000 metres by bus.

She arrives at the bus stop outside the school 15 minutes after she sets off from home.

a Draw a distance–time graph of the journey.

b Work out the speed of the bus, first in metres per minute, then in km per hour.

4 Kunal drove to a football stadium to watch a match.

The travel graph shows this part of his journey. He arrived at the football stadium at 13.40.

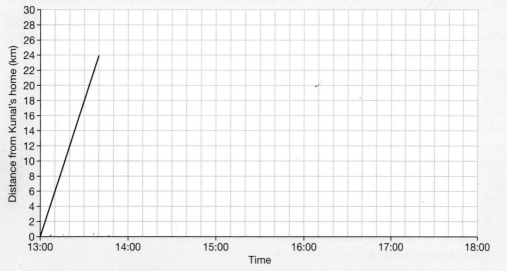

a How far was Kunal from home at 13.20?

b How far is the football stadium from Kunal's home?

c Work out Kunal's speed as he drove to the football stadium.
   Give your answer in km/h.

Kunal stayed at the football stadium for $2\frac{1}{2}$ hours.

On the way home the traffic was very slow.

Kunal drove home at an average speed of 18 km/h.

d Copy and complete the travel graph.

8.6 You can draw and use graphs of quadratic functions to solve equations

Key Points

⦿ For quadratic graphs such as $y = ax^2 + b$:
  ⦿ the number (b) that is on its own moves the graph up or down
  ⦿ the number (a) that is in front of the x^2 brings the graph closer to the y-axis
  ⦿ if there is a minus sign in front of the x^2 then the graph turns upside down.
⦿ You can solve a quadratic equation by drawing the graph and then finding where the graph crosses the x-axis, where $y = 0$.

Example 10 On a coordinate grid with values of x from -3 to $+3$, draw the graph of $y = x^2 - 2$.

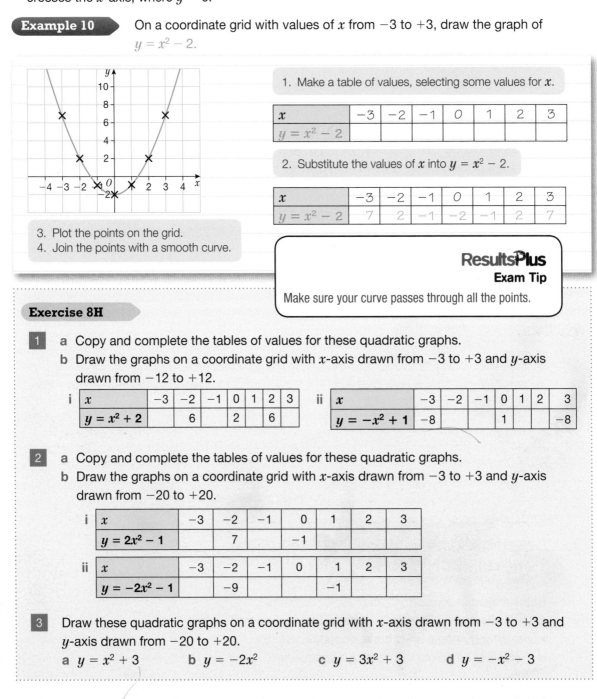

1. Make a table of values, selecting some values for x.

x	-3	-2	-1	0	1	2	3
$y = x^2 - 2$							

2. Substitute the values of x into $y = x^2 - 2$.

x	-3	-2	-1	0	1	2	3
$y = x^2 - 2$	7	2	-1	-2	-1	2	7

3. Plot the points on the grid.
4. Join the points with a smooth curve.

ResultsPlus
Exam Tip

Make sure your curve passes through all the points.

Exercise 8H

1 a Copy and complete the tables of values for these quadratic graphs.
   b Draw the graphs on a coordinate grid with x-axis drawn from -3 to $+3$ and y-axis drawn from -12 to $+12$.

i
x	-3	-2	-1	0	1	2	3
$y = x^2 + 2$		6		2		6	

ii
x	-3	-2	-1	0	1	2	3
$y = -x^2 + 1$	-8			1			-8

2 a Copy and complete the tables of values for these quadratic graphs.
   b Draw the graphs on a coordinate grid with x-axis drawn from -3 to $+3$ and y-axis drawn from -20 to $+20$.

i
x	-3	-2	-1	0	1	2	3
$y = 2x^2 - 1$		7			-1		

ii
x	-3	-2	-1	0	1	2	3
$y = -2x^2 - 1$		-9			-1		

3 Draw these quadratic graphs on a coordinate grid with x-axis drawn from -3 to $+3$ and y-axis drawn from -20 to $+20$.

a $y = x^2 + 3$ b $y = -2x^2$ c $y = 3x^2 + 3$ d $y = -x^2 - 3$

C

Example 11

a On a coordinate grid with values of x from -3 to $+3$, draw the graph of
$y = x^2 + 2x - 5$.

b Use your graph to solve the equations i $x^2 + 2x - 5 = 0$ ii $x^2 + 2x - 5 = 4$

a

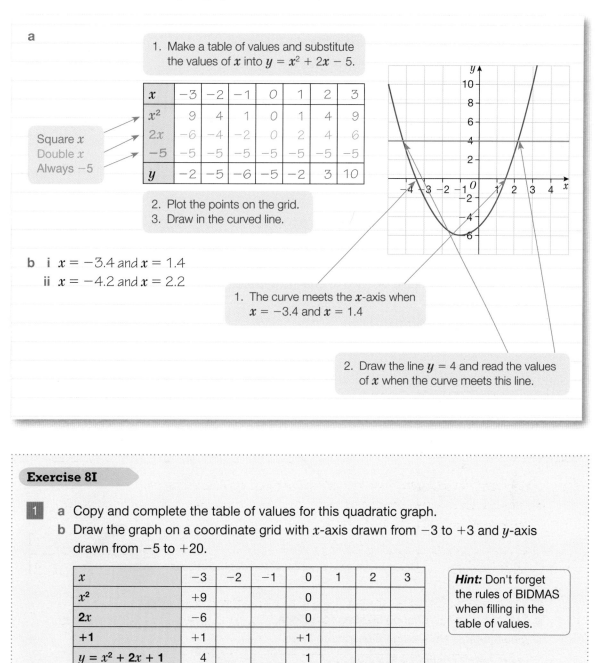

1. Make a table of values and substitute the values of x into $y = x^2 + 2x - 5$.

x	-3	-2	-1	0	1	2	3
x^2	9	4	1	0	1	4	9
$2x$	-6	-4	-2	0	2	4	6
-5	-5	-5	-5	-5	-5	-5	-5
y	-2	-5	-6	-5	-2	3	10

Square x
Double x
Always -5

2. Plot the points on the grid.
3. Draw in the curved line.

b i $x = -3.4$ and $x = 1.4$
   ii $x = -4.2$ and $x = 2.2$

1. The curve meets the x-axis when
$x = -3.4$ and $x = 1.4$

2. Draw the line $y = 4$ and read the values of x when the curve meets this line.

Exercise 8I

1 a Copy and complete the table of values for this quadratic graph.
  b Draw the graph on a coordinate grid with x-axis drawn from -3 to $+3$ and y-axis drawn from -5 to $+20$.

x	-3	-2	-1	0	1	2	3
x^2	$+9$			0			
$2x$	-6			0			
$+1$	$+1$			$+1$			
$y = x^2 + 2x + 1$	4			1			

Hint: Don't forget the rules of BIDMAS when filling in the table of values.

2 a Draw the graph of $y = x^2 - 3x - 2$ for values of x from -2 to $+5$.
  b Use your graph to solve the equations.
    i $x^2 - 3x - 2 = 0$ ii $x^2 - 3x - 2 = 5$

3 a Draw the graph of $y = 2x^2 - 3x$ for values of x from -2 to $+3$.
  b Use your graph to solve the equations.
    i $2x^2 - 3x = 0$ ii $2x^2 - 3x = 4$

C

Exam review

Self-assessment checklist

I can:

- fill in a table of values and use it to draw a straight-line graph   [p. 74]
- draw a straight-line graph without a table of values   [p. 76]
- find the midpoint of a line segment.   [p. 78]
- draw and interpret straight-line graphs from everyday life   [p. 79]
- draw and interpret conversion graphs   [p. 79]
- draw and interpret distance–time graphs   [p. 82]
- work out the speed from a distance–time graph   [p. 82]
- draw a graph for a quadratic function   [p. 84]
- use a quadratic graph to solve equations   [p. 84]

Exam practice

E

1   This conversion graph can be used to change between litres and gallons.

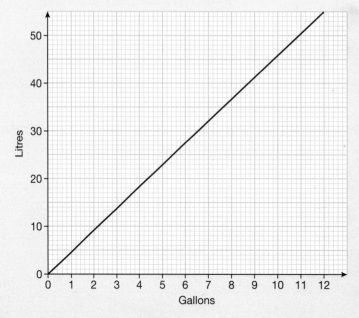

   a Use the graph to change 50 litres to gallons.

   b Use the graph to change 6 gallons to litres.

   1 litre of petrol costs £1.15.

   c Work out the cost of 50 litres of petrol.

   d Work out an estimate for the cost of 1 gallon of petrol.   *June 2010*

D **A02**

2   **a** Draw a graph of $2y + x = 8$ for values of x from -2 to 4.

     b On the same axes draw the graph of $y = x$ for values of x from -2 to 4.

     c P is the point on the graph of $2y + x = 8$ for which the value of x is the same as the value of y.

        Estimate the value of x.

D

3 On the coordinate grid draw the graph of $y = 2x - 3$.
Use values of x from -2 to $+2$.

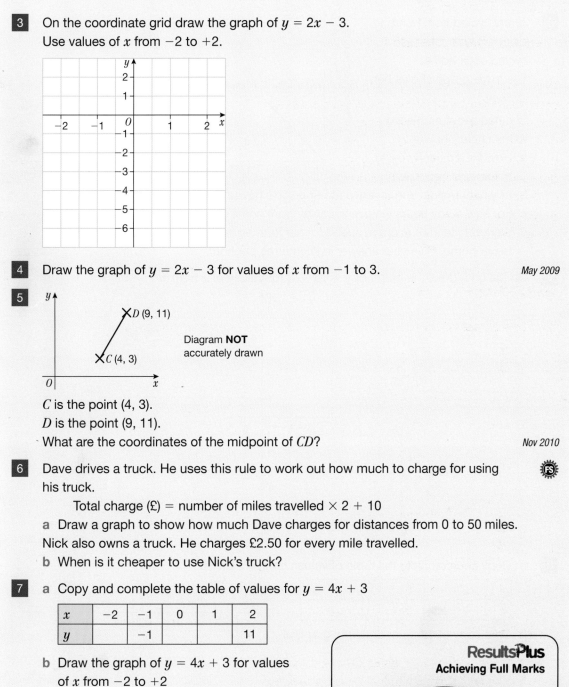

4 Draw the graph of $y = 2x - 3$ for values of x from -1 to 3. *May 2009*

A02

5

$\times D$ (9, 11)

Diagram **NOT**
accurately drawn

$\times C$ (4, 3)

C is the point (4, 3).
D is the point (9, 11).
What are the coordinates of the midpoint of CD? *Nov 2010*

6 Dave drives a truck. He uses this rule to work out how much to charge for using his truck.

        Total charge (£) = number of miles travelled × 2 + 10

a Draw a graph to show how much Dave charges for distances from 0 to 50 miles.

Nick also owns a truck. He charges £2.50 for every mile travelled.

b When is it cheaper to use Nick's truck?

A02
A03

7 **a** Copy and complete the table of values for $y = 4x + 3$

x	-2	-1	0	1	2
y		-1			11

b Draw the graph of $y = 4x + 3$ for values of x from -2 to $+2$

March 2008

ResultsPlus
Achieving Full Marks

■ C candidates
■ D candidates
100% 100%

To get full marks on this question, draw and label a coordinate grid, plot all the points and draw a straight line through them.

8 Jenny cycled from home to visit her uncle. She also cycled back home.
The travel graph shows her journey.

She had a rest on the way to her uncle's house.

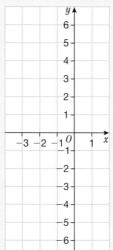

a How far did Jenny cycle before she had a rest?

b At what time did Jenny arrive at her uncle's house?

c For how many hours was Jenny away from home?

d Work out Jenny's average speed for her journey from her uncle's house back to her home. Give your answer in kilometres per hour.

Nov 2009

9 On the grid, draw the graph of $y = 2x + 3$ for values of x from $x = -3$ to $x = 1$

March 2011

10 a Copy and complete the table of values for $y = 2x + 2$

x	-2	-1	0	1	2	3
y		0	2			

b On a copy of the grid, draw the graph of $y = 2x + 2$

c Use your graph to find

  i the value of y when $x = -1.5$

  ii the value of x when $y = 7$

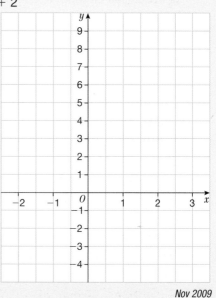

Nov 2009

11 The graph shows the cost, C, of a hiring a sander for d days from Hire It.

Find:

a a formula linking C with d

b the cost of hiring the sander for 10 days.

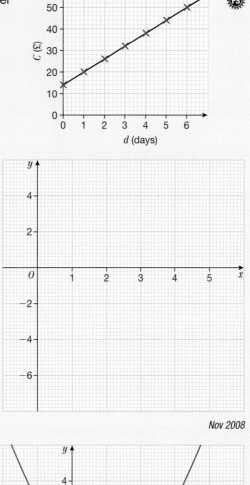

12 **a** Copy and complete the table of values for $y = x^2 - 4x - 2$.

x	-1	0	1	2	3	4	5
y		-2	-5			-2	3

b Copy the grid and draw the graph of $y = x^2 - 4x - 2$.

c Use your graph to find estimates of the solutions of $x^2 - 4x - 2 = 0$.

Nov 2008

13 The graph of $y = x^2 - 2x$ has been drawn on the grid.

Copy the graph and use it to find estimates of the solutions of

a $x^2 - 2x = 0$

b $x^2 - 2x = 2$

c $x^2 - 2x = -1$

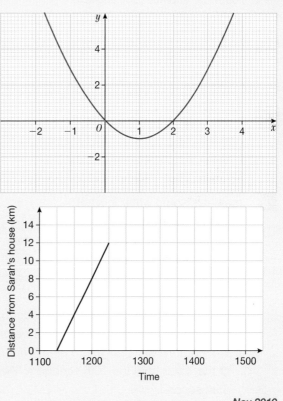

14 Each Saturday, Sarah cycles from her house to the gym.

The travel graph shows Sarah's journey to the gym.

a What time does she leave home?

b How far is the gym from Sarah's house?

Sarah stays at the gym for $1\frac{1}{2}$ hours.
She then cycles back to her house at 18 km/h.

c Copy and complete the travel graph.

Nov 2010

15 A journey in Jill's taxi costs a fixed charge plus £1.00 for each mile travelled.

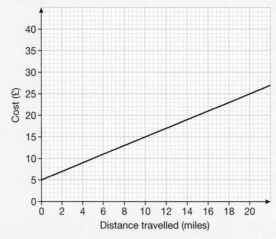

a How much is the fixed charge?

A taxi journey in Matt's taxi costs £1.50 per mile. There is no fixed charge. Liz is going to make a taxi journey. She wants to know whether Jill's taxi or Matt's taxi is cheaper.

b Compare the cost of using Jill's taxi with the cost of using Matt's taxi. In your answer, you should refer to the distance travelled.

* **16** The graph gives information about the costs of taxi fares from Kari Cabs.
Aleph Taxis charge £4 plus 90p per mile.
Which company is better value?
You must explain your answer.

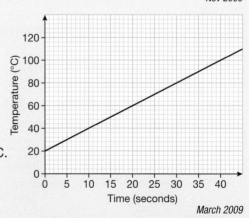

17 The coordinates of the point A are $(-3, 9)$.
The coordinates of the point B are $(5, 1)$.
M is the midpoint of the line AB.
What are the coordinates of the point M?

Nov 2009

18 Joe heats some water in a kettle.
The graph gives information about the temperature of the water in the kettle and the length of time it has been heated.

a Write down the temperature of the water when Joe started to heat the water.

b Use the graph to find how many seconds it took the water to reach a temperature of 70°C.

c Work out the increase in the temperature of the water from the 10th second to the 35th second.

March 2009

B

19 **a** Copy and complete the table of values for $y = x^3 - 7$

x	−2	−1	0	1	2	3
y		−8				20

b On a copy of the grid, draw the graph of $y = x^3 - 7$ for values of x from −2 to 3

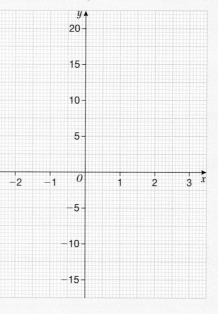

Nov 2010

9 EQUATIONS AND INEQUALITIES

9.1 You can solve equations with variables on one side

Key Points

⦿ You can solve an equation by rearranging it so that the variable is on its own on one side of the equation.

⦿ 'Solve' means find the value of the variable.

⦿ In an equation with two operations, deal with the $+$ or $-$ first.

⦿ Solutions to equations can be whole numbers, fractions or decimals.

⦿ Solutions to linear equations can be negative.

Example 1   Solve   **a** $5m - 8 = 3$ **b** $\frac{x}{5} + 2 = 6$

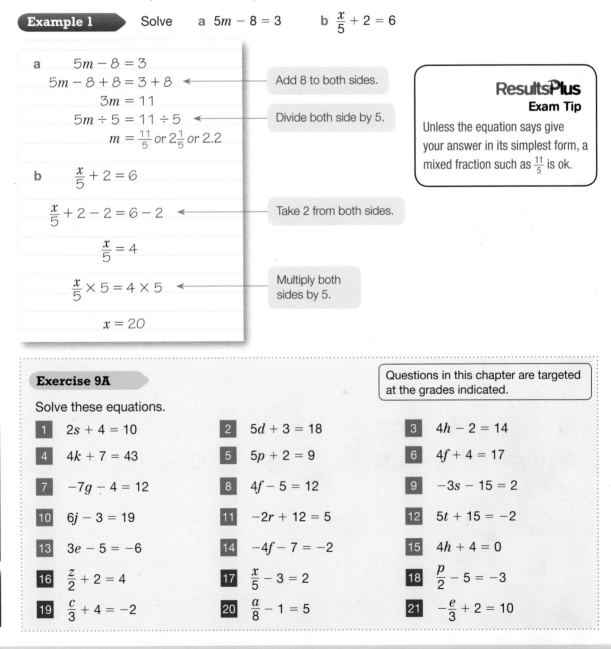

a $5m - 8 = 3$

$5m - 8 + 8 = 3 + 8$ ←   Add 8 to both sides.

$3m = 11$

$5m \div 5 = 11 \div 5$ ←   Divide both side by 5.

$m = \frac{11}{5} \text{ or } 2\frac{1}{5} \text{ or } 2.2$

b $\frac{x}{5} + 2 = 6$

$\frac{x}{5} + 2 - 2 = 6 - 2$ ←   Take 2 from both sides.

$\frac{x}{5} = 4$

$\frac{x}{5} \times 5 = 4 \times 5$ ←   Multiply both sides by 5.

$x = 20$

ResultsPlus
Exam Tip

Unless the equation says give your answer in its simplest form, a mixed fraction such as $\frac{11}{5}$ is ok.

Exercise 9A

Questions in this chapter are targeted at the grades indicated.

Solve these equations.

1 $2s + 4 = 10$ **2** $5d + 3 = 18$ **3** $4h - 2 = 14$

4 $4k + 7 = 43$ **5** $5p + 2 = 9$ **6** $4f + 4 = 17$

7 $-7g - 4 = 12$ **8** $4f - 5 = 12$ **9** $-3s - 15 = 2$

10 $6j - 3 = 19$ **11** $-2r + 12 = 5$ **12** $5t + 15 = -2$

13 $3e - 5 = -6$ **14** $-4f - 7 = -2$ **15** $4h + 4 = 0$

16 $\frac{z}{2} + 2 = 4$ **17** $\frac{x}{5} - 3 = 2$ **18** $\frac{p}{2} - 5 = -3$

19 $\frac{c}{3} + 4 = -2$ **20** $\frac{a}{8} - 1 = 5$ **21** $-\frac{e}{3} + 2 = 10$

9.2 You can solve equations with brackets

Key Point

- In an equation with brackets, expand the bracket first.

Example 2 Solve the equation $5(2x + 3) = 7$.

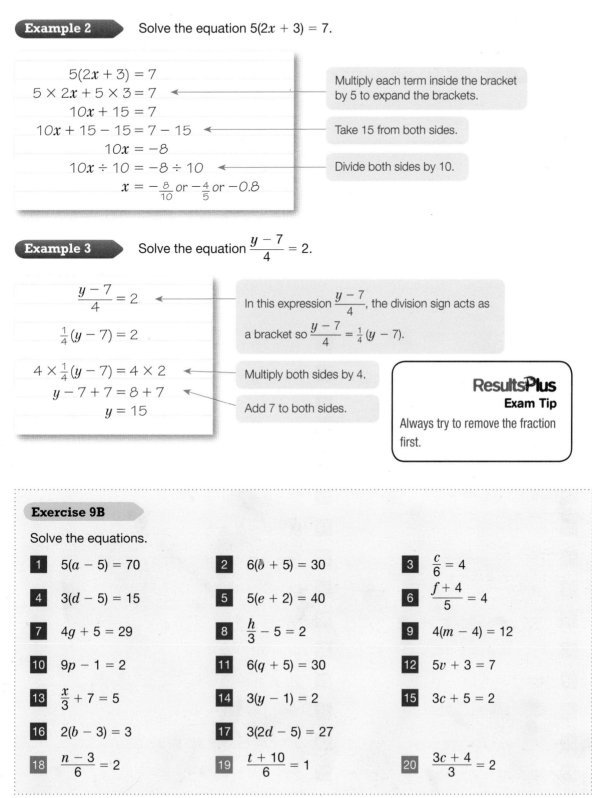

$$5(2x + 3) = 7$$
$$5 \times 2x + 5 \times 3 = 7$$
$$10x + 15 = 7$$
$$10x + 15 - 15 = 7 - 15$$
$$10x = -8$$
$$10x \div 10 = -8 \div 10$$
$$x = -\frac{8}{10} \text{ or } -\frac{4}{5} \text{ or } -0.8$$

Multiply each term inside the bracket by 5 to expand the brackets.

Take 15 from both sides.

Divide both sides by 10.

Example 3 Solve the equation $\dfrac{y - 7}{4} = 2$.

$$\frac{y - 7}{4} = 2$$
$$\frac{1}{4}(y - 7) = 2$$
$$4 \times \frac{1}{4}(y - 7) = 4 \times 2$$
$$y - 7 + 7 = 8 + 7$$
$$y = 15$$

In this expression $\dfrac{y - 7}{4}$, the division sign acts as a bracket so $\dfrac{y - 7}{4} = \dfrac{1}{4}(y - 7)$.

Multiply both sides by 4.

Add 7 to both sides.

ResultsPlus
Exam Tip

Always try to remove the fraction first.

Exercise 9B

Solve the equations.

1. $5(a - 5) = 70$
2. $6(b + 5) = 30$
3. $\dfrac{c}{6} = 4$
4. $3(d - 5) = 15$
5. $5(e + 2) = 40$
6. $\dfrac{f + 4}{5} = 4$
7. $4g + 5 = 29$
8. $\dfrac{h}{3} - 5 = 2$
9. $4(m - 4) = 12$
10. $9p - 1 = 2$
11. $6(q + 5) = 30$
12. $5v + 3 = 7$
13. $\dfrac{x}{3} + 7 = 5$
14. $3(y - 1) = 2$
15. $3c + 5 = 2$
16. $2(b - 3) = 3$
17. $3(2d - 5) = 27$
18. $\dfrac{n - 3}{6} = 2$
19. $\dfrac{t + 10}{6} = 1$
20. $\dfrac{3c + 4}{3} = 2$

D

C

9.3 You can solve equations with variables on both sides

Key Point

⦾ In an equation with a variable on both sides, use the balance method to rearrange the equation so that the variable is on one side only.

Example 4   Find the value of p in the equation $5p - 2 = 3p + 6$.

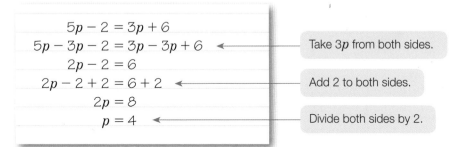

$$5p - 2 = 3p + 6$$
$$5p - 3p - 2 = 3p - 3p + 6 \quad \leftarrow \quad \text{Take } 3p \text{ from both sides.}$$
$$2p - 2 = 6$$
$$2p - 2 + 2 = 6 + 2 \quad \leftarrow \quad \text{Add 2 to both sides.}$$
$$2p = 8$$
$$p = 4 \quad \leftarrow \quad \text{Divide both sides by 2.}$$

Exercise 9C

Solve the equations.

1. $2a + 9 = a + 5$

2. $3c - 1 = c + 9$

3. $5p - 7 = 2p + 11$

4. $8b + 9 = 3b + 14$

5. $9q - 8 = 2q + 13$

6. $x + 13 = 5x + 1$

7. $4d + 17 = 8d - 3$

8. $7y = 2y + 15$

9. $3n + 14 = 5n$

10. $5k + 1 = 2k + 1$

11. $4u + 3 = 2u + 8$

12. $7r - 3 = 2r + 9$

13. $6v - 7 = 3v + 7$

14. $9t + 5 = 4t + 9$

15. $7m - 2 = 3m + 8$

16. $3g + 4 = 9g - 1$

17. $5b + 6 = 7b + 5$

18. $2h + 7 = 8h - 1$

19. $3e = 7e - 18$

20. $9f = 3f + 4$

21. $7(x + 2) = 2x + 17$

22. $8x - 3 = 3(2x + 5)$

23. $4(3x - 1) = 7x - 34$

24. $5(x - 4) = 3(x - 7)$

25. $5(x + 2) = 3x - 20$

26. $7x - 1 = 3x$

27. $6 = 2(x + 5)$

28. $8(5 - x) = 2x - 1$

29. $3y + 2(1 + y) = 6y$

30. $5(2x - 1) = 8(x - 1)$

9.4 You can solve equations with negative coefficients

Key Points

◉ A coefficient is the number in front of an unknown.

◉ You solve equations with negative coefficients using the balance method you have used in the previous sections.

Example 5 Solve the equations.

a $7 - 3x = 19$ b $4 - 3x = 7 - 5x$

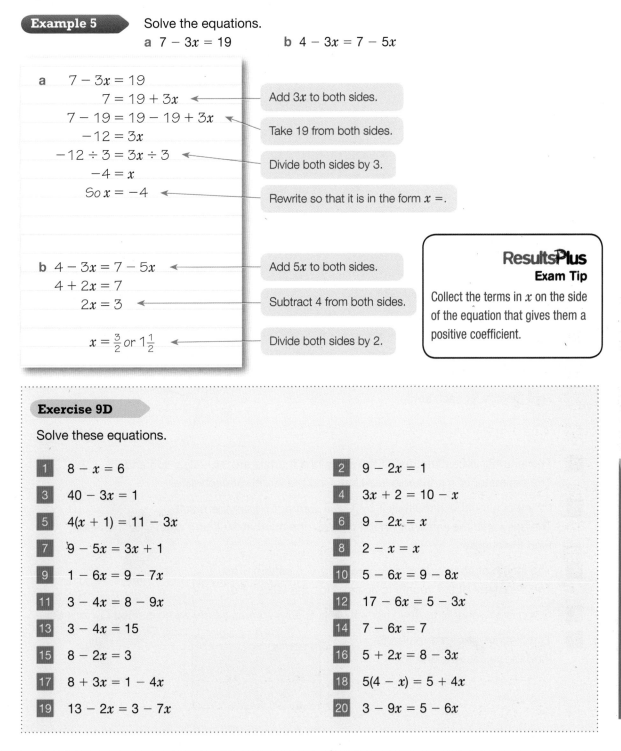

a $\quad 7 - 3x = 19$

$\quad\quad\quad 7 = 19 + 3x$ — Add $3x$ to both sides.

$\quad 7 - 19 = 19 - 19 + 3x$ — Take 19 from both sides.

$\quad\quad -12 = 3x$

$\quad -12 \div 3 = 3x \div 3$ — Divide both sides by 3.

$\quad\quad\quad -4 = x$

$\quad\quad\quad So\ x = -4$ — Rewrite so that it is in the form $x =$.

b $\quad 4 - 3x = 7 - 5x$ — Add $5x$ to both sides.

$\quad\quad 4 + 2x = 7$

$\quad\quad\quad 2x = 3$ — Subtract 4 from both sides.

$\quad\quad\quad x = \frac{3}{2}$ or $1\frac{1}{2}$ — Divide both sides by 2.

ResultsPlus
Exam Tip

Collect the terms in x on the side of the equation that gives them a positive coefficient.

Exercise 9D

Solve these equations.

1 $8 - x = 6$

2 $9 - 2x = 1$

3 $40 - 3x = 1$

4 $3x + 2 = 10 - x$

5 $4(x + 1) = 11 - 3x$

6 $9 - 2x = x$

7 $9 - 5x = 3x + 1$

8 $2 - x = x$

9 $1 - 6x = 9 - 7x$

10 $5 - 6x = 9 - 8x$

11 $3 - 4x = 8 - 9x$

12 $17 - 6x = 5 - 3x$

13 $3 - 4x = 15$

14 $7 - 6x = 7$

15 $8 - 2x = 3$

16 $5 + 2x = 8 - 3x$

17 $8 + 3x = 1 - 4x$

18 $5(4 - x) = 5 + 4x$

19 $13 - 2x = 3 - 7x$

20 $3 - 9x = 5 - 6x$

C

9.5 You can use equations to solve problems

> **Key Point**
>
> ⊙ You can solve problems in mathematics and other subjects by setting up equations and solving them.

Example 6   In the diagram, ABC is a straight line.
Work out the size of angle DBC.

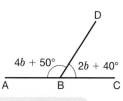

$4b + 50 + 2b + 40 = 180$ ← Write an equation in terms of b, using the sum of the angles on a straight line = 180°.

$6b + 90 = 180$ ← Collect the terms.

$6b = 180 - 90$

$6b = 90$ ← Divide both sides by 6.

$b = 15$

angle DBC $= 2b + 40$

$= 2 \times 15 + 40$ ← Substitute $b = 15$.

$= 30 + 40$

$= 70°$

Exercise 9E

1   The sizes of the angles of a triangle are $a + 30°$, $a + 40°$ and $a - 10°$.
Find the size of the largest angle.

2   The diagram shows three angles at a point.
Find the size of each angle.

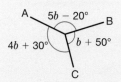

3   The lengths, in centimetres, of the sides of a triangle are $3x - 4$, $x + 5$ and $15 - 2x$.
The perimeter of the triangle is 24 cm. Find the length of each side.

4   I think of a number. I multiply it by 7 and subtract 6 from the result.
The answer is the same as when I multiply the number by 4 and add 27 to the result.
Find the number.

5   The length of each side of a square is $2y - 5$ centimetres.
The perimeter of the square is 36 cm. Find the value of y.

6   Gwen is 39 years older than her son. She is also 4 times as old as he is. Find Gwen's age.

7   The diagram shows a rectangle.
Find the values of x and y.

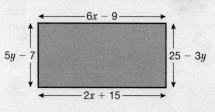

9.6 You can solve equations by trial and improvement

Key Points

● There are some equations that can only be solved using the method known as 'trial and improvement'.

● It is helpful to set out your work in a table (see Example 7).

Example 7   Use trial and improvement to solve the equation $x^3 + x = 16$.
Give your answer correct to 2 d.p.

> $x^3 + x = 16$ is a *cubic equation*. The highest power of x is cubed.

Method
Estimate a value for x.
Calculate $x^3 + x$ using your estimate.
Compare your answer with 16.
If your answer is too small, choose a bigger value for x.
If your answer is too big, choose a smaller value for x.
Keep repeating this process until you find a value for x correct to 2 d.p. which makes $x^3 + x$ as close as possible to 16.

x	$x^3 + x$	Bigger or smaller than 16?
2	10	Too small
3	30	Too big
2.5	18.125	Too big
2.4	16.224	Too big
2.3	14.467	Too small
2.35	15.327 875	Too small
2.36	15.504 256	Too small
2.37	15.682 053	Too small
2.38	15.861 272	Too small
2.39	16.041 919	Too big
2.385	15.951 416 63	Too small

> Try $x = 2.385$ to find out whether the solution is closer to 2.38 or 2.39.

The solution lies between 2.385 and 2.39.
So $x = 2.39$ to 2 d.p.

Exercise 9F

1   Use trial and improvement to solve $x^3 + x = 8$, giving your answer correct to 1 d.p.

2   Use trial and improvement to solve $x^3 + 4x = 100$, giving your answer correct to 1 d.p.

3   Use trial and improvement to solve $\dfrac{x^3}{2 + x} = 50$, giving your answer correct to 1 d.p.

4   Use trial and improvement to solve $2x^3 + 2x = 50$, giving your answer correct to 2 d.p.

C

9.7 You understand inequalities and can represent inequalities on a number line

Key Points

- ⊙ > means greater than.
- ⊙ ⩾ means greater than or equal to.
- ⊙ < means less than.
- ⊙ ⩽ means less than or equal to.
- ⊙ You can show inequalities on a number line.
- ⊙ An empty circle shows that the value is not included and a filled circle shows that the value is included (see Example 10).

Example 8

Write down the values of x that are integers and satisfy these inequalities.

$$\text{a } 3 < x < 8 \qquad \text{b } -3 \leqslant x < 2$$

a $3 < x < 8$
$4, 5, 6, 7$

This means x is greater than 3 but less than 8.
Integers are the same as positive and negative whole numbers.
These whole numbers would satisfy this statement.

b $-3 \leqslant x < 2$
$-3, -2, -1, 0, 1$

This means x is greater than or equal to -3 and less than 2.

Write the numbers in order of size.

Exercise 9G

1 Put the correct sign (< or >) between each pair of numbers to make a true statement.

a 4, 6	**b** 5, 2	**c** 12, 8	**d** 6, 6
e 15, 8	**f** 3, 24	**g** 10, 3	**h** 0, 0.1
i 6, 0.7	**j** 4.5, 4.5	**k** 0.2, 0.5	**l** 4.8, 4.79

2 Write down whether each statement is true or false. If it is false, write down the pair of numbers with the correct sign.

a $6 > 4$	**b** $2 > 6$	**c** $6 > 6$	**d** $6 > 8$
e $6 < 5$	**f** $8 = 14$	**g** $7 < 6.99$	**h** $6 > 6.01$
i $7 < 0$	**j** $4 < 4$	**k** $6 = 4$	**l** $6 > 0.84$

3 Write down the values of x that are whole numbers and satisfy these inequalities.

a $4 < x < 6$	**b** $3 < x < 8$	**c** $0 \leqslant x < 4$	**d** $3 < x < 6$
e $1 < x \leqslant 4$	**f** $2 < x < 6$	**g** $4 \leqslant x < 7$	**h** $-2 \leqslant x < 4$
i $-1 < x < 5$	**j** $-2 < x \leqslant 6$	**k** $-3 \leqslant x < 3$	**l** $-4 \leqslant x \leqslant 2$
m $0 < x < 5$	**n** $-1 < x \leqslant 4$	**o** $-5 \leqslant x < 0$	**p** $-3 \leqslant x \leqslant 3$

Example 9

Draw a number line from 0 to 10. Show the inequality $x > 4$.

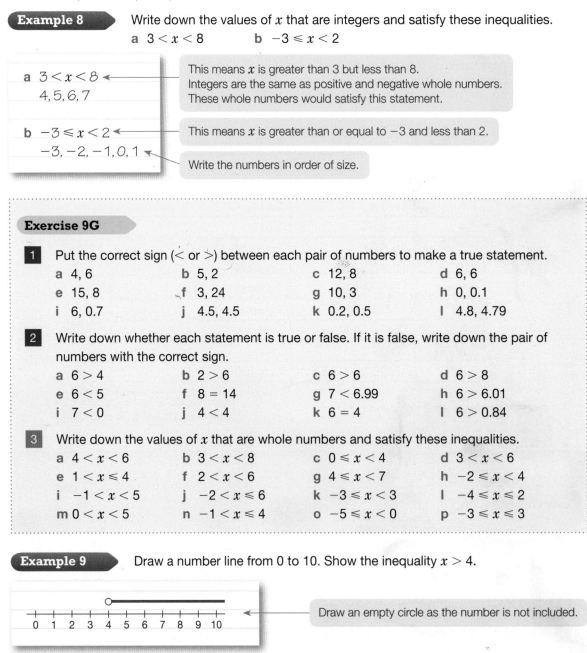

Draw an empty circle as the number is not included.

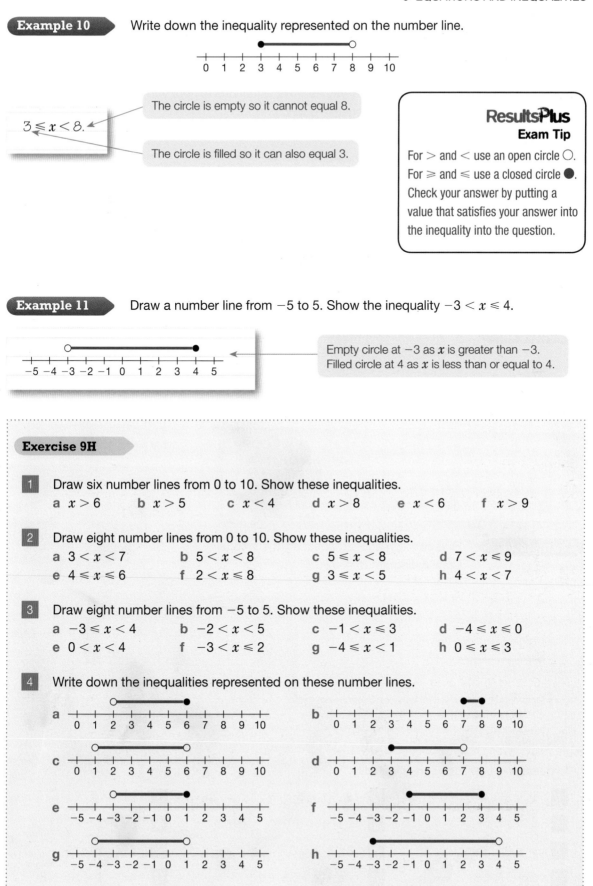

Example 10

Write down the inequality represented on the number line.

The circle is empty so it cannot equal 8.

$3 \leqslant x < 8.$

The circle is filled so it can also equal 3.

ResultsPlus
Exam Tip

For $>$ and $<$ use an open circle ○.
For $\geqslant$ and $\leqslant$ use a closed circle ●.
Check your answer by putting a value that satisfies your answer into the inequality into the question.

Example 11

Draw a number line from -5 to 5. Show the inequality $-3 < x \leqslant 4$.

Empty circle at -3 as x is greater than -3.
Filled circle at 4 as x is less than or equal to 4.

Exercise 9H

1 Draw six number lines from 0 to 10. Show these inequalities.

  a $x > 6$ **b** $x > 5$ **c** $x < 4$ **d** $x > 8$ **e** $x < 6$ **f** $x > 9$

2 Draw eight number lines from 0 to 10. Show these inequalities.

  a $3 < x < 7$ **b** $5 < x < 8$ **c** $5 \leqslant x < 8$ **d** $7 < x \leqslant 9$
  e $4 \leqslant x \leqslant 6$ **f** $2 < x \leqslant 8$ **g** $3 \leqslant x < 5$ **h** $4 < x < 7$

3 Draw eight number lines from -5 to 5. Show these inequalities.

  a $-3 \leqslant x < 4$ **b** $-2 < x < 5$ **c** $-1 < x \leqslant 3$ **d** $-4 \leqslant x \leqslant 0$
  e $0 < x < 4$ **f** $-3 < x \leqslant 2$ **g** $-4 \leqslant x < 1$ **h** $0 \leqslant x \leqslant 3$

4 Write down the inequalities represented on these number lines.

C

9.8 You can solve inequalities

Key Point

⦿ You can solve inequalities in the same way as linear equations except you must **not**:
- ⦿ multiply both sides by the same negative quantity
- ⦿ divide both sides by the same negative quantity.

Example 12　　a Solve the inequality $2x - 1 < 4$.
　　　　　　　　b Show the solution on a number line.

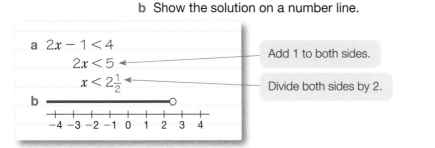

a $2x - 1 < 4$
　　$2x < 5$　　　　　　　Add 1 to both sides.
　　　$x < 2\frac{1}{2}$　　　　　Divide both sides by 2.

b （number line from −4 to 4, open circle at $2\frac{1}{2}$）

Example 13　　a Solve the inequality $2x + 3 \leqslant 5x + 7$.
　　　　　　　　b Write down the smallest integer that satisfies this inequality.

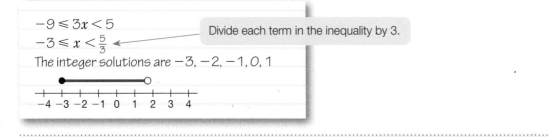

a $2x + 3 \leqslant 5x + 7$
　　　$3 \leqslant 3x + 7$　　　　Subtract $2x$ from both sides.
　　$-4 \leqslant 3x$　　　　　Subtract 7 from both sides.　　$-4 \leqslant 3x$ is the same as $3x \geqslant -4$
　　　$x \geqslant -1\frac{1}{3}$　　　　Divide both sides by 3.

b The smallest integer that satisfies this inequality is -1.

Example 14　　Find all the integers that satisfy the inequality $-9 \leqslant 3x < 5$.
　　　　　　　　Draw a diagram to help.

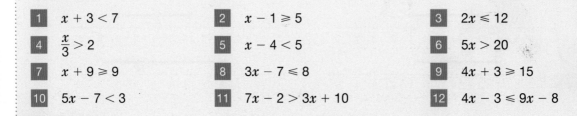

$-9 \leqslant 3x < 5$
$-3 \leqslant x < \frac{5}{3}$　　　　Divide each term in the inequality by 3.
The integer solutions are $-3, -2, -1, 0, 1$

（number line from −4 to 4, closed circle at −3, open circle at $\frac{5}{3}$）

Exercise 9I

In questions 1–12, solve the inequality.

1 $x + 3 < 7$	**2** $x - 1 \geqslant 5$	**3** $2x \leqslant 12$
4 $\frac{x}{3} > 2$	**5** $x - 4 < 5$	**6** $5x > 20$
7 $x + 9 \geqslant 9$	**8** $3x - 7 \leqslant 8$	**9** $4x + 3 \geqslant 15$
10 $5x - 7 < 3$	**11** $7x - 2 > 3x + 10$	**12** $4x - 3 \leqslant 9x - 8$

In questions 13–18, solve the inequality and show the solution on a number line.

13 $4x > 11$

14 $6x \leqslant 3$

15 $3x + 7 \geqslant 1$

16 $8x - 3 > 7$

17 $2x + 5 < 2$

18 $7x - 5 \leqslant 3x - 2$

In questions 19–27, find all the integers that satisfy the inequality.

19 $4 \leqslant 2x \leqslant 8$

20 $-9 \leqslant 3x < 6$

21 $-15 < 5x \leqslant 5$

22 $0 \leqslant 6x < 24$

23 $-16 < 4x \leqslant 0$

24 $2 \leqslant 3x < 7$

25 $-7 < 5x \leqslant 15$

26 $-5 < 2x < 5$

27 $-10 < 3x < 0$

In questions 28–39, solve the inequality.

28 $5x > -15$

29 $\dfrac{x}{4} > -2$

30 $4x - 9 \geqslant 2$

31 $6x + 7 \leqslant 3$

32 $8x - 1 > 6$

33 $9 < 7x + 2$

34 $7x + 2 \leqslant 3x - 2$

35 $5(x + 2) > 10$

36 $3(x + 1) < x + 9$

37 $7 - x \leqslant 1$

38 $4(x - 3) \leqslant 3 - x$

39 $6 - 5x \leqslant 2 - 3x$

40 Solve the inequality $7x + 5 > 4x - 9$.
Write down the smallest integer that satisfies it.

41 Solve the inequality $3x + 4 \leqslant 1 - 2x$.
Write down the largest integer that satisfies it.

42 Lucy has x pence. Ben has 10p more than Lucy. Alice has twice as much as Ben.
They need at least £2 altogether to buy a sandwich to share.
What is the smallest value x must be to buy the sandwich?

43

2x	x + 4	2x

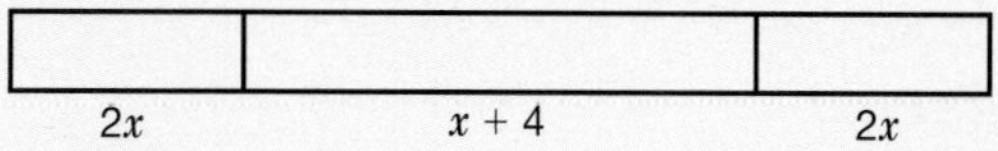

Here is a bar made of three parts. The length in centimetres of each part is shown
on the diagram.
The total length of the bar must be greater then 20 cm and less than 30 cm.
Work out the set of possible values of x.

44 The diagram shows a triangle. All the measurements are in cm.

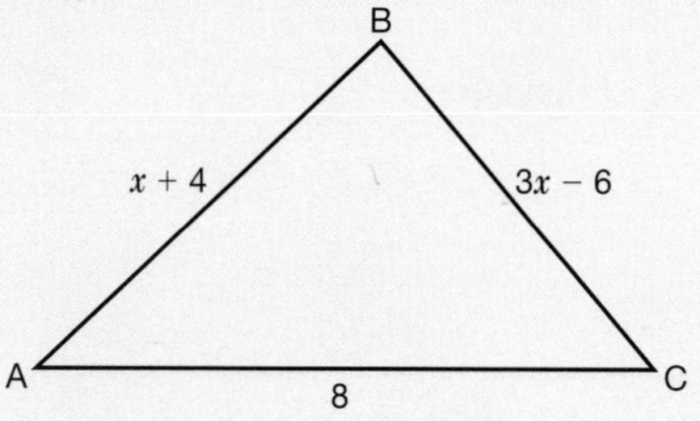

a Explain why $4x - 2 > 8$.
b Find the smallest integer value of x for which $4x - 2 > 8$.

9.9 You can solve simultaneous equations

Key Points

- When there are two unknowns you need two equations. These are called simultaneous equations.
- Simultaneous equations can be solved using elimination and then substitution.
- To eliminate an unknown, multiply the equations so that the coefficients of that unknown are the same. Add or subtract the equations to eliminate the chosen unknown.
  Sometimes the equations have to be multiplied by numbers before an unknown can be eliminated.
- Once you know one unknown, you can use substitution to find the other.

Example 15   Solve the simultaneous equations $4x - y = 3$
$$x + y = 7$$

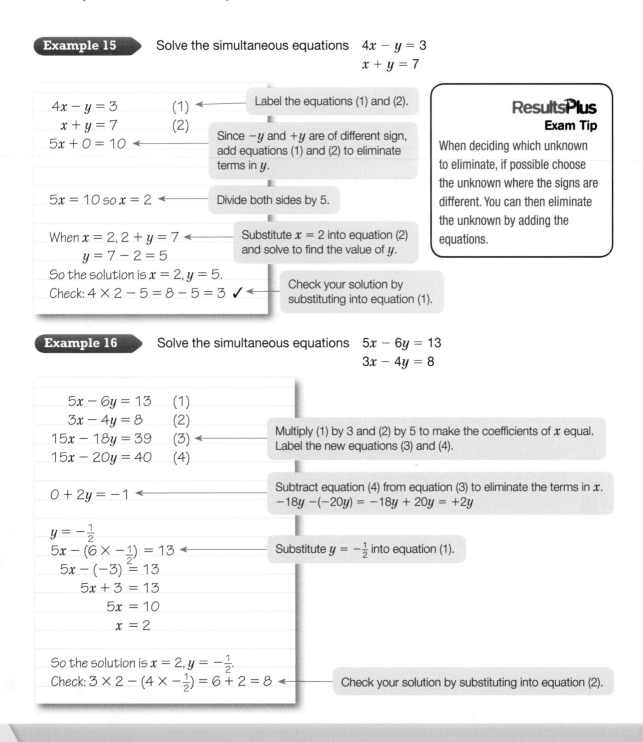

$4x - y = 3$ (1) ←   Label the equations (1) and (2).
$x + y = 7$ (2)
$5x + 0 = 10$ ←   Since $-y$ and $+y$ are of different sign, add equations (1) and (2) to eliminate terms in y.

$5x = 10$ so $x = 2$ ←   Divide both sides by 5.

When $x = 2, 2 + y = 7$ ←   Substitute $x = 2$ into equation (2) and solve to find the value of y.
$y = 7 - 2 = 5$
So the solution is $x = 2, y = 5$.
Check: $4 \times 2 - 5 = 8 - 5 = 3$ ✓ ←   Check your solution by substituting into equation (1).

ResultsPlus
Exam Tip

When deciding which unknown to eliminate, if possible choose the unknown where the signs are different. You can then eliminate the unknown by adding the equations.

Example 16   Solve the simultaneous equations $5x - 6y = 13$
$$3x - 4y = 8$$

$5x - 6y = 13$ (1)
$3x - 4y = 8$ (2)
$15x - 18y = 39$ (3) ←   Multiply (1) by 3 and (2) by 5 to make the coefficients of x equal. Label the new equations (3) and (4).
$15x - 20y = 40$ (4)

$0 + 2y = -1$ ←   Subtract equation (4) from equation (3) to eliminate the terms in x. $-18y - (-20y) = -18y + 20y = +2y$

$y = -\frac{1}{2}$
$5x - (6 \times -\frac{1}{2}) = 13$ ←   Substitute $y = -\frac{1}{2}$ into equation (1).
$5x - (-3) = 13$
$5x + 3 = 13$
$5x = 10$
$x = 2$

So the solution is $x = 2, y = -\frac{1}{2}$.
Check: $3 \times 2 - (4 \times -\frac{1}{2}) = 6 + 2 = 8$ ←   Check your solution by substituting into equation (2).

Example 17   Solve the simultaneous equations
$$3x + 5y = 16$$
$$y = 2x + 11$$

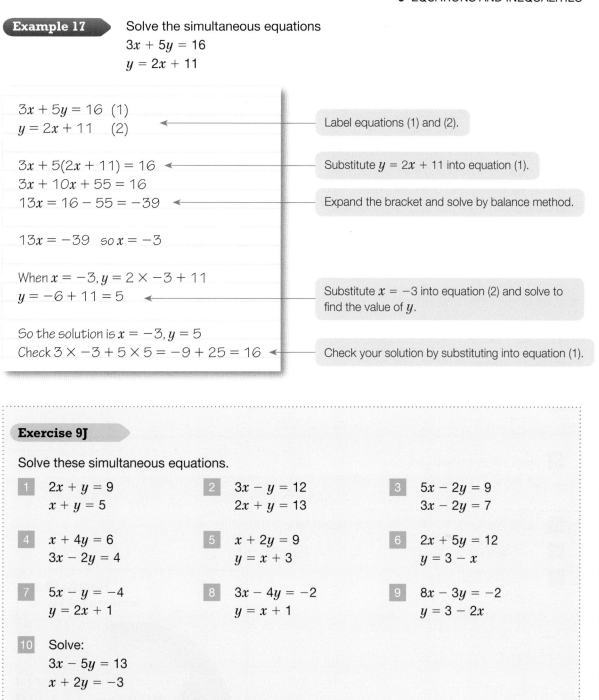

$3x + 5y = 16$ (1)
$y = 2x + 11$ (2)

Label equations (1) and (2).

$3x + 5(2x + 11) = 16$
$3x + 10x + 55 = 16$
$13x = 16 - 55 = -39$

Substitute $y = 2x + 11$ into equation (1).

Expand the bracket and solve by balance method.

$13x = -39$ so $x = -3$

When $x = -3, y = 2 \times -3 + 11$
$y = -6 + 11 = 5$

Substitute $x = -3$ into equation (2) and solve to find the value of y.

So the solution is $x = -3, y = 5$
Check $3 \times -3 + 5 \times 5 = -9 + 25 = 16$

Check your solution by substituting into equation (1).

Exercise 9J

Solve these simultaneous equations.

1   $2x + y = 9$
    $x + y = 5$

2   $3x - y = 12$
    $2x + y = 13$

3   $5x - 2y = 9$
    $3x - 2y = 7$

4   $x + 4y = 6$
    $3x - 2y = 4$

5   $x + 2y = 9$
    $y = x + 3$

6   $2x + 5y = 12$
    $y = 3 - x$

7   $5x - y = -4$
    $y = 2x + 1$

8   $3x - 4y = -2$
    $y = x + 1$

9   $8x - 3y = -2$
    $y = 3 - 2x$

10   Solve:
     $3x - 5y = 13$
     $x + 2y = -3$

11   Two pens and three pencils cost £1.35.
     Five pens and two pencils cost £2.55.
     Work out the cost each of a pen and a pencil.

A03 A

B

Exam review

Self-assessment checklist

I can

◉ solve equations with variables on one side [p.92]
◉ solve equations with brackets [p.93]
◉ solve equations with variables on both sides [p.94]
◉ solve equations with negative coefficients [p.95]
◉ set up equations and use them to solve problems [p.96]
◉ solve equations by trial and improvement [p.97]
◉ understand inequalities [p.98]
◉ solve inequalities on a number line [p.98]
◉ interpret inequalities on a number line and write down the inequality [p.98]
◉ solve inequalities [p.100]
◉ solve simultaneous equations. [p.102]

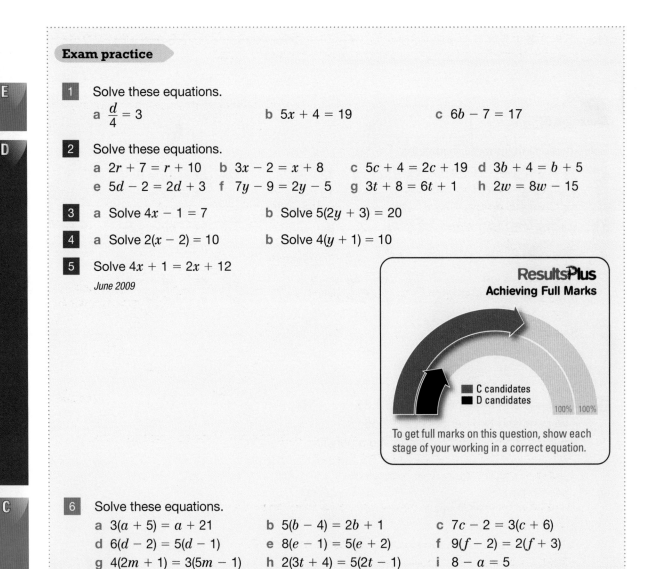

Exam practice

E

1 Solve these equations.

  a $\dfrac{d}{4} = 3$ **b** $5x + 4 = 19$ **c** $6b - 7 = 17$

D

2 Solve these equations.

  a $2r + 7 = r + 10$ **b** $3x - 2 = x + 8$ **c** $5c + 4 = 2c + 19$ **d** $3b + 4 = b + 5$
  e $5d - 2 = 2d + 3$ **f** $7y - 9 = 2y - 5$ **g** $3t + 8 = 6t + 1$ **h** $2w = 8w - 15$

3   **a** Solve $4x - 1 = 7$ **b** Solve $5(2y + 3) = 20$

4   **a** Solve $2(x - 2) = 10$ **b** Solve $4(y + 1) = 10$

5 Solve $4x + 1 = 2x + 12$

June 2009

> **ResultsPlus**
> **Achieving Full Marks**
>
> ■ C candidates
> ■ D candidates
>   100% 100%
>
> To get full marks on this question, show each
> stage of your working in a correct equation.

C

6 Solve these equations.

  a $3(a + 5) = a + 21$ **b** $5(b - 4) = 2b + 1$ **c** $7c - 2 = 3(c + 6)$
  d $6(d - 2) = 5(d - 1)$ **e** $8(e - 1) = 5(e + 2)$ **f** $9(f - 2) = 2(f + 3)$
  g $4(2m + 1) = 3(5m - 1)$ **h** $2(3t + 4) = 5(2t - 1)$ **i** $8 - a = 5$

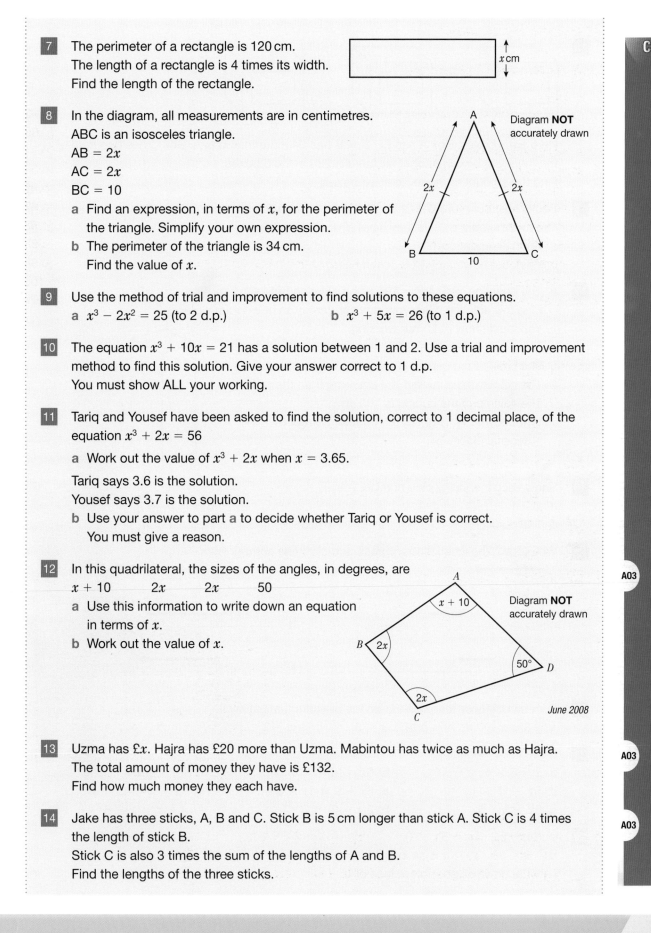

7 The perimeter of a rectangle is 120 cm.
The length of a rectangle is 4 times its width.
Find the length of the rectangle.

x cm

8 In the diagram, all measurements are in centimetres.
ABC is an isosceles triangle.
AB = $2x$
AC = $2x$
BC = 10
a Find an expression, in terms of x, for the perimeter of the triangle. Simplify your own expression.
b The perimeter of the triangle is 34 cm. Find the value of x.

Diagram **NOT** accurately drawn

9 Use the method of trial and improvement to find solutions to these equations.
a $x^3 - 2x^2 = 25$ (to 2 d.p.)   **b** $x^3 + 5x = 26$ (to 1 d.p.)

10 The equation $x^3 + 10x = 21$ has a solution between 1 and 2. Use a trial and improvement method to find this solution. Give your answer correct to 1 d.p.
You must show ALL your working.

11 Tariq and Yousef have been asked to find the solution, correct to 1 decimal place, of the equation $x^3 + 2x = 56$
a Work out the value of $x^3 + 2x$ when $x = 3.65$.

Tariq says 3.6 is the solution.
Yousef says 3.7 is the solution.
b Use your answer to part **a** to decide whether Tariq or Yousef is correct.
You must give a reason.

12 In this quadrilateral, the sizes of the angles, in degrees, are
$x + 10$ $2x$ $2x$ 50
a Use this information to write down an equation in terms of x.
b Work out the value of x.

Diagram **NOT** accurately drawn

June 2008

A03

13 Uzma has £x. Hajra has £20 more than Uzma. Mabintou has twice as much as Hajra.
The total amount of money they have is £132.
Find how much money they each have.

A03

14 Jake has three sticks, A, B and C. Stick B is 5 cm longer than stick A. Stick C is 4 times the length of stick B.
Stick C is also 3 times the sum of the lengths of A and B.
Find the lengths of the three sticks.

A03

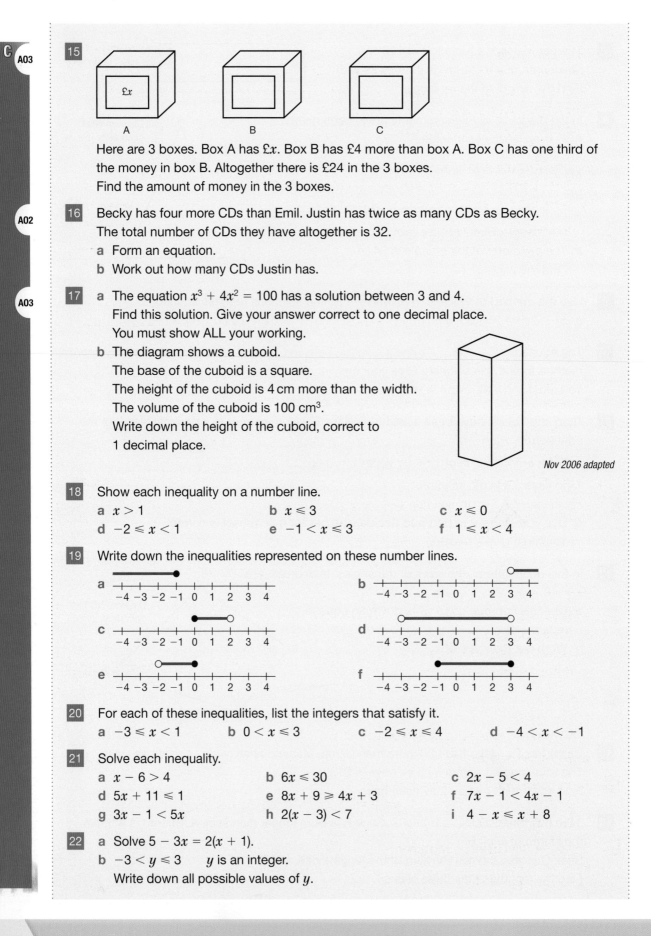

C AO3

15

A   B   C

Here are 3 boxes. Box A has £x. Box B has £4 more than box A. Box C has one third of the money in box B. Altogether there is £24 in the 3 boxes.
Find the amount of money in the 3 boxes.

AO2

16 Becky has four more CDs than Emil. Justin has twice as many CDs as Becky.
The total number of CDs they have altogether is 32.
a Form an equation.
b Work out how many CDs Justin has.

AO3

17 a The equation $x^3 + 4x^2 = 100$ has a solution between 3 and 4.
     Find this solution. Give your answer correct to one decimal place.
     You must show ALL your working.
   b The diagram shows a cuboid.
     The base of the cuboid is a square.
     The height of the cuboid is 4 cm more than the width.
     The volume of the cuboid is 100 cm³.
     Write down the height of the cuboid, correct to
     1 decimal place.

Nov 2006 adapted

18 Show each inequality on a number line.
   a $x > 1$ b $x \leqslant 3$ c $x \leqslant 0$
   d $-2 \leqslant x < 1$ e $-1 < x \leqslant 3$ f $1 \leqslant x < 4$

19 Write down the inequalities represented on these number lines.

a
−4 −3 −2 −1 0 1 2 3 4

b
−4 −3 −2 −1 0 1 2 3 4

c
−4 −3 −2 −1 0 1 2 3 4

d
−4 −3 −2 −1 0 1 2 3 4

e
−4 −3 −2 −1 0 1 2 3 4

f
−4 −3 −2 −1 0 1 2 3 4

20 For each of these inequalities, list the integers that satisfy it.
   a $-3 \leqslant x < 1$ b $0 < x \leqslant 3$ c $-2 \leqslant x \leqslant 4$ d $-4 < x < -1$

21 Solve each inequality.
   a $x - 6 > 4$ b $6x \leqslant 30$ c $2x - 5 < 4$
   d $5x + 11 \leqslant 1$ e $8x + 9 \geqslant 4x + 3$ f $7x - 1 < 4x - 1$
   g $3x - 1 < 5x$ h $2(x - 3) < 7$ i $4 - x \leqslant x + 8$

22 a Solve $5 - 3x = 2(x + 1)$.
   b $-3 < y \leqslant 3$ y is an integer.
     Write down all possible values of y.

23 Here are 3 rods.

Diagram **NOT** accurately drawn

The length of rod A is x cm.
Rod B is 4 cm longer than rod A.
The length of rod C is twice the length of rod B.
The total length of all 3 rods is L cm.

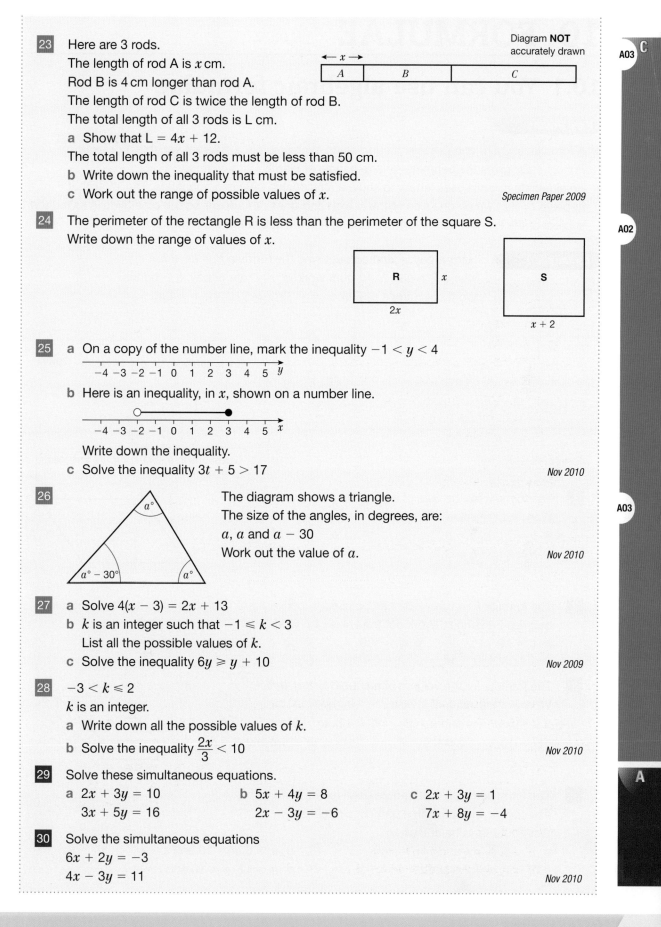

a Show that L = $4x + 12$.
The total length of all 3 rods must be less than 50 cm.
b Write down the inequality that must be satisfied.
c Work out the range of possible values of x.

Specimen Paper 2009

24 The perimeter of the rectangle R is less than the perimeter of the square S.
Write down the range of values of x.

25 a On a copy of the number line, mark the inequality $-1 < y < 4$

b Here is an inequality, in x, shown on a number line.

Write down the inequality.
c Solve the inequality $3t + 5 > 17$

Nov 2010

26

The diagram shows a triangle.
The size of the angles, in degrees, are:
a, a and $a - 30$
Work out the value of a.

Nov 2010

27 a Solve $4(x - 3) = 2x + 13$
b k is an integer such that $-1 \leqslant k < 3$
List all the possible values of k.
c Solve the inequality $6y \geqslant y + 10$

Nov 2009

28 $-3 < k \leqslant 2$
k is an integer.
a Write down all the possible values of k.
b Solve the inequality $\dfrac{2x}{3} < 10$

Nov 2010

29 Solve these simultaneous equations.

a $2x + 3y = 10$
$3x + 5y = 16$

b $5x + 4y = 8$
$2x - 3y = -6$

c $2x + 3y = 1$
$7x + 8y = -4$

30 Solve the simultaneous equations
$6x + 2y = -3$
$4x - 3y = 11$

Nov 2010

10 FORMULAE

10.1 You can use algebraic formulae

Key Points

⦿ A formula is where one variable is equal to an expression in a different variable. For example, $P = 2l + 2w$ gives the perimeter of a rectangle of length l and width w.

⦿ An algebraic formula uses letters to show a relationship between quantities. The letter that appears on its own on one side of the $=$ sign and does not appear on the other side is called the subject of the formula. In the formula above, P is the subject of the formula.

Example 1

Harry's pay is worked out using the formula $P = hr + b$
where P = pay, h = hours worked, r = rate of pay, b = bonus.
Work out Harry's pay when $h = 35$, $r = £10$ and $b = £45$.

$P = hr + b$
$P = 35 \times 10 + 45$ ⟵ Substitute $h = 35$, $r = 10$ and $b = 45$.
$P = 350 + 45 = £395$

Exercise 10A

Questions in this chapter are targeted at the grades indicated.

1 The formula for the area of a parallelogram is $A = bh$.
Work out the value of A when
  a $b = 7$ and $h = 3$ **b** $b = 9$ and $h = 7$
  c $b = 6$ and $h = 3.7$ **d** $b = 8.4$ and $h = 4.5$

2 The formula $F = 1.8C + 32$ can be used to convert a temperature from degrees Celsius to degrees Fahrenheit. Work out the value of F when
  a $C = 10$ **b** $C = 100$ **c** $C = -30$ **d** $C = 0$

3 The formula for the volume of a cuboid is $V = lwh$.
Work out the value of V when
  a $l = 5$, $w = 4$ and $h = 2$ **b** $l = 8$, $w = 5$ and $h = 3.5$
  c $l = 10$, $w = 6$ and $h = 4$ **d** $l = 9.3$, $w = 4.2$ and $h = 5.1$

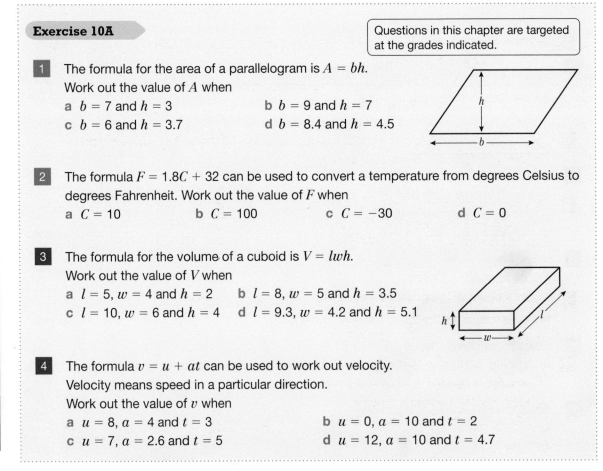

4 The formula $v = u + at$ can be used to work out velocity.
Velocity means speed in a particular direction.
Work out the value of v when
  a $u = 8$, $a = 4$ and $t = 3$ **b** $u = 0$, $a = 10$ and $t = 2$
  c $u = 7$, $a = 2.6$ and $t = 5$ **d** $u = 12$, $a = 10$ and $t = 4.7$

10.2 You can write an algebraic formula to represent a problem

Key Point

⦿ You can use information given in words to write an algebraic formula to solve a problem.

Example 2

Florence's pay is worked out using the formula
pay = number of hours work × rate per hour + commission.

   a Write this as an algebraic formula.
   b Work out Florence's pay when she works 30 hours at £7.50 per hour and gets a commission of £20.

a $P = nr + c$ ⟵ | Use letter for pay = P, number of hours worked = n, rate per hour = r and commission = c.

b $P = nr + c$ ⟵ | Substitute $n = 30$, $r = £7.50$ and $c = 20$.
$P = 30 \times 7.50 + 20$
$P = 225 + 20$
$P = £245$

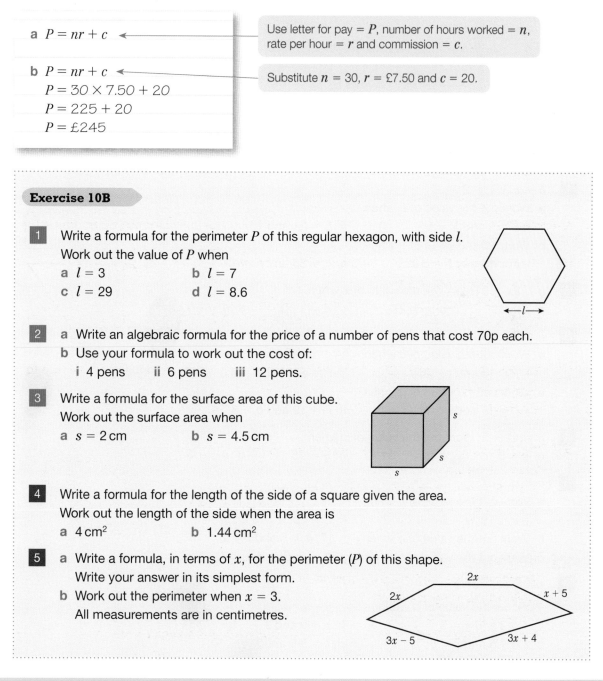

Exercise 10B

1. Write a formula for the perimeter P of this regular hexagon, with side l.
   Work out the value of P when
   a $l = 3$ **b** $l = 7$
   c $l = 29$ **d** $l = 8.6$

2. **a** Write an algebraic formula for the price of a number of pens that cost 70p each.
   b Use your formula to work out the cost of:
     i 4 pens   **ii** 6 pens   **iii** 12 pens.

3. Write a formula for the surface area of this cube.
   Work out the surface area when
   a $s = 2$ cm   **b** $s = 4.5$ cm

4. Write a formula for the length of the side of a square given the area.
   Work out the length of the side when the area is
   a 4 cm²   **b** 1.44 cm²

5. **a** Write a formula, in terms of x, for the perimeter (P) of this shape.
   Write your answer in its simplest form.
   b Work out the perimeter when $x = 3$.
   All measurements are in centimetres.

E

D

10.3 You can find the value of a term in a formula which is not the subject of the formula

Key Point

- To find out the value of a term which is not the subject of a formula, put the given values into the formula and then solve the resulting equation.

Example 3

$P = 2a + b$

Work out the value of a when $P = 25$ and $b = 7$.

$25 = 2a + 7$ ⟵ Solve this equation.

$2a = 18$ ⟵ Subtract 7 from both sides.

$a = 9$ ⟵ Divide both sides by 2.

ResultsPlus
Exam Tip
Substitute the value of the term back into the formula to check your answer.

Exercise 10C

D

1 $E = F + V - 2$
   a Work out the value of F when
      i $E = 9$ and $V = 5$ ii $E = 21$ and $V = 9$
   b Work out the value of V when
      i $E = 15$ and $F = 10$ ii $E = 30$ and $F = 12$

2 $y = 2x + 3$ Work out the value of x when
   a $y = 15$ b $y = 27$ c $y = -10$ d $y = -3$

3 $P = 2a + b$
   a Work out the value of b when
      i $P = 15$ and $a = 6$ ii $P = 23$ and $a = 4.5$
   b Work out the value of a when
      i $P = 11$ and $b = 5$ ii $P = 19$ and $b = 8$

4 $y = 4x - 5$ Work out the value of x when
   a $y = 3$ b $y = -31$ c $y = 75$ d $y = -6$

5 $v = u + at$
   a Work out the value of u when
      i $v = 19$, $a = 7$ and $t = 2$ ii $v = 25$, $a = 6$ and $t = 3$
   b Work out the value of a when $v = 17$, $u = 5$ and $t = 2$.
   c Work out the value of t when $v = 31$, $u = 3$ and $a = 7$.

6 $t = \dfrac{d}{s}$
   Work out the value of d when
   a $t = 3$ and $s = 5$ b $t = 9$ and $s = -8$
   c $t = 7.5$ and $s = 6$ d $t = 5.6$ and $s = -10.4$

10.4 You can change the subject of a formula

Key Point

◉ You can change the subject of a formula by carrying out the same operations on both sides of the equals sign.

Example 4   Make t the subject of the formula $v = u + at$.

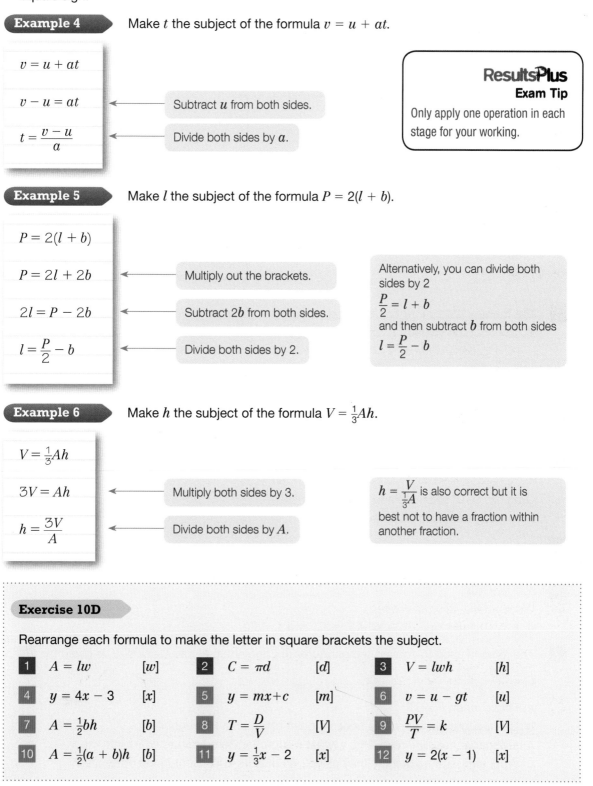

$v = u + at$

$v - u = at$ ←   Subtract u from both sides.

$t = \dfrac{v - u}{a}$ ←   Divide both sides by a.

ResultsPlus
Exam Tip
Only apply one operation in each stage for your working.

Example 5   Make l the subject of the formula $P = 2(l + b)$.

$P = 2(l + b)$

$P = 2l + 2b$ ←   Multiply out the brackets.

$2l = P - 2b$ ←   Subtract $2b$ from both sides.

$l = \dfrac{P}{2} - b$ ←   Divide both sides by 2.

Alternatively, you can divide both sides by 2
$$\frac{P}{2} = l + b$$
and then subtract b from both sides
$$l = \frac{P}{2} - b$$

Example 6   Make h the subject of the formula $V = \frac{1}{3}Ah$.

$V = \frac{1}{3}Ah$

$3V = Ah$ ←   Multiply both sides by 3.

$h = \dfrac{3V}{A}$ ←   Divide both sides by A.

$h = \dfrac{V}{\frac{1}{3}A}$ is also correct but it is best not to have a fraction within another fraction.

Exercise 10D

Rearrange each formula to make the letter in square brackets the subject.

1   $A = lw$ $[w]$ 2 $C = \pi d$ $[d]$ 3 $V = lwh$ $[h]$

4   $y = 4x - 3$ $[x]$ 5 $y = mx + c$ $[m]$ 6 $v = u - gt$ $[u]$

7   $A = \frac{1}{2}bh$ $[b]$ 8 $T = \dfrac{D}{V}$ $[V]$ 9 $\dfrac{PV}{T} = k$ $[V]$

10   $A = \frac{1}{2}(a + b)h$ $[b]$ 11 $y = \frac{1}{3}x - 2$ $[x]$ 12 $y = 2(x - 1)$ $[x]$

D

C

Exam review

Self-assessment checklist

I can:

- substitute number values for the letters in a formula to work out a quantity [p. 108]
- write an algebraic formula to solve a problem [p. 109]
- find the value of a term in an algebraic formula when it is not the subject of the formula [p. 110]
- rearrange a formula to make a different variable the subject of the formula. [p. 111]

D

Exam practice

1 $F = 1.8C + 32$

  a Work out the value of F when $C = -8$

  b Work out the value of C when $F = 68$

  June 2009

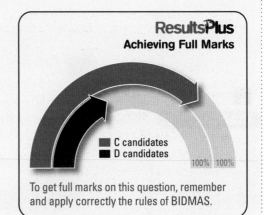

ResultsPlus

Achieving Full Marks

■ C candidates
■ D candidates

100% 100%

To get full marks on this question, remember and apply correctly the rules of BIDMAS.

2 The formula $v = u - gt$ can be used to work out velocity.

  a Work out the value of v when $u = 45$, $g = 10$ and $t = 3$.

  b Work out the value of u when $v = 8$, $g = 10$ and $t = 2$.

3 **a** Write a formula for the perimeter of a rectangle.

  b Work out the perimeter when

    i $l = 9$ and $w = 4$

    ii $l = 6.7$ and $w = 3.4$

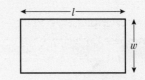

4 The cost, C in £, of buying t trees and b bushes together with delivery is given by the formula

$$C = 10t + 6b + 15.$$

Greg has £315 to spend and needs 35 bushes.

How many trees can he afford?

5 $p = 2$

Work out the value of $5p^2$.

6 $v = u + 10t$

Work out the value of v when

  a $u = 10$ and $t = 7$ **b** $u = -2.5$ and $t = 3.2$

7 The formula used to convert temperatures in Fahrenheit, F, into Celsius, C, is given by: ✦

$$C = \frac{5(F - 32)}{9}$$

  a Find C when $F = 77$.

  b Use the formula to find the freezing point of water in Fahrenheit.

  A newspaper headline read 'Phew, what a scorcher! Temperature soars into the 100s.'

  c What temperature unit are they using? What is its equivalent in the other unit?

8

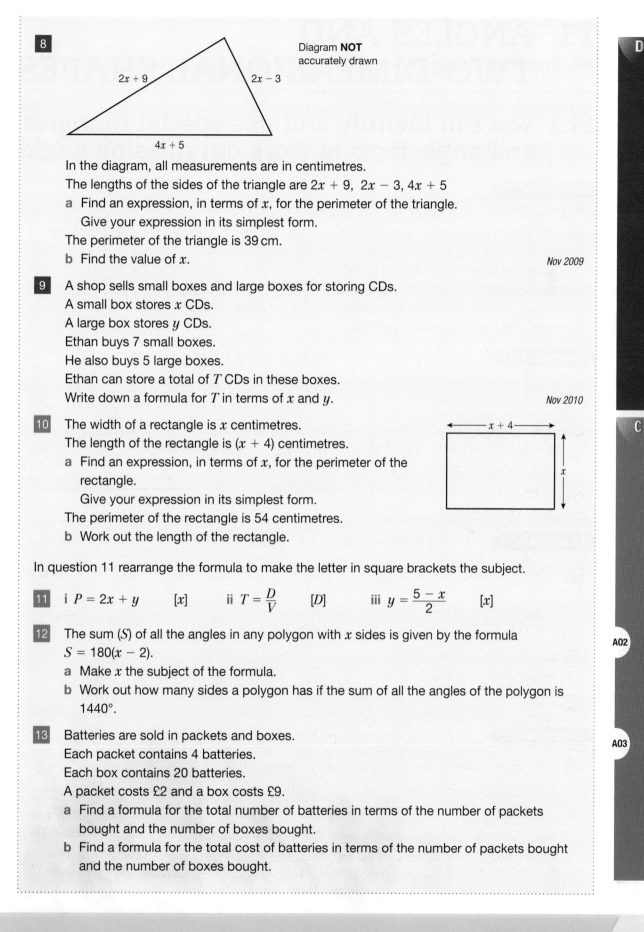

Diagram **NOT** accurately drawn

2x + 9   2x − 3

4x + 5

In the diagram, all measurements are in centimetres.

The lengths of the sides of the triangle are $2x + 9$, $2x − 3$, $4x + 5$

a Find an expression, in terms of x, for the perimeter of the triangle.
   Give your expression in its simplest form.

The perimeter of the triangle is 39 cm.

b Find the value of x.

Nov 2009

9 A shop sells small boxes and large boxes for storing CDs.

A small box stores x CDs.

A large box stores y CDs.

Ethan buys 7 small boxes.

He also buys 5 large boxes.

Ethan can store a total of T CDs in these boxes.

Write down a formula for T in terms of x and y.

Nov 2010

10 The width of a rectangle is x centimetres.

The length of the rectangle is $(x + 4)$ centimetres.

a Find an expression, in terms of x, for the perimeter of the
   rectangle.
   Give your expression in its simplest form.

The perimeter of the rectangle is 54 centimetres.

b Work out the length of the rectangle.

In question 11 rearrange the formula to make the letter in square brackets the subject.

11 i $P = 2x + y$ $[x]$ ii $T = \dfrac{D}{V}$ $[D]$ iii $y = \dfrac{5 − x}{2}$ $[x]$

12 The sum (S) of all the angles in any polygon with x sides is given by the formula
$S = 180(x − 2)$.

a Make x the subject of the formula.

b Work out how many sides a polygon has if the sum of all the angles of the polygon is
   1440°.

13 Batteries are sold in packets and boxes.

Each packet contains 4 batteries.

Each box contains 20 batteries.

A packet costs £2 and a box costs £9.

a Find a formula for the total number of batteries in terms of the number of packets
   bought and the number of boxes bought.

b Find a formula for the total cost of batteries in terms of the number of packets bought
   and the number of boxes bought.

D

C

A02

A03

11 ANGLES AND TWO-DIMENSIONAL SHAPES

11.1 You can identify and use special triangles and angle facts to work out missing angles

Key Points

- The interior angles of a triangle add up to 180°.
- Knowledge of the properties of special triangles can be used to work out the size of missing angles.
- The angles on a straight line add up to 180°.
- The angles around a point add up to 360°.
- Where two straight lines cross, the opposite angles are equal. They are called vertically opposite angles.

Example 1   Work out the missing angles in this triangle.

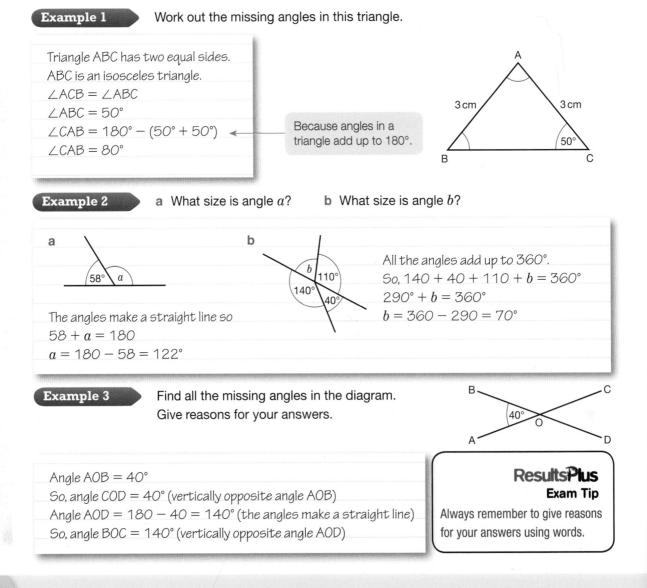

Triangle ABC has two equal sides.
ABC is an isosceles triangle.
$\angle ACB = \angle ABC$
$\angle ABC = 50°$
$\angle CAB = 180° - (50° + 50°)$ ← Because angles in a triangle add up to 180°.
$\angle CAB = 80°$

Example 2   **a** What size is angle a?   **b** What size is angle b?

a

58° a

The angles make a straight line so
$58 + a = 180$
$a = 180 - 58 = 122°$

b

b 110°
140° 40°

All the angles add up to 360°.
So, $140 + 40 + 110 + b = 360°$
$290° + b = 360°$
$b = 360 - 290 = 70°$

Example 3   Find all the missing angles in the diagram.
Give reasons for your answers.

Angle AOB = 40°
So, angle COD = 40° (vertically opposite angle AOB)
Angle AOD = 180 - 40 = 140° (the angles make a straight line)
So, angle BOC = 140° (vertically opposite angle AOD)

ResultsPlus
Exam Tip

Always remember to give reasons for your answers using words.

Exercise 11A

Questions in this chapter are targeted at the grades indicated.

1 Find the value of the letters in the diagrams below.
   Give reasons for your answers.

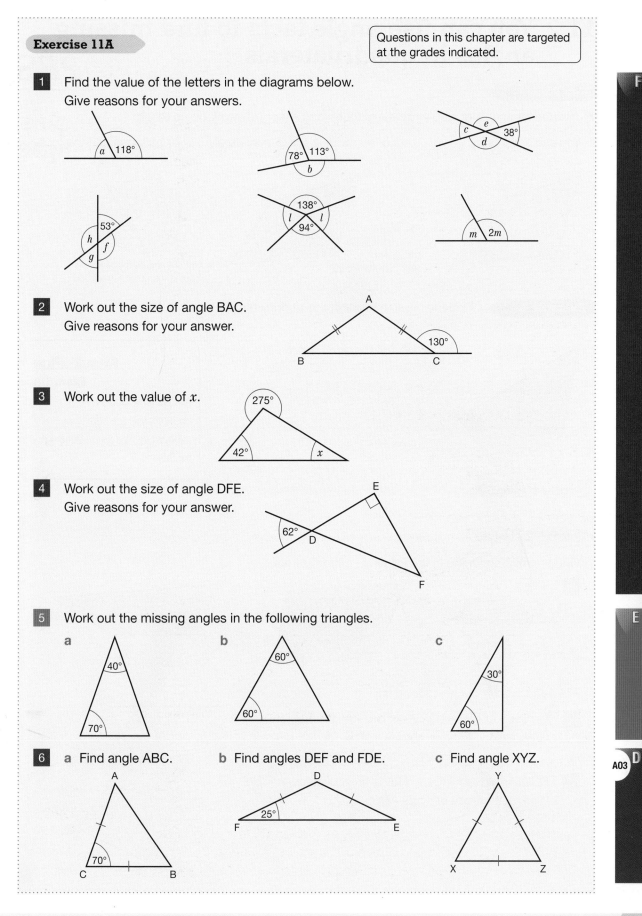

2 Work out the size of angle BAC.
   Give reasons for your answer.

3 Work out the value of x.

4 Work out the size of angle DFE.
   Give reasons for your answer.

5 Work out the missing angles in the following triangles.

   a   b   c

6 a Find angle ABC.   b Find angles DEF and FDE.   c Find angle XYZ.

F

E

A03 D

11.2 You can use angle facts to find missing angles in quadrilaterals

Key Point

◉ The interior angles of a quadrilateral (a four-sided shape) always add up to 360°.

You can see this by measuring the angles…

… or by dividing the quadrilateral into two triangles…

The angles of the two triangles add up to:
180° + 180° = 360°

… or by tearing off the four corners of a quadrilateral.

Put the angles together. They make a full turn of 360°.

Example 4   Find the missing angle in this quadrilateral.

The total of the three angles
marked = 128° + 100° + 83° = 311°
So a = 360° − 311°
a = 49°

ResultsPlus
Exam Tip

Always write down all the numbers you are adding or subtracting. You get method marks for this.

Exercise 11B

Find the missing angles in the following quadrilaterals.

1   a   b   c

2   Here is a quadrilateral. Work out the size of angle a.
    Give reasons for your answer.

3   BCDE is a quadrilateral. ABE is an equilateral triangle.
    Work out the size of angle ABC.

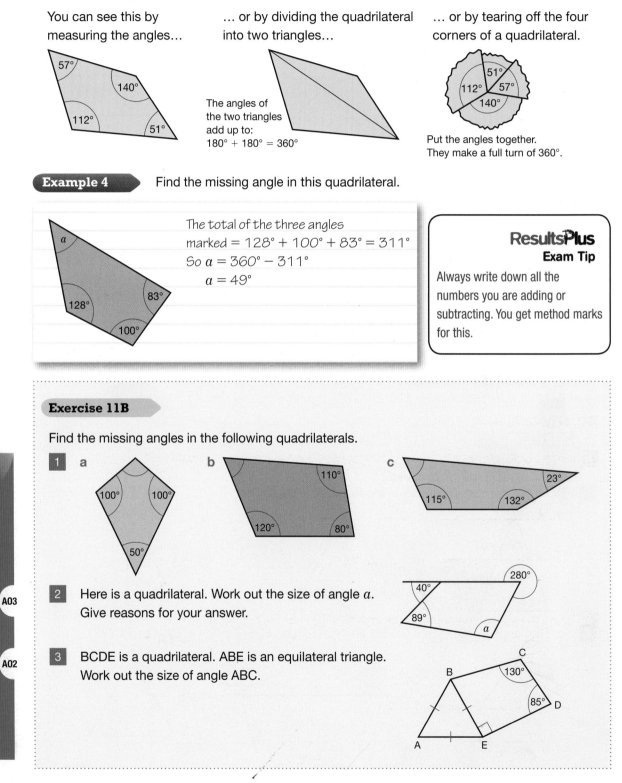

11.3 You can use corresponding and alternate angles to find missing angles

Key Points

- The marked angles below are equal. They are called corresponding angles.

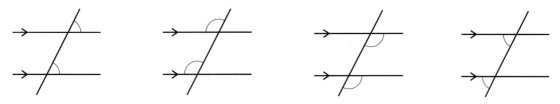

- The marked angles below are equal. They are called alternate angles.

Example 5   Find the size of the lettered angles, giving reasons for your answers.

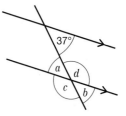

$a = 37°$	alternate angles are equal.
$b = 37°$	corresponding angles are equal.
$c = 143°$	angles on a straight line add up to 180°.
$d = 143°$	vertically opposite angles are equal.

Exercise 11C

1   In the diagrams below, find the size of each angle marked with a letter.
Give reasons for your answers.

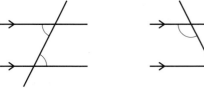

2   Find the size of the angles marked with a letter in the diagrams below.

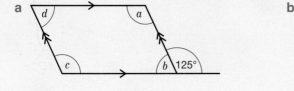
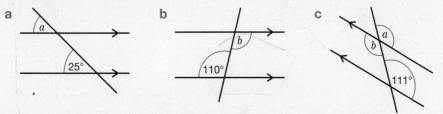

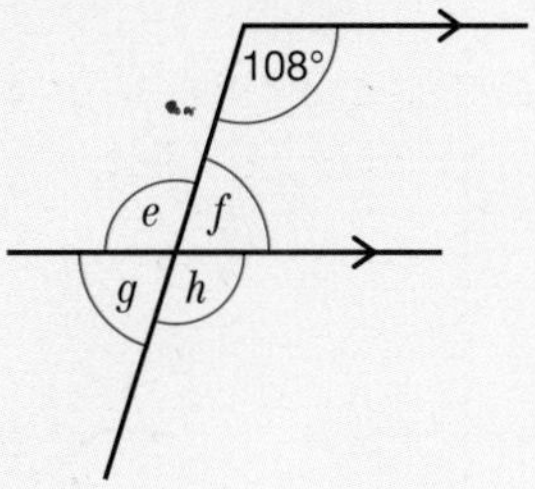

D

A02

11.4 You can understand and identify line symmetry

Key Points

- A shape is symmetrical if you can fold it in half and one half is the mirror image of the other half. The dividing line is called a line of symmetry or a mirror line.
- You can use tracing paper to help you. Trace the diagram and then fold it in half on the mirror line. You can then check if each half folds exactly onto the other half.

Example 6   Draw all the lines of symmetry for a rectangle.

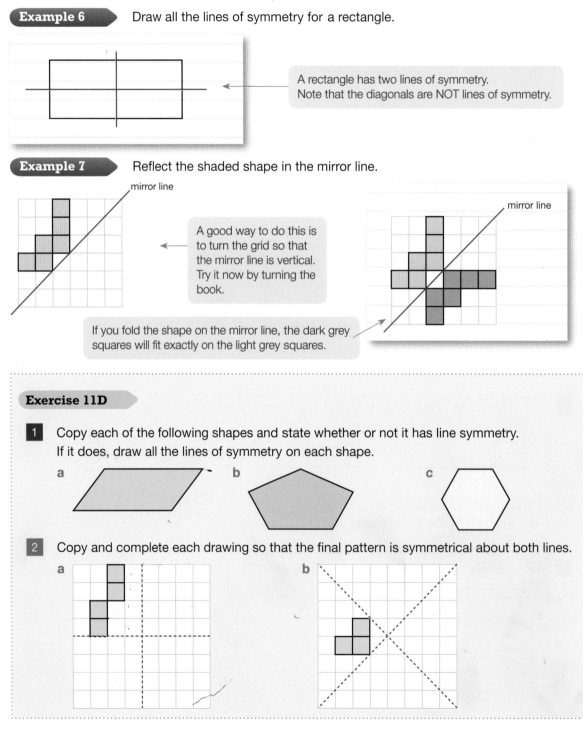

A rectangle has two lines of symmetry.
Note that the diagonals are NOT lines of symmetry.

Example 7   Reflect the shaded shape in the mirror line.

mirror line

A good way to do this is to turn the grid so that the mirror line is vertical. Try it now by turning the book.

mirror line

If you fold the shape on the mirror line, the dark grey squares will fit exactly on the light grey squares.

Exercise 11D

1   Copy each of the following shapes and state whether or not it has line symmetry. If it does, draw all the lines of symmetry on each shape.

a   b   c

2   Copy and complete each drawing so that the final pattern is symmetrical about both lines.

a   b

11.5 You can understand and identify rotational symmetry

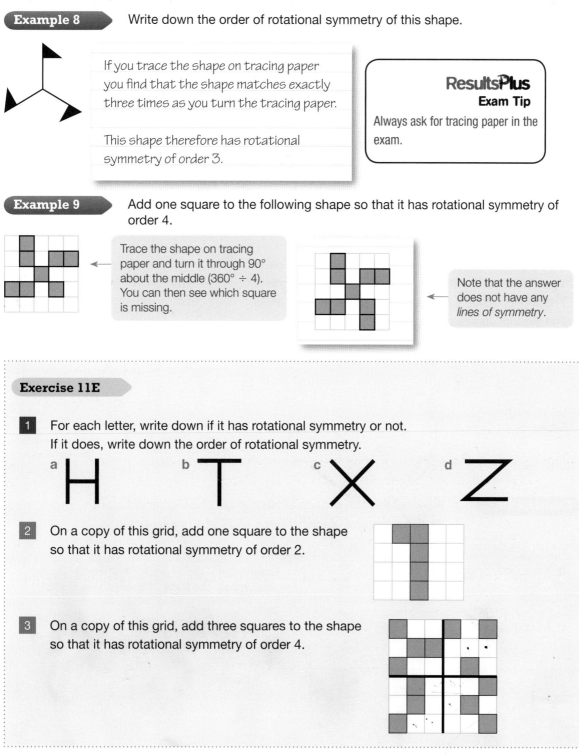

Key Point

⊙ To see if a shape has rotational symmetry, rotate it one full turn and see how many times along the rotation the shape still looks the same.

Example 8   Write down the order of rotational symmetry of this shape.

If you trace the shape on tracing paper you find that the shape matches exactly three times as you turn the tracing paper.

This shape therefore has rotational symmetry of order 3.

ResultsPlus
Exam Tip

Always ask for tracing paper in the exam.

Example 9   Add one square to the following shape so that it has rotational symmetry of order 4.

Trace the shape on tracing paper and turn it through 90° about the middle (360° ÷ 4). You can then see which square is missing.

Note that the answer does not have any *lines of symmetry*.

Exercise 11E

1   For each letter, write down if it has rotational symmetry or not.
     If it does, write down the order of rotational symmetry.

     a H   b T   c X   d Z

2   On a copy of this grid, add one square to the shape so that it has rotational symmetry of order 2.

3   On a copy of this grid, add three squares to the shape so that it has rotational symmetry of order 4.

F

E

11.6 You can work out the exterior and interior angles of regular polygons

Key Points

◉ A polygon is a regular polygon if its sides are all the same length and its angles are all the same size. You need to know the names of the following special polygons:

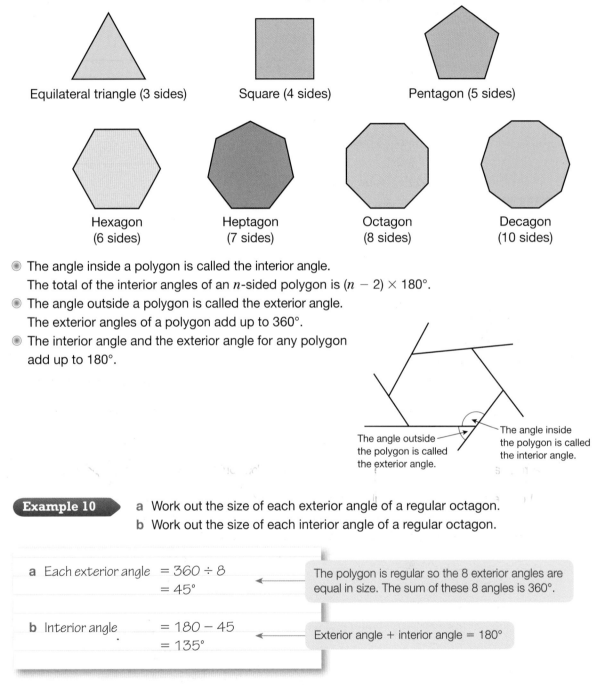

Equilateral triangle (3 sides)　　Square (4 sides)　　Pentagon (5 sides)

Hexagon
(6 sides)　　Heptagon
(7 sides)　　Octagon
(8 sides)　　Decagon
(10 sides)

◉ The angle inside a polygon is called the interior angle.
The total of the interior angles of an n-sided polygon is $(n - 2) \times 180°$.
◉ The angle outside a polygon is called the exterior angle.
The exterior angles of a polygon add up to 360°.
◉ The interior angle and the exterior angle for any polygon add up to 180°.

The angle outside the polygon is called the exterior angle.

The angle inside the polygon is called the interior angle.

Example 10　　a Work out the size of each exterior angle of a regular octagon.
　　b Work out the size of each interior angle of a regular octagon.

a Each exterior angle $= 360 \div 8$
$= 45°$

The polygon is regular so the 8 exterior angles are equal in size. The sum of these 8 angles is 360°.

b Interior angle $= 180 - 45$
$= 135°$

Exterior angle + interior angle = 180°

Example 11 An *n*-sided regular polygon has an interior angle of 160°.

    a Calculate the exterior angle of the polygon.

    b Use your answer to part **a** to work out how many sides the polygon has.

---

a The interior angle and the exterior angle of the polygon add up to 180°.

  Therefore 160° + exterior angle = 180°.

  So the exterior angle = 20°.

b The exterior angles of a polygon add up to 360°.

  So $n \times 20 = 360$

         $n = 360 \div 20$

         $n = 18$ The polygon has 18 sides.

> **ResultsPlus**
> **Watch Out!**
>
> The formula each exterior angle = 360° ÷ *n* does not work for irregular polygons.

Exercise 11F

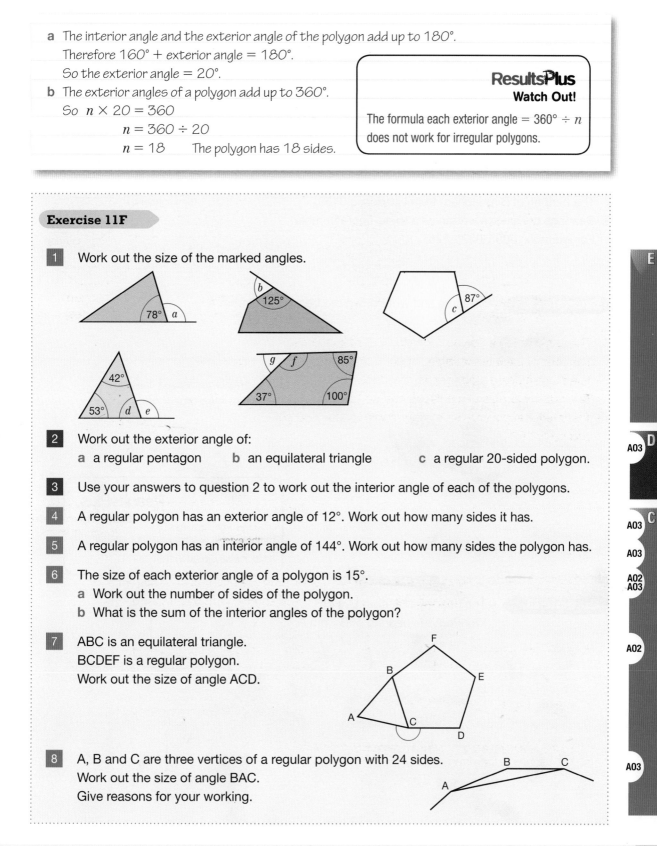

1 Work out the size of the marked angles.

2 Work out the exterior angle of:

  a a regular pentagon   **b** an equilateral triangle   **c** a regular 20-sided polygon.

3 Use your answers to question 2 to work out the interior angle of each of the polygons.

4 A regular polygon has an exterior angle of 12°. Work out how many sides it has.

5 A regular polygon has an interior angle of 144°. Work out how many sides the polygon has.

6 The size of each exterior angle of a polygon is 15°.

  a Work out the number of sides of the polygon.

  b What is the sum of the interior angles of the polygon?

7 ABC is an equilateral triangle.

  BCDEF is a regular polygon.

  Work out the size of angle ACD.

8 A, B and C are three vertices of a regular polygon with 24 sides.

  Work out the size of angle BAC.

  Give reasons for your working.

A03   D

A03   C

A03

A02
A03

A02

A03

E

11.7 You know what a bearing is and can use bearings to solve problems

◉ Bearings are used to describe directions with angles.

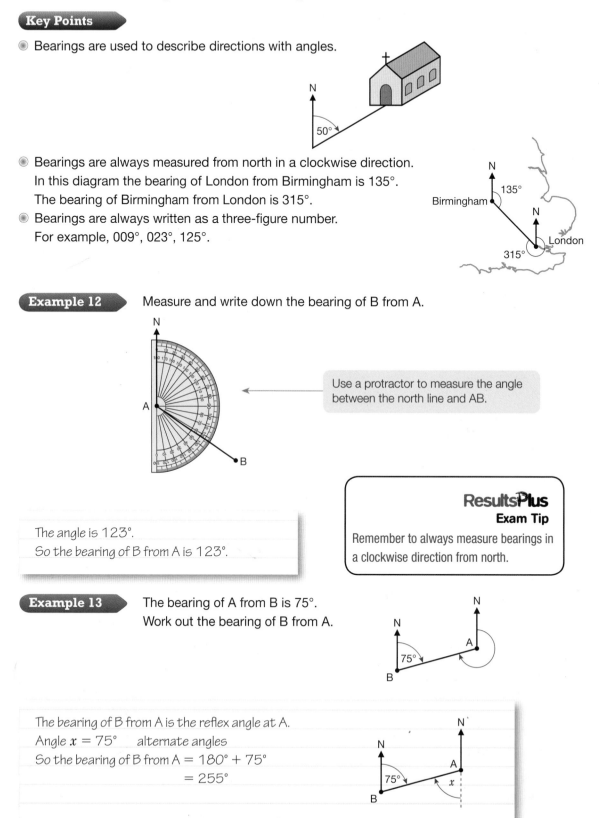

◉ Bearings are always measured from north in a clockwise direction.
In this diagram the bearing of London from Birmingham is 135°.
The bearing of Birmingham from London is 315°.

◉ Bearings are always written as a three-figure number.
For example, 009°, 023°, 125°.

Example 12   Measure and write down the bearing of B from A.

Use a protractor to measure the angle between the north line and AB.

The angle is 123°.
So the bearing of B from A is 123°.

ResultsPlus
Exam Tip

Remember to always measure bearings in a clockwise direction from north.

Example 13   The bearing of A from B is 75°.
Work out the bearing of B from A.

The bearing of B from A is the reflex angle at A.
Angle $x = 75°$ alternate angles
So the bearing of B from A = $180° + 75°$
                        = $255°$

Exercise 11G

1   Write down the bearing of:
    a   B from A
    b   C from B
    c   B from C.

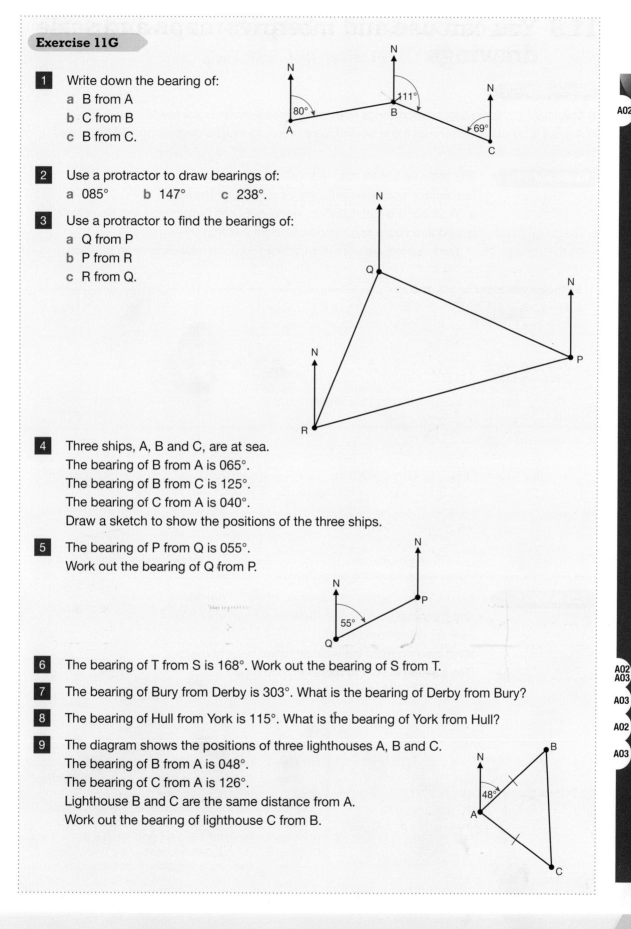

2   Use a protractor to draw bearings of:
    a   085°   b   147°   c   238°.

3   Use a protractor to find the bearings of:
    a   Q from P
    b   P from R
    c   R from Q.

4   Three ships, A, B and C, are at sea.
    The bearing of B from A is 065°.
    The bearing of B from C is 125°.
    The bearing of C from A is 040°.
    Draw a sketch to show the positions of the three ships.

5   The bearing of P from Q is 055°.
    Work out the bearing of Q from P.

6   The bearing of T from S is 168°. Work out the bearing of S from T.

7   The bearing of Bury from Derby is 303°. What is the bearing of Derby from Bury?

8   The bearing of Hull from York is 115°. What is the bearing of York from Hull?

9   The diagram shows the positions of three lighthouses A, B and C.
    The bearing of B from A is 048°.
    The bearing of C from A is 126°.
    Lighthouse B and C are the same distance from A.
    Work out the bearing of lighthouse C from B.

D

A02

A02
A03

A03

A02

A03

11.8 You can use and interpret maps and scale drawings

Key Points

- Maps and plans are accurate drawings from which measurements are made.
- A scale is a ratio which shows the relationship between a length on a drawing and the actual length in real life.

Example 14

The scale on a road map is 1 : 200 000.
Sunderland and Newcastle are 9 cm apart on the map.
  a Work out the real distance, in km, between Sunderland and Newcastle.
  b Middlesbrough is 55 km in a straight line from Newcastle.
     Work out the distance of Middlesbrough from Newcastle on the map.

a The distance on the map is 9 cm.

   real distance = 9 cm × 200 000 = 1 800 000 cm

   real distance = 18 000 m   ← Divide by 100 to change cm to m.

   The real distance between Sunderland and Newcastle is 18 km.   ← Divide by 1000 to change m to km.

b The real distance is 55 km.

   real distance = 55 × 1000 = 55 000 m   ← Multiply by 1000 to change km to m.

   real distance = 55 000 × 100 = 5 500 000 cm   ← Multiply by 100 to change m to cm.

   Distance on the map = $\dfrac{5500000}{200000} = 27.5$ cm   ← Divide by 200 000 to find the distance on the map.

> Remember:
> 100 cm = 1 m
> 1000 m = 1 km

Example 15

Irie walks for 2 miles on a bearing of 060° from home.
She then walks a further 4 miles on a bearing of 300°.
How far is Irie from home?
What bearing must Irie walk on to get back home?
Use a scale of 2 cm to represent one mile.

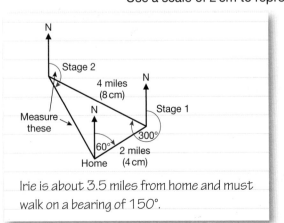

Irie is about 3.5 miles from home and must walk on a bearing of 150°.

Step 1 Draw the bearing of 060° from home.
Step 2 As the scale is 2 cm for 1 mile, you need to draw a line that is 4 cm long.
Step 3 Put in a new north line at the end of Stage 1.
Step 4 Draw the bearing of 300° from Stage 1.
Step 5 Make the line 8 cm long (4 miles is 4 × 2 cm).
Step 6 Put in a new north line at the end of Stage 2.
Step 7 Measure the distance from Stage 2 to home.
Step 8 Measure the bearing from Stage 2 to home.

Exercise 11H

1 The scale on a map is 1 cm to 2 km.
The distance between Ashton and Dacreville is 5.5 cm on the map.
How many kilometres apart are Ashton and Dacreville in real life?

2 A map is drawn on a scale of 3 cm to 1 km.
a Work out the real length of a lake, which is 4.2 cm long on the map.
b The distance between the church in Canwick and the town hall in Barnton is 5.8 km.
Work out the distance between them on the map.

3 Jane walks for 10 miles on a bearing of 060°.
Use a scale of 1 cm to represent 1 mile to show the journey.

4 Sam runs for 4 km on a bearing of 120°. Use a scale of 1 cm to represent 2 km to show the journey.

5 Witley is 2 km due south of Milford. The bearing of Hydestile from Milford is 125° and the distance from Milford to Hydestile is 2.8 km.
a Make a scale drawing to show the three villages. Use a scale of 1 : 25 000.
b Use your drawing to find
   i the distance of Hydestile from Witley
   ii the bearing of Hydestile from Witley.

6 This is a sketch of Arfan's bedroom. It is *not* drawn to scale.
Draw an accurate scale drawing on cm squared paper of Arfan's bedroom.
Use a scale of 1 : 50.

7 Ian sails his boat from the Isle of Wight for 20 km on a bearing of 135°.
He then sails on a bearing of 240° for 10 km.
How far is Ian from his starting point?
What bearing does he need to sail on to get back to the start?
Use a scale of 1 cm to represent 2 km.

8 Peg Leg the pirate buried his treasure 100 yards from the big tree on a bearing of 045°.
One-Eyed Rick dug up the treasure and moved it 50 yards on a bearing of 310° from where it had been buried.
How far is the treasure from the big tree now?
What bearing is the new hiding place of the treasure?
Use a scale of 1 cm to represent 10 yards.

9 Ray flew his plane on a bearing of 300° for 200 km. He then changed direction and flew on a bearing of 150° for 100 km.
What bearing must Ray fly on to get back to the start?
How far is he away from the start?

125

Exam review

Self-assessment checklist

I can:

- recognise and use the properties of right-angled, isosceles and equilateral triangles [p.114]
- find a missing angle using the fact that angles on a straight line add up to 180° [p.114]
- find a missing angle using the fact that angles at a point add up to 360° [p.114]
- find a missing angle using the fact that angles in a triangle add up to 180° [p.114]
- recognise vertically opposite angles [p.114]
- find a missing angle using the fact that angles in a quadrilateral add up to 360° [p.116]
- recognise alternate angles [p.117]
- recognise corresponding angles [p.117]
- understand line symmetry and identify and draw lines of symmetry of a 2D shape [p.118]
- understand rotational symmetry and identify the order of rotational symmetry of a 2D shape [p.119]
- recognise and name regular polygons [p.120]
- work out the size of the exterior angle of a regular polygon using the fact that the sum of the exterior angles of any polygon is 360° [p.120]
- work out the sum of the interior angles of a polygon with n sides using $(n - 2) \times 180°$ [p.120]
- use the fact that the interior angle and the exterior angle for any polygon add up to 180° [p.120]
- measure a bearing, starting at the north line, measuring it in a clockwise direction and using three figures for the bearing [p.122]
- work out the bearing of B from A given the bearing of A from B [p.122]
- use and interpret maps and scale drawings and use the scale on a map to work out distances in real life from distances on the map and vice versa. [p.124]

Exam practice

1 a Work out the size of the angle marked x.
   b Give a reason for your answer.

Diagram **NOT** accurately drawn

130°

x

June 2010

2 a On a copy of the shape, draw all the lines of symmetry.

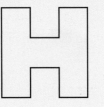

The shape below has rotational symmetry.
   b Write down the order of rotational symmetry.

Nov 2010

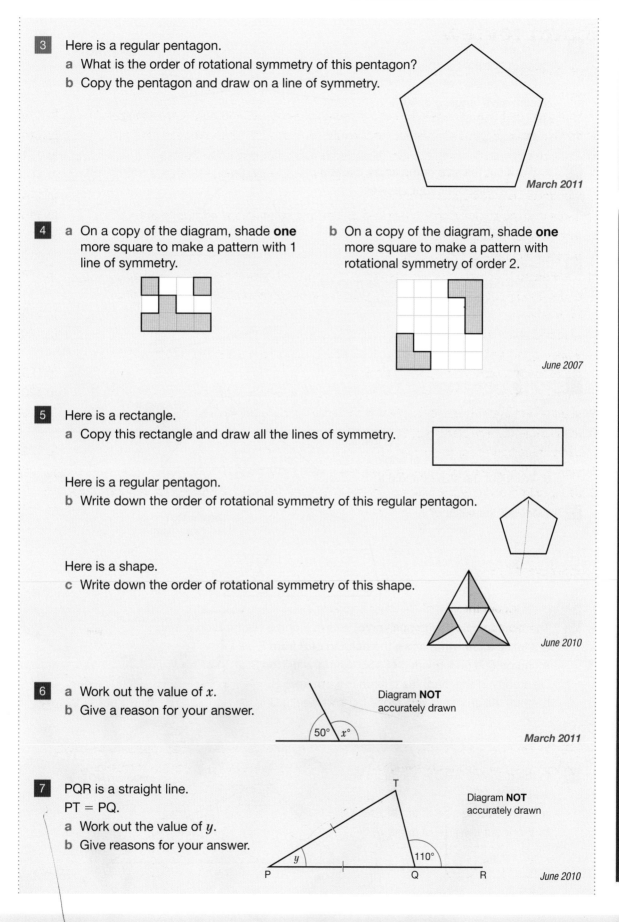

3 Here is a regular pentagon.
   a What is the order of rotational symmetry of this pentagon?
   b Copy the pentagon and draw on a line of symmetry.

March 2011

4 a On a copy of the diagram, shade **one** more square to make a pattern with 1 line of symmetry.
   b On a copy of the diagram, shade **one** more square to make a pattern with rotational symmetry of order 2.

June 2007

5 Here is a rectangle.
   a Copy this rectangle and draw all the lines of symmetry.

   Here is a regular pentagon.
   b Write down the order of rotational symmetry of this regular pentagon.

   Here is a shape.
   c Write down the order of rotational symmetry of this shape.

June 2010

6 a Work out the value of x.
   b Give a reason for your answer.

   Diagram **NOT** accurately drawn

   50° $x°$

March 2011

7 PQR is a straight line.
   PT = PQ.
   a Work out the value of y.
   b Give reasons for your answer.

   T

   Diagram **NOT** accurately drawn

   y 110°

   P   Q   R   *June 2010*

127

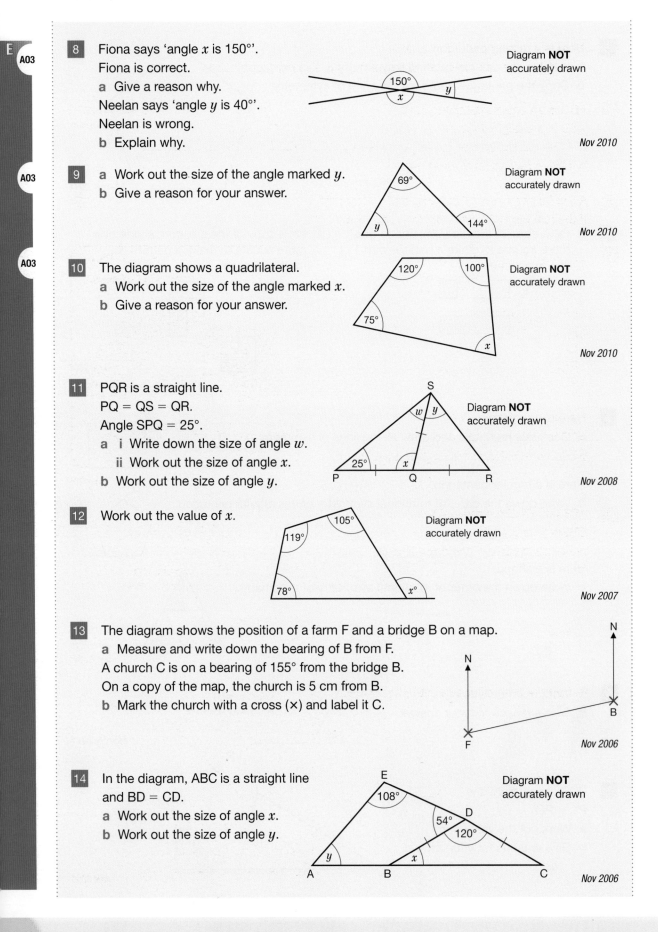

8 Fiona says 'angle x is 150°'.
Fiona is correct.
a Give a reason why.
Neelan says 'angle y is 40°'.
Neelan is wrong.
b Explain why.

150°

y

x

Diagram **NOT**
accurately drawn

Nov 2010

9 **a** Work out the size of the angle marked y.
b Give a reason for your answer.

69°

y

144°

Diagram **NOT**
accurately drawn

Nov 2010

10 The diagram shows a quadrilateral.
a Work out the size of the angle marked x.
b Give a reason for your answer.

120° 100°

75°

x

Diagram **NOT**
accurately drawn

Nov 2010

11 PQR is a straight line.
PQ = QS = QR.
Angle SPQ = 25°.
a **i** Write down the size of angle w.
  ii Work out the size of angle x.
b Work out the size of angle y.

S

w y

25° x

P Q R

Diagram **NOT**
accurately drawn

Nov 2008

12 Work out the value of x.

105°

119°

78°

$x°$

Diagram **NOT**
accurately drawn

Nov 2007

13 The diagram shows the position of a farm F and a bridge B on a map.
a Measure and write down the bearing of B from F.
A church C is on a bearing of 155° from the bridge B.
On a copy of the map, the church is 5 cm from B.
b Mark the church with a cross (×) and label it C.

N

N

B

F

Nov 2006

14 In the diagram, ABC is a straight line
and BD = CD.
a Work out the size of angle x.
b Work out the size of angle y.

E

108°

54° D

120°

y x

A B C

Diagram **NOT**
accurately drawn

Nov 2006

128

15 A car is 4 m long and 1.8 m wide.

A model of the car, similar in all respects, is 5 cm long. How wide is it?

16 ABC is an equilateral triangle.

ACD is a straight line.

  a Work out the size of the angle marked x.

  b Give a reason for your answer.

Diagram **NOT** accurately drawn

Nov 2010

17 A model of a car is 12 cm long and 5.2 cm high.

If the real car is 3.36 m long, how high is it?

18

Diagram **NOT** accurately drawn

ABC is an equilateral triangle.

ACD is a right-angled triangle.

Work out the size of the angle marked x.

ResultsPlus
Achieving Full Marks

■ C candidates
■ D candidates
100% 100%

To get full marks on this question, work out the size of angle *DAC* and angle *BAC* then add your answers together.

Nov 2009

19 AFB and CHD are parallel lines.

EFD is a straight line.

Work out the size of the angle marked x.

Diagram **NOT** accurately drawn

Nov 2010

20 Reflect the shaded shape in the line $y = x$.

Nov 2010

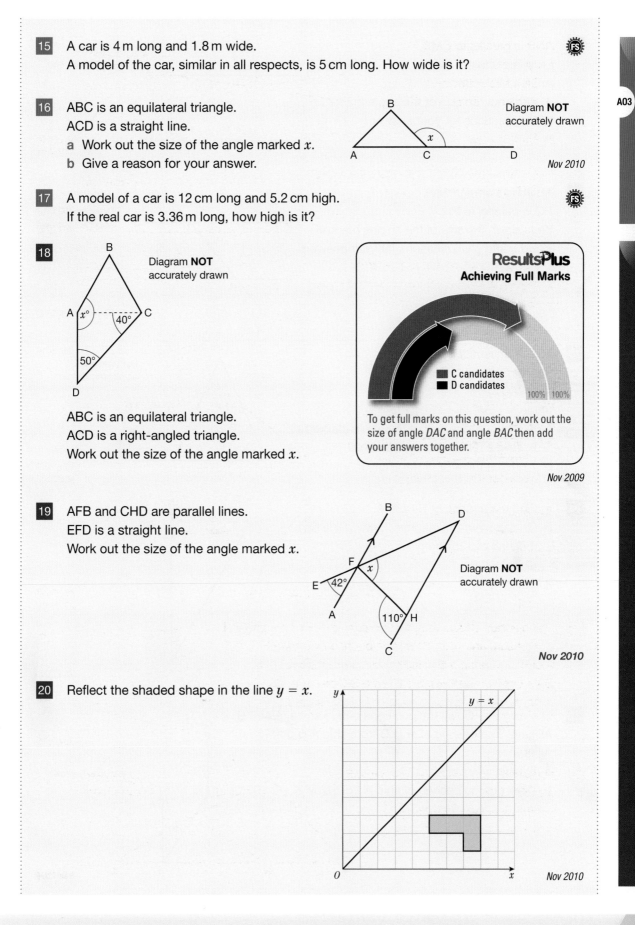

129

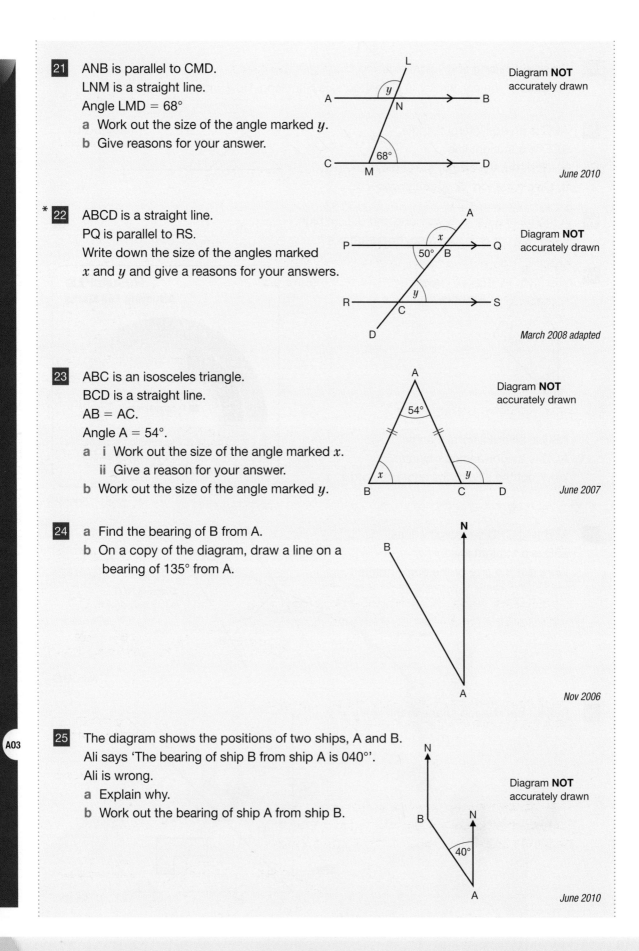

21 ANB is parallel to CMD.
LNM is a straight line.
Angle LMD = 68°
a Work out the size of the angle marked y.
b Give reasons for your answer.

A ————————————————— B

Diagram **NOT** accurately drawn

68°

C ————————————————— D

June 2010

*22 ABCD is a straight line.
PQ is parallel to RS.
Write down the size of the angles marked
x and y and give a reasons for your answers.

P ————————————— Q

Diagram **NOT** accurately drawn

50°

R ————————————— S

March 2008 adapted

23 ABC is an isosceles triangle.
BCD is a straight line.
AB = AC.
Angle A = 54°.
a **i** Work out the size of the angle marked x.
ii Give a reason for your answer.
b Work out the size of the angle marked y.

54°

Diagram **NOT** accurately drawn

June 2007

24 **a** Find the bearing of B from A.
b On a copy of the diagram, draw a line on a
bearing of 135° from A.

N

Nov 2006

A03

25 The diagram shows the positions of two ships, A and B.
Ali says 'The bearing of ship B from ship A is 040°'.
Ali is wrong.
a Explain why.
b Work out the bearing of ship A from ship B.

N

Diagram **NOT** accurately drawn

40°

June 2010

26 Work out the size of an exterior angle of a regular pentagon.

Diagram **NOT** accurately drawn

June 2010

27 The diagram shows the position of two airports, A and B.
A plane flies from airport A to airport B.
  a Measure the size of the angle marked x.
  b Work out the real distance between airport A and airport B.
     Use the scale 1 cm represents 50 km.
Airport C is 350 km on a bearing of 060° from airport B.
  c On a copy of the diagram, mark airport C with a cross (×).
     Label it C.

Scale: 1 cm repreasents 50 km

May 2008

28 Work out the bearing of B from A.

Diagram **NOT** accurately drawn

June 2010

29 The interior angle of a regular polygon is 160°.
  a Write down the size of an exterior angle of the polygon.
  b Work out the number of sides of the polygon.

160°

Diagram **NOT** accurately drawn

March 2011

30 The diagram shows part of a regular 10-sided polygon.
Work out the size of the angle marked x.

x

Diagram **NOT** accurately drawn

Nov 2008

31 The diagram shows three sides of a regular polygon.
Each interior angle of the regular polygon is 140°.
Work out the number of sides of the regular polygon.

Diagram **NOT** accurately drawn

140°   140°

Nov 2010

D

C

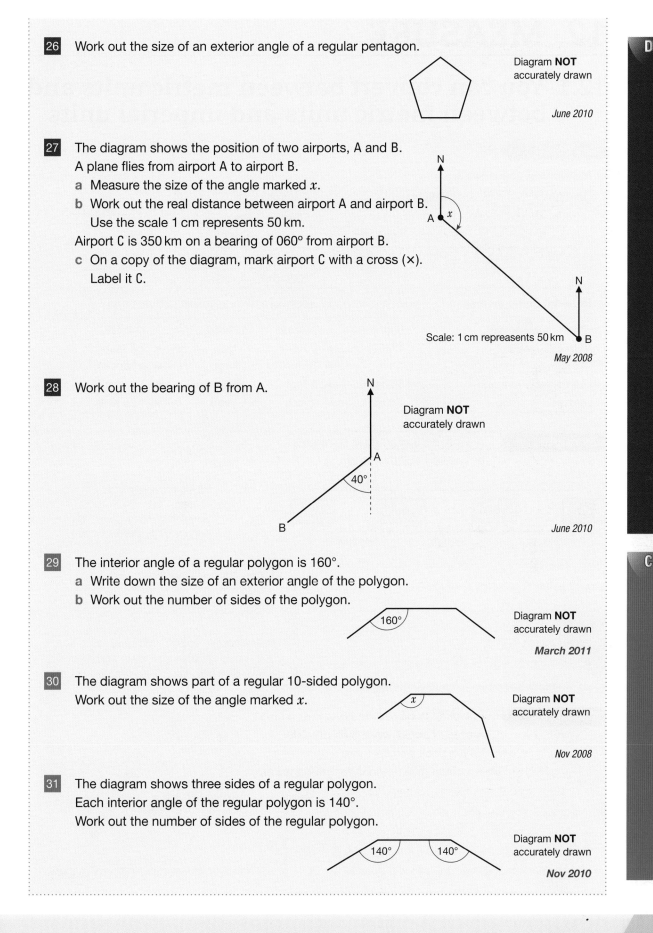

12 MEASURE

12.1 You can convert between metric units and between metric units and imperial units

Key Points

- **Metric unit** conversions

Length	Weight	Capacity
10 mm = 1 cm	1000 mg = 1 g	100 cl = 1 litre
100 cm = 1 m	1000 g = 1 kg	1000 ml = 1 litre
1000 mm = 1 m	1000 kg = 1 tonne	1000 l = 1 cubic metre
1000 m = 1 km		1000 cm^3 = 1 litre

- **Imperial unit** conversions

12 inches = 1 foot
3 feet = 1 yard
16 ounces = 1 pound
14 pounds = 1 stone
8 pints = 1 gallon

- Metric–imperial approximate equivalent conversions

Metric	Imperial	Metric	Imperial
8 km ⟶ 5 miles		1 kg ⟶ 2.2 pounds	
1 m ⟶ 39 inches		25 g ⟶ 1 ounce	
30 cm ⟶ 1 foot		4.5 litres ⟶ 1 gallon	
2.5 cm ⟶ 1 inch		1 litre ⟶ 1.75 pints	

Example 1

  a Convert 3 kilometres to metres.

  b Convert 450 mm to cm.

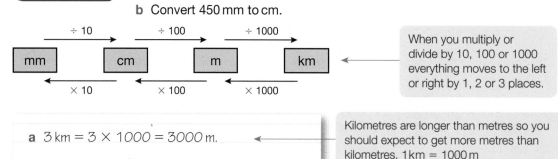

When you multiply or divide by 10, 100 or 1000 everything moves to the left or right by 1, 2 or 3 places.

  a 3 km = 3 × 1000 = 3000 m.

Kilometres are longer than metres so you should expect to get more metres than kilometres. 1 km = 1000 m

  b 450 mm = 450 ÷ 10 = 45 cm.

Millimetres are smaller than centimetres so you should expect to get fewer centimetres than millimetres. 10 mm = 1 cm

Example 2

A sack of flour weighs 20 kg.

A sack of sugar weighs 35 pounds.

Which sack weighs more?

You must give reasons for your answer.

Use 1 kg = 2.2 pounds

So 20 kg = 20 × 2.2 = 44 pounds

The sack of flour weighs more as it weighs 44 pounds and the sack of sugar weighs only 35 pounds.

Give your final answer clearly with a reason.

Example 3   Convert 20 km into miles.

Use 8 km = 5 miles
20 km = 20 ÷ 8 × 5 miles = 12.5 miles.

ResultsPlus
Exam Tip
In the exam, you will be expected to know the metric–imperial conversions.

Exercise 12A

Questions in this chapter are targeted at the grades indicated.

1   A large box contains 3 kg of plastic cubes. Each cube weighs 6 grams. How many cubes are there in the box?   A02

2   A jar contains 450 ml of water. A tank can fill 200 of these jars. What is the capacity, in litres, of the tank?   A02

3   One lap of a running track is 400 m. How many laps must be run to complete a 10 km race?   A02

4   Convert the following measurements.
   a 15 miles into kilometres   b 10 kg into pounds   c 4 litres into pints
   d 6 inches into cm   e 48 km into miles   f 11 pounds into kg

5   A tank holds 18 litres. How many gallons is this?

6   A baby needs 1 pint of milk a day. His bottle contains 0.2 litres. How many bottles will his carer have to make for him in one day?   A02 A03

7   Yasmin travels from London to Scotland. The distance is 400 miles. What is the distance in kilometres?

8   A family on holiday in Majorca travel 150 km while touring the island. How many miles do they travel?

9   A group of men can lay 300 m of pipe in one day. Working at the same rate, how long should it take them to lay the pipe for a length of 15 km?   A02

10   A scuba diver weighs 110 lb. She needs to weigh a total of 57 kg to dive. Her airtank weighs 5 kg. How many half pound weights does she need to wear?   A02 A03

11   The petrol tank on Keith's car will hold 14 gallons of petrol.
   The petrol tank is empty.
   Keith wants to fill up the petrol tank with petrol.
   Petrol costs £1.32 per litre.
   How much will it cost Keith to fill up his petrol tank?   A03

12   Shop A is selling 4 kg of potatoes for £1.60. Shop B is selling a 5-pound bag of potatoes for £1.60.
   Which is the better buy?   A02 A03

12.2 You can solve problems using speed, distance and time

Key Points

- Speed = $\dfrac{\text{distance}}{\text{time}}$

- Time = $\dfrac{\text{distance}}{\text{speed}}$

- Distance = speed × time

- Average speed = $\dfrac{\text{total distance travelled}}{\text{total time taken}}$

- Units of speed are usually miles per hour (mph), kilometres per hour (km/h) or metres per second (m/s).

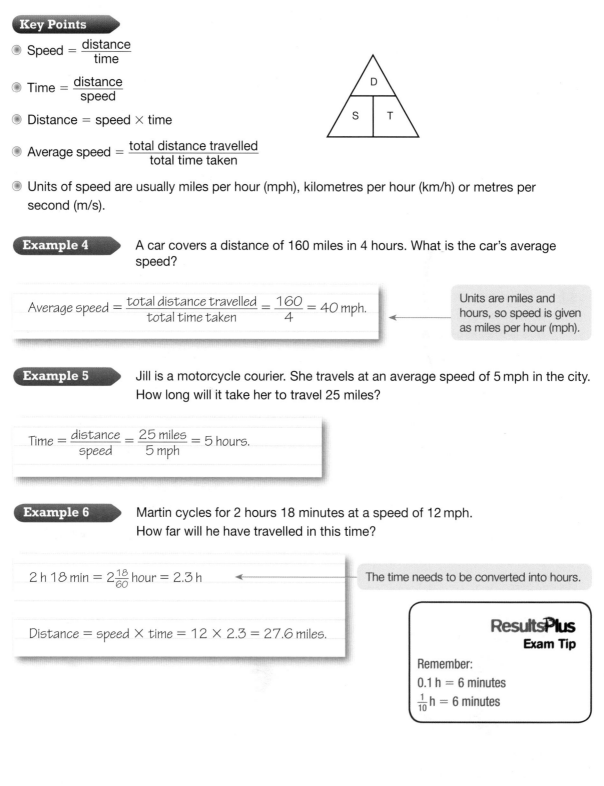

Example 4   A car covers a distance of 160 miles in 4 hours. What is the car's average speed?

Average speed = $\dfrac{\text{total distance travelled}}{\text{total time taken}} = \dfrac{160}{4} = 40$ mph.

> Units are miles and hours, so speed is given as miles per hour (mph).

Example 5   Jill is a motorcycle courier. She travels at an average speed of 5 mph in the city. How long will it take her to travel 25 miles?

Time = $\dfrac{\text{distance}}{\text{speed}} = \dfrac{25 \text{ miles}}{5 \text{ mph}} = 5$ hours.

Example 6   Martin cycles for 2 hours 18 minutes at a speed of 12 mph. How far will he have travelled in this time?

2 h 18 min = $2\frac{18}{60}$ hour = 2.3 h

> The time needs to be converted into hours.

Distance = speed × time = 12 × 2.3 = 27.6 miles.

ResultsPlus
Exam Tip

Remember:
0.1 h = 6 minutes
$\frac{1}{10}$ h = 6 minutes

134

Exercise 12B

1. A car travels for 2 hours at 40 mph. How far will the car have gone?

2. Find the time taken to travel 12 km at 3 km/h.

3. What is the average speed of a car that takes 3 hours to travel 90 miles?

4. Giles ran for 2 hours and covered 16 miles. At what average speed was he running?

5. How long does it take to travel 60 miles at an average speed of 40 mph?

6. Find the time taken to walk 10 miles at an average walking speed of $2\frac{1}{2}$ mph.

7. An aeroplane flew at 400 mph. How far did it travel in $3\frac{1}{2}$ hours?

8. Rajesh travels for $2\frac{1}{2}$ hours at 64 mph. Calculate the distance he travelled.

9. Mandy swam 5 miles. It took her $2\frac{1}{2}$ hours. What was her average speed?

10. Ahmed travelled 200 miles on a business trip. He left home at 9 am and arrived at his destination at 1 pm. What was his average speed?

11. What is the average speed of a train that takes $2\frac{1}{2}$ hours to travel 80 km?

12. Jon travels 40 km in 30 minutes. Calculate his average speed in km/h.

13. An aeroplane flies 1400 km in $3\frac{1}{2}$ hours. What is its average speed?

14. How far will you have gone if you travel for 1 hour 45 minutes at 50 mph?

15. A cyclist rode at a speed of 10 mph. She covered a distance of 32 miles. For how long was she cycling? (Give your answer in hours and minutes.)

16. A lorry made a journey of 390 km at an average speed of 50 km/h. How long did it take? Give your answer in hours and minutes.

17. A horse takes 6 minutes to gallop 5 km. What is the average speed of the horse?

18. **a** A racing car travels at 85 m/s. Work out the distance the car travels in 0.4 seconds.
    b Change a speed of 85 m/s into km/h.

19. A lorry travels at an average speed of 60 km/h.
    A van travels at an average speed of 45 miles per hour.
    Which vehicle travels faster?
    You must explain your answer.

20. Rob cycles 20 miles in $2\frac{1}{2}$ hours.
    Jean cycles 45 km in 3 hours.
    Who cycles the fastest?
    You must explain your answer.

E

D

C

A02
A03

A02
A03

12.3 You can recognise the inaccuracy of measurements

Key Points

- Measured with a ruler, the length of a piece of A4 paper is 297 mm.
- The exact length of the piece of A4 paper is somewhere between 296.5 mm and 297.5 mm.
- So 297 mm to the nearest millimetre means that the minimum (least) possible length is 296.5 mm, and the maximum (greatest) possible length is 297.5 mm.
- Measurements given to the nearest whole unit may be inaccurate by up to one half of a unit below and one half of a unit above.
- The upper bound of a number written to 1 decimal place is the highest value which rounds down to that number.
- The lower bound of a number written to 1 decimal place is the lowest value which rounds up to that number.

		mm
270 280	290 300	310

29.65 ‖ 29.75

Example 7

The weight of a cocker spaniel is 14 kg correct to the nearest kilogram.
Write down

  a the smallest possible weight
  b the greatest possible weight.

> We are looking for the range of values that give 14 kg when correct to the nearest kg.

  a 13.5 kg   b 14.5 kg

> The range of values is 13.5 kg to 14.5 kg.

Example 8

  a $x = 6.4$ (correct to 1 decimal place)
     Write down the upper bound and the lower bound of x.
  b $y = 248$ (correct to 3 significant figures)
     Write down the upper bound and the lower bound of y.

> **ResultsPlus**
> **Exam Tip**
>
> Remember that the upper bound is the same distance above x as the lower bound is below x.

  a Upper bound of $x = 6.45$

> For 1 decimal place the upper bound is 0.05 above the stated value.

     Lower bound of $x = 6.35$

> For 1 decimal place the lower bound is 0.05 below the stated value.

  b Upper bound of $y = 248.5$

> 248.5 is the largest value which will round down to 248 correct to 3 significant figures.

     Lower bound of $y = 247.5$

Exercise 12C

1. The length of a pencil is 12 cm correct to the nearest centimetre.
   Write down the maximum length it could be.

2. The weight of an envelope is 45 grams correct to the nearest gram.
   Write down the minimum weight it could be.

3. The capacity of a jug is 4 litres correct to the nearest litre.
   Write down the minimum capacity of the jug.

4. The radius of a plate is 9.7 cm correct to the nearest millimetre.
   Write down:
   a the least possible length it could be   b the greatest possible length it could be.

5. Magda's height is 1.59 m correct to the nearest centimetre. Write down in metres:
   a the minimum possible height she could be
   b the maximum possible height she could be.

6. The length of a pencil is 10 cm correct to the nearest cm.
   The length of a pencil case is 102 mm correct to the nearest mm.
   Explain why the pen might not fit in the case.

7. The width of a cupboard is measured to be 82 cm correct to the nearest centimetre.
   There is a gap of 817 mm correct to the nearest mm in the wall.
   Explain how the cupboard might fit in the wall.

8. Write down: i the upper bound and ii the lower bound of these numbers.
   a 84 (2 significant figures)   b 84.0 (3 significant figures)   c 84.00 (4 significant figures)

9. Write down: i the upper bound and ii the lower bound of these numbers.
   a 0.9 (1 decimal place)   b 0.90 (2 decimal places)   c 0.09 (2 decimal places)

10. The length of a line is 118 cm correct to the nearest cm. Write down:
    a the upper bound   b the lower bound of the length of the line.
    Give your answers in cm.

11. The mass of a stone is 6.4 kg correct to the nearest one tenth of a kg. Write down:
    a the upper bound   b the lower bound of the mass of the stone.
    Give your answers in grams.

12. The amount of fuel in a tank is 48.0 litres correct to the nearest tenth of a litre. Write down:
    a the upper bound   b the lower bound of the amount of fuel in the tank.
    Give your answers in litres.

13. The length of a piece of wood is 1 metre correct to the nearest cm. Write down:
    a the upper bound   b the lower bound of the length of the piece of wood.
    Give your answers in metres.

C

A

Exam review

Self-assessment checklist

I can:

- convert between metric units [p.132]
- convert between metric units and imperial units [p.132]
- remember the metric units conversions [p.132]

Length	Weight	Capacity
10 mm = 1 cm	1000 mg = 1 g	100 cl = 1 litre
100 cm = 1 m	1000 g = 1 kg	1000 ml = 1 litre
1000 mm = 1 m	1000 kg = 1 tonne	1000 l = 1 cubic metre
1000 m = 1 km		1000 cm^3 = 1 litre

- remember the common metric–imperial conversions [p.132]

		Metric	Imperial	Metric	Imperial
12 inches = 1 foot		8 km ⟶ 5 miles		1 kg ⟶ 2.2 pounds	
3 feet = 1 yard		1 m ⟶ 39 inches		25 g ⟶ 1 ounce	
16 ounces = 1 pound		30 cm ⟶ 1 foot		4.5 litres ⟶ 1 gallon	
14 pounds = 1 stone		2.5 cm ⟶ 1 inch		1 litre ⟶ 1.75 pints	
8 pints = 1 gallon					

- solve problems involving distance, speed and time using the formula [p.134]

$$\text{speed} = \frac{\text{distance}}{\text{time}} \text{ or}$$

- recognise that measurements given to the nearest whole unit may be inaccurate by up to one half in either direction [p.136]
- find the upper and lower bound of a number given the accuracy to which it has been written. [p.136]

E

D A02 A03

Exam practice

1 The distance from London to New York is 3456 miles.
A plane takes 8 hours to fly from London to New York.
Work out the average speed of the plane.

June 2008

2 The motorway speed limit in Great Britain is
70 miles per hour. The motorway speed limit in
Spain is 120 kilometres per hour.
Which of these speed limits is the lowest speed?
You must show working to explain your answer.

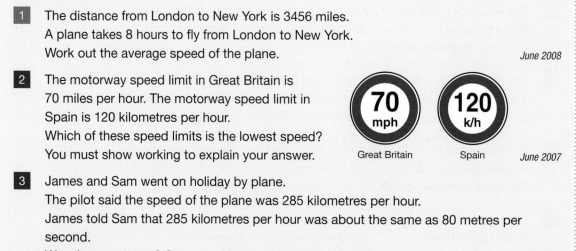

70 mph
Great Britain

120 k/h
Spain

June 2007

3 James and Sam went on holiday by plane.
The pilot said the speed of the plane was 285 kilometres per hour.
James told Sam that 285 kilometres per hour was about the same as 80 metres per second.
Was James correct? Show working to justify your answer.

June 2005

4 John travelled 30 km in 1.5 hours.
Kamala travelled 42 km in 2 hours.
Who had the greater average speed?
You must show your working.

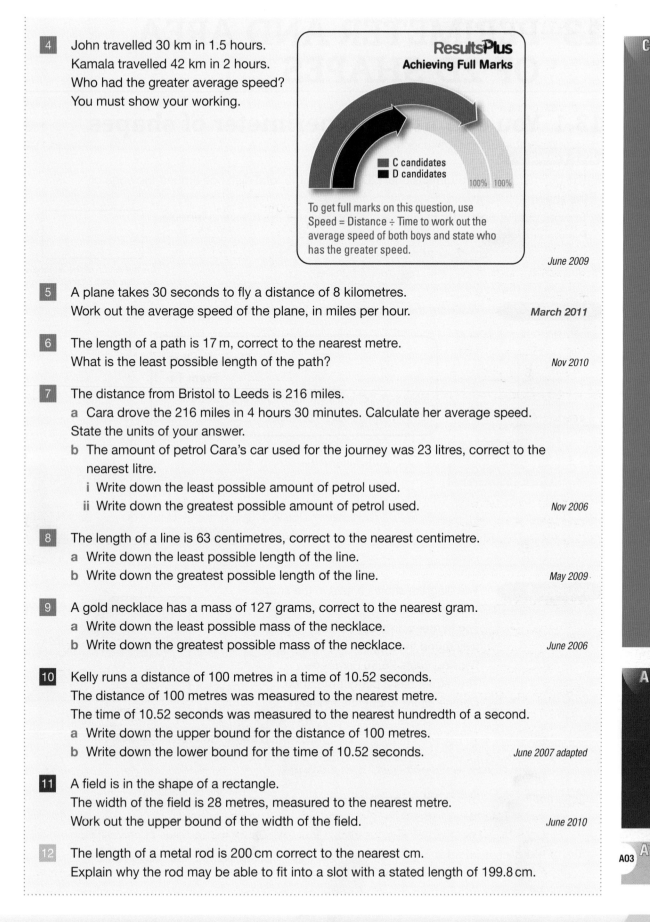

ResultsPlus
Achieving Full Marks

■ C candidates
■ D candidates
100% 100%

To get full marks on this question, use
Speed = Distance ÷ Time to work out the
average speed of both boys and state who
has the greater speed.

June 2009

5 A plane takes 30 seconds to fly a distance of 8 kilometres.
Work out the average speed of the plane, in miles per hour.   **March 2011**

6 The length of a path is 17 m, correct to the nearest metre.
What is the least possible length of the path?   *Nov 2010*

7 The distance from Bristol to Leeds is 216 miles.
  a Cara drove the 216 miles in 4 hours 30 minutes. Calculate her average speed.
  State the units of your answer.
  b The amount of petrol Cara's car used for the journey was 23 litres, correct to the
  nearest litre.
    i Write down the least possible amount of petrol used.
    ii Write down the greatest possible amount of petrol used.   *Nov 2006*

8 The length of a line is 63 centimetres, correct to the nearest centimetre.
  a Write down the least possible length of the line.
  b Write down the greatest possible length of the line.   *May 2009*

9 A gold necklace has a mass of 127 grams, correct to the nearest gram.
  a Write down the least possible mass of the necklace.
  b Write down the greatest possible mass of the necklace.   *June 2006*

10 Kelly runs a distance of 100 metres in a time of 10.52 seconds.
The distance of 100 metres was measured to the nearest metre.
The time of 10.52 seconds was measured to the nearest hundredth of a second.
  a Write down the upper bound for the distance of 100 metres.
  b Write down the lower bound for the time of 10.52 seconds.   *June 2007 adapted*

11 A field is in the shape of a rectangle.
The width of the field is 28 metres, measured to the nearest metre.
Work out the upper bound of the width of the field.   *June 2010*

12 The length of a metal rod is 200 cm correct to the nearest cm.
Explain why the rod may be able to fit into a slot with a stated length of 199.8 cm.

C

A

A03 A*

13 PERIMETER AND AREA OF 2D SHAPES

13.1 You can find the perimeter of shapes

Key Points

- The perimeter of a two-dimensional (2D) shape is the total distance around the edge of the shape.
- To work out the perimeter of a rectangle you can use the following formula.

Perimeter of a rectangle $= l + w + l + w$
$$= 2l + 2w$$

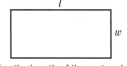

l = the length of the rectangle
w = the width of the rectangle

Example 1   Work out the perimeter of the following shape.

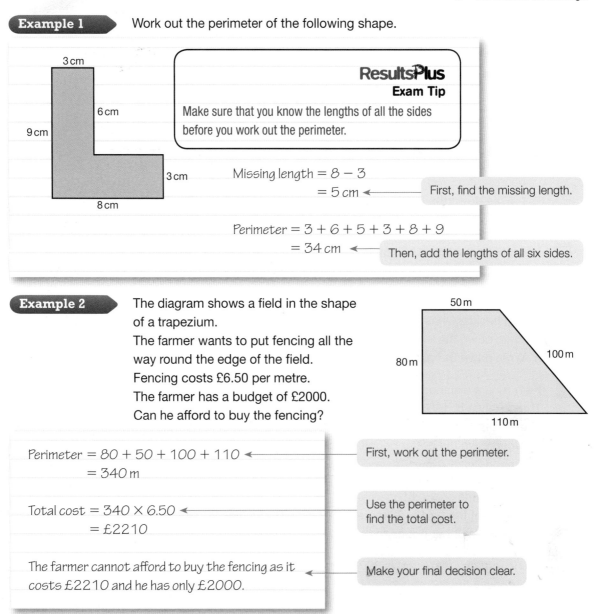

ResultsPlus
Exam Tip

Make sure that you know the lengths of all the sides before you work out the perimeter.

Missing length $= 8 - 3$
$$= 5\,cm$$ First, find the missing length.

Perimeter $= 3 + 6 + 5 + 3 + 8 + 9$
$$= 34\,cm$$ Then, add the lengths of all six sides.

Example 2   The diagram shows a field in the shape of a trapezium.
The farmer wants to put fencing all the way round the edge of the field.
Fencing costs £6.50 per metre.
The farmer has a budget of £2000.
Can he afford to buy the fencing?

Perimeter $= 80 + 50 + 100 + 110$ First, work out the perimeter.
$$= 340\,m$$

Total cost $= 340 \times 6.50$ Use the perimeter to find the total cost.
$$= £2210$$

The farmer cannot afford to buy the fencing as it costs £2210 and he has only £2000.   Make your final decision clear.

Exercise 13A

Questions in this chapter are targeted at the grades indicated.

1 Work out the perimeters of the following shapes.

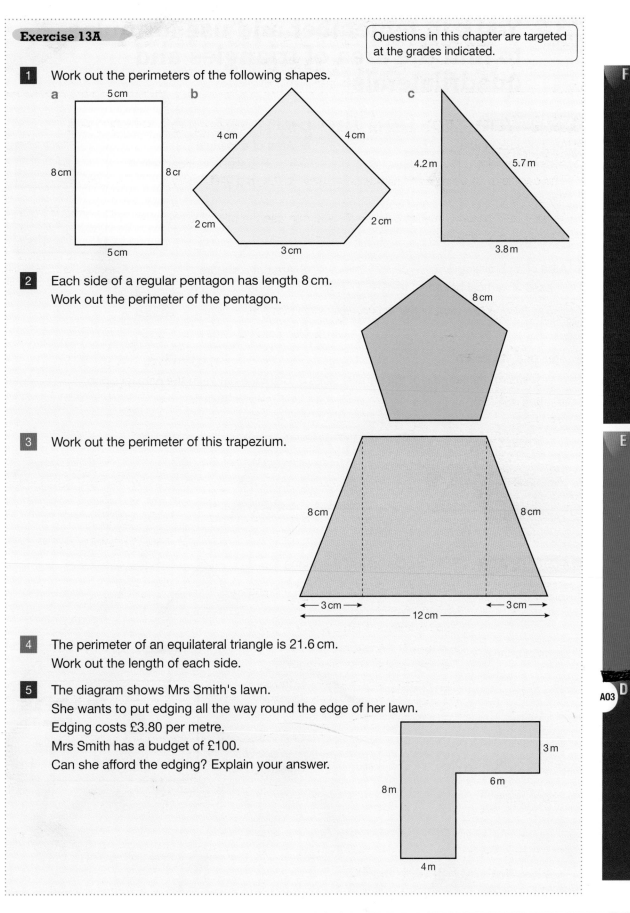

a

5 cm

8 cm   8 cr

5 cm

b

4 cm   4 cm

2 cm   2 cm

3 cm

c

4.2 m   5.7 m

3.8 m

2 Each side of a regular pentagon has length 8 cm.
Work out the perimeter of the pentagon.

8 cm

3 Work out the perimeter of this trapezium.

8 cm   8 cm

3 cm   3 cm
12 cm

4 The perimeter of an equilateral triangle is 21.6 cm.
Work out the length of each side.

5 The diagram shows Mrs Smith's lawn.
She wants to put edging all the way round the edge of her lawn.
Edging costs £3.80 per metre.
Mrs Smith has a budget of £100.
Can she afford the edging? Explain your answer.

3 m

6 m

8 m

4 m

F

E

A03 D

13.2 You can remember and use formulae to find the area of triangles and quadrilaterals

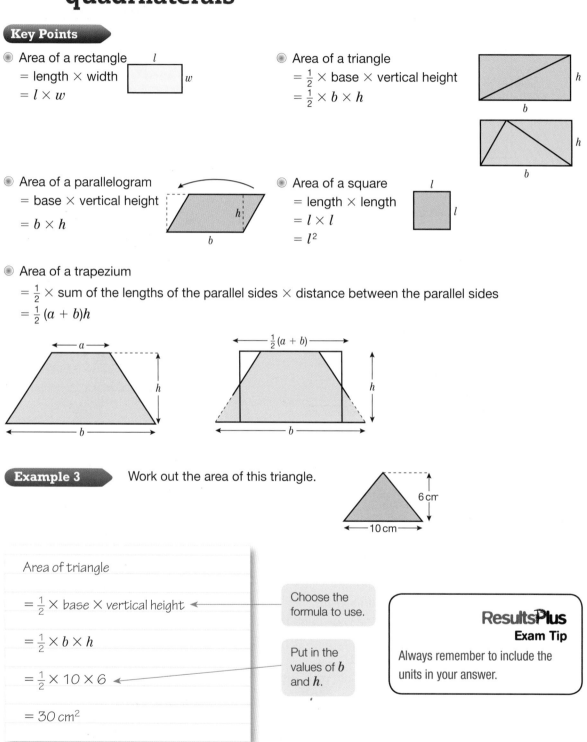

Key Points

- Area of a rectangle
  = length × width
  = $l \times w$

- Area of a triangle
  = $\frac{1}{2}$ × base × vertical height
  = $\frac{1}{2} \times b \times h$

- Area of a parallelogram
  = base × vertical height
  = $b \times h$

- Area of a square
  = length × length
  = $l \times l$
  = l^2

- Area of a trapezium
  = $\frac{1}{2}$ × sum of the lengths of the parallel sides × distance between the parallel sides
  = $\frac{1}{2}(a + b)h$

Example 3   Work out the area of this triangle.

6 cm

10 cm

Area of triangle

= $\frac{1}{2}$ × base × vertical height   ←   Choose the formula to use.

= $\frac{1}{2} \times b \times h$

= $\frac{1}{2} \times 10 \times 6$ ←   Put in the values of b and h.

= 30 cm²

ResultsPlus
Exam Tip

Always remember to include the units in your answer.

Example 4　　　Work out the area of this trapezium.

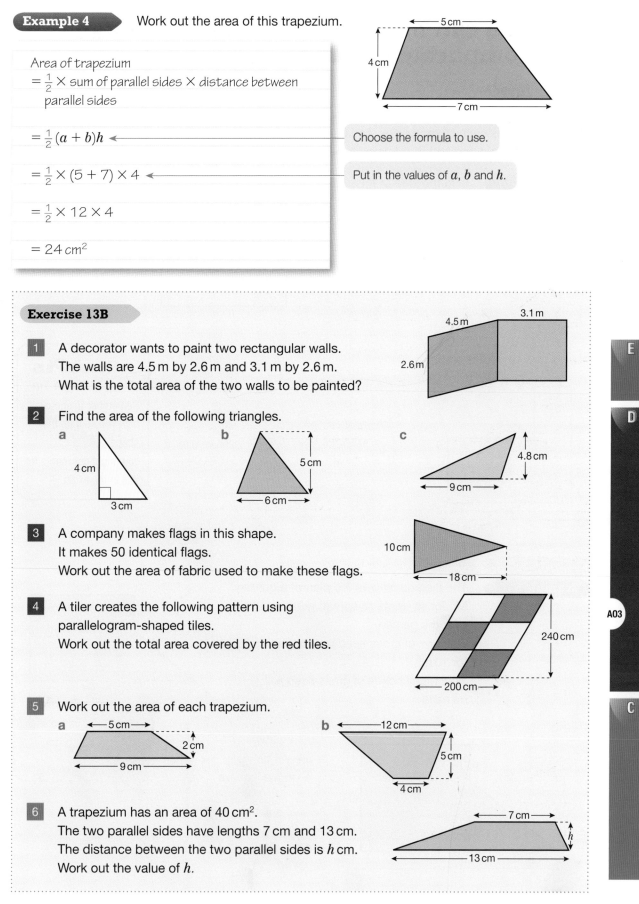

Area of trapezium
= $\frac{1}{2}$ × sum of parallel sides × distance between parallel sides

= $\frac{1}{2}(a + b)h$ ←————————————— Choose the formula to use.

= $\frac{1}{2}$ × (5 + 7) × 4 ←————————————— Put in the values of a, b and h.

= $\frac{1}{2}$ × 12 × 4

= 24 cm²

Exercise 13B

1　A decorator wants to paint two rectangular walls.
The walls are 4.5 m by 2.6 m and 3.1 m by 2.6 m.
What is the total area of the two walls to be painted?

2　Find the area of the following triangles.

　a

　b

　c

3　A company makes flags in this shape.
It makes 50 identical flags.
Work out the area of fabric used to make these flags.

4　A tiler creates the following pattern using
parallelogram-shaped tiles.
Work out the total area covered by the red tiles.

5　Work out the area of each trapezium.

　a

　b

6　A trapezium has an area of 40 cm².
The two parallel sides have lengths 7 cm and 13 cm.
The distance between the two parallel sides is h cm.
Work out the value of h.

13.3 You can find the areas of more complicated shapes

Key Point

⦿ To find the area of more complicated shapes you will need to split the shape into a number of simpler shapes such as rectangles, squares, triangles or parallelograms. You can then find the area of each part and add these areas together to find the total area.

Example 5   Find the area of this shape.

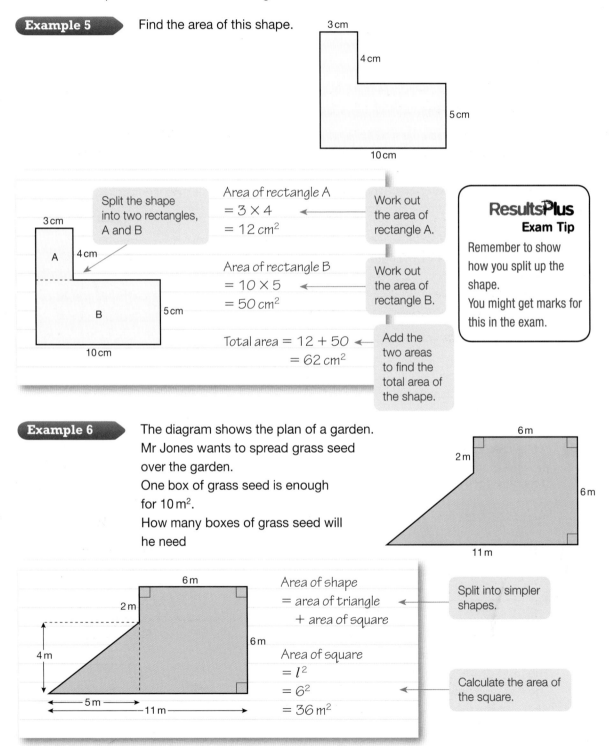

Split the shape into two rectangles, A and B

Area of rectangle A
$= 3 \times 4$
$= 12 \, cm^2$

Work out the area of rectangle A.

Area of rectangle B
$= 10 \times 5$
$= 50 \, cm^2$

Work out the area of rectangle B.

Total area $= 12 + 50$
$= 62 \, cm^2$

Add the two areas to find the total area of the shape.

ResultsPlus
Exam Tip

Remember to show how you split up the shape.
You might get marks for this in the exam.

Example 6   The diagram shows the plan of a garden.
Mr Jones wants to spread grass seed over the garden.
One box of grass seed is enough for 10 m².
How many boxes of grass seed will he need

Area of shape
= area of triangle
   + area of square

Split into simpler shapes.

Area of square
$= l^2$
$= 6^2$
$= 36 \, m^2$

Calculate the area of the square.

Area of triangle $= \frac{1}{2} \times b \times h$

$\qquad = \frac{1}{2} \times 5 \times 4 = 10 \, \text{m}^2$ ◄

Work out any unknown lengths you need and mark them on the diagram. Then calculate the area of the triangle.

Total area $= 10 + 36 = 46 \, \text{m}^2$ ◄

Add the two areas to find the total area of the shape.

Amount of grass seed $= 46 \div 10$

$\qquad = 4.6 = 5 \, \text{boxes}$ ◄

The number has got to be the next whole number higher than the answer, not just rounded to the nearest whole number.

Exercise 13C

1 The floor of the hall in a house is a 225 cm by 150 cm rectangle. Tiles which are squares of side 15 cm are used to tile the floor. Work out how many tiles are needed.

A02 **D**

2 Liam wants to replace the carpet in his room. The floor of the room is a rectangle measuring 4 metres by 3 metres. The carpet he wants to buy costs £8.65 per square metre.
Work out how much it will cost Liam to buy enough carpet to cover the floor.

A02

3 Libby wants to buy some grass seed so that she can sow a new lawn in her garden. She wants the lawn to be a rectangle measuring 3.2 metres by 2.5 metres. She needs 35 grams of lawn seed for every square metre of lawn. One box of lawn seed contains 250 g.
   a How many boxes of lawn seed will Libby need to buy?
   b How much lawn seed will be left over?

A03

4 Find the area of the following shapes.

A02
A03 **C**

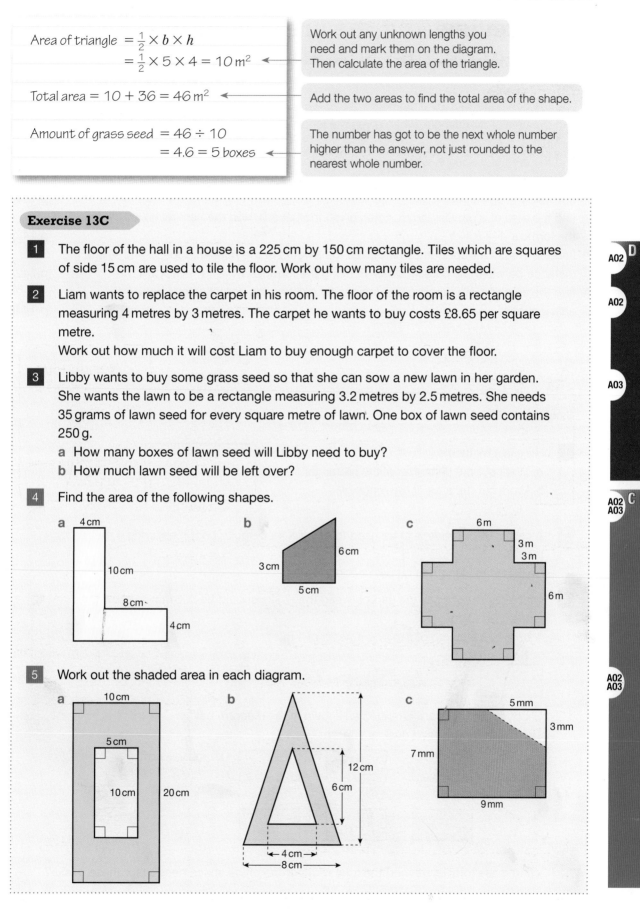

5 Work out the shaded area in each diagram.

A02
A03

Exam review

Self-assessment checklist

I can:

- find the perimeter of a 2D shape [p.140]
- find the area of a rectangle, when given the length, l, and the width, w, using the
  formula $A = l \times w$ [p.142]
- find the area of a square, when given the length, l, using the formula $A = l^2$ [p.142]
- find the area of a triangle, when given the base, b, and vertical height, h, using the
  formula $A = \frac{1}{2} \times b \times h$ [p.142]
- find the area of a parallelogram, when given the base, b, and the vertical height, h, using
  the formula $A = b \times h$ [p.142]
- find the area of a trapezium, when given the lengths of the parallel sides, a and b, and the
  distance between the parallel sides, h, using the formula $A = \frac{1}{2}(a + b) \times h$ [p.142]
- find the area of more complicated shapes by splitting the complicated shape into
  easier shapes. [p.144]

Exam practice

1 Here is a rectangle.
  a Work out the perimeter of the rectangle.   10 cm
  b Work out the area of the rectangle.

Diagram **NOT** accurately drawn

20 cm

Nov 2008

2 A carpet 60 cm wide is to be used to cover a rectangular floor measuring 4 metres by 9 metres.
Calculate the length of carpet needed.

3 Office regulations say the gap between the desks should be 900 mm to allow for wheelchair users.
A desk has a length of 2 m and a width of 1 m.

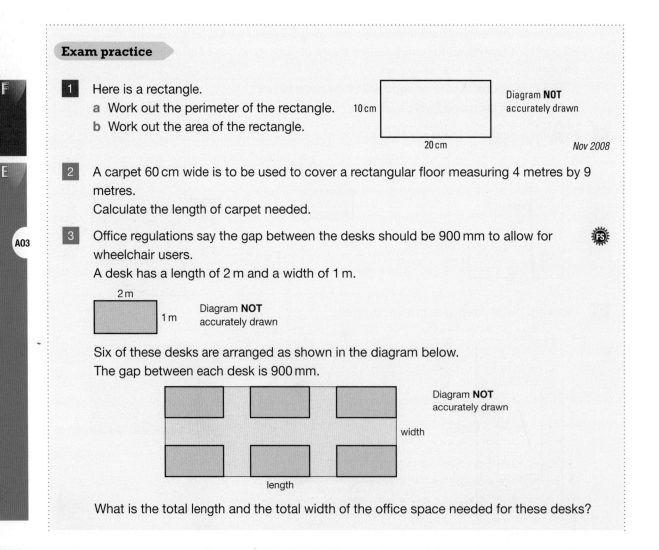

2 m

1 m

Diagram **NOT** accurately drawn

Six of these desks are arranged as shown in the diagram below.
The gap between each desk is 900 mm.

Diagram **NOT** accurately drawn

width

length

What is the total length and the total width of the office space needed for these desks?

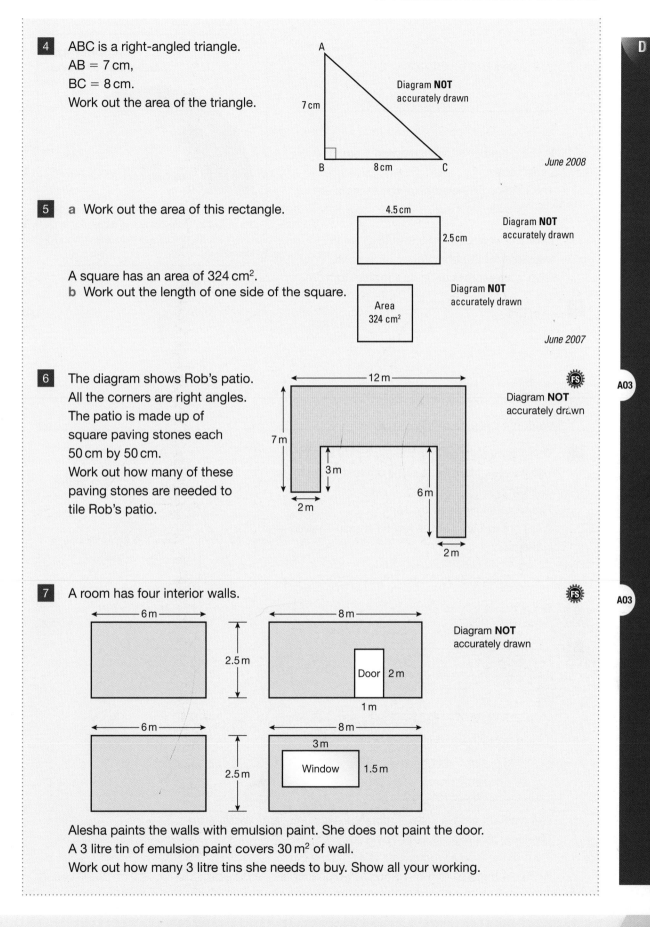

4 ABC is a right-angled triangle.
AB = 7 cm,
BC = 8 cm.
Work out the area of the triangle.

A

7 cm

Diagram **NOT**
accurately drawn

B   8 cm   C

June 2008

5 **a** Work out the area of this rectangle.

4.5 cm

Diagram **NOT**
accurately drawn

2.5 cm

A square has an area of 324 cm².
b Work out the length of one side of the square.

Diagram **NOT**
accurately drawn

Area
324 cm²

June 2007

6 The diagram shows Rob's patio.
All the corners are right angles.
The patio is made up of
square paving stones each
50 cm by 50 cm.
Work out how many of these
paving stones are needed to
tile Rob's patio.

12 m

Diagram **NOT**
accurately drawn

7 m

3 m

2 m

6 m

2 m

A03

7 A room has four interior walls.

6 m

2.5 m

8 m

Diagram **NOT**
accurately drawn

Door 2 m

1 m

6 m

2.5 m

8 m

3 m

Window 1.5 m

Alesha paints the walls with emulsion paint. She does not paint the door.
A 3 litre tin of emulsion paint covers 30 m² of wall.
Work out how many 3 litre tins she needs to buy. Show all your working.

A03

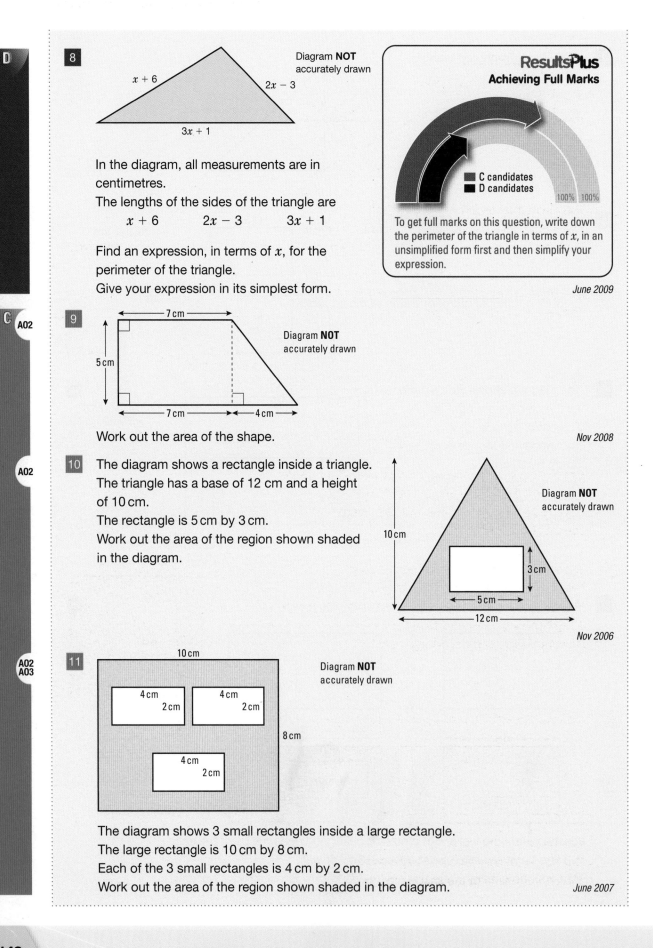

8

$x + 6$

$2x - 3$

$3x + 1$

Diagram **NOT** accurately drawn

In the diagram, all measurements are in centimetres.
The lengths of the sides of the triangle are

$x + 6$ $2x - 3$ $3x + 1$

Find an expression, in terms of x, for the perimeter of the triangle.
Give your expression in its simplest form.

ResultsPlus
Achieving Full Marks

C candidates
D candidates
100% 100%

To get full marks on this question, write down the perimeter of the triangle in terms of x, in an unsimplified form first and then simplify your expression.

June 2009

9

7 cm

5 cm

7 cm

4 cm

Diagram **NOT** accurately drawn

Work out the area of the shape.

Nov 2008

10 The diagram shows a rectangle inside a triangle.
The triangle has a base of 12 cm and a height of 10 cm.
The rectangle is 5 cm by 3 cm.
Work out the area of the region shown shaded in the diagram.

10 cm

Diagram **NOT** accurately drawn

3 cm

5 cm

12 cm

Nov 2006

11

10 cm

4 cm
2 cm

4 cm
2 cm

8 cm

4 cm
2 cm

Diagram **NOT** accurately drawn

The diagram shows 3 small rectangles inside a large rectangle.
The large rectangle is 10 cm by 8 cm.
Each of the 3 small rectangles is 4 cm by 2 cm.
Work out the area of the region shown shaded in the diagram.

June 2007

C

12

75 m
30 m
Diagram NOT accurately drawn
100 m
160 m

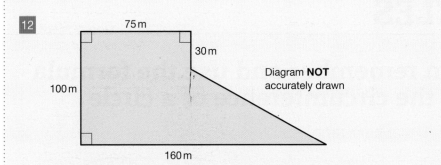

The diagram shows the plan of a field.
The farmer sells the field for £3 per square metre.
Work out the total amount of money the farmer should get.

March 2007

13 Mrs Kunal's garden is in the shape of a rectangle.
Part of the garden is a patio in the shape of a triangle.
The rest of the garden is grass.

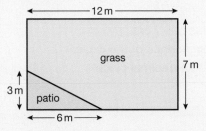

A03

12 m
grass
7 m
3 m
patio
6 m
Diagram NOT accurately drawn

Mrs Kunal wants to spread fertiliser over all her grass.
One box of fertiliser is enough for 32 m^2 of grass.
How many boxes of fertiliser will she need?
You must show your working.

Nov 2010

14 The diagram shows a garden with a pond.
The pond is in the shape of a triangle.
George is going to cover the shaded area with gravel.
35 kg of gravel is needed to cover 1 m^2.
How much gravel does George need?

A03

8 m
3 m
7 m
4 m

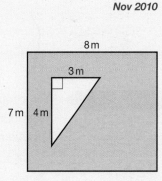

15 A piece of card is in the shape of a trapezium.

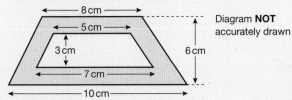

A02

8 cm
5 cm
3 cm
6 cm
7 cm
10 cm
Diagram NOT accurately drawn

A hole is cut in the card.
The hole is in the shape of a trapezium.
Work out the area of the shaded region.

March 2011

14 CIRCLES

14.1 You can remember and use the formula to find the circumference of a circle

Key points

- The formula to calculate the circumference of a circle:
  $C = \pi \times d$ or $C = \pi d$
- As the diameter is twice the radius, we can also use this formula:
  $C = 2 \times \pi \times r$ or $C = 2\pi r$
- To find the diameter (or radius) of a circle when given the circumference, use the formula:
  $d = \dfrac{C}{\pi}$ or $r = \dfrac{C}{2\pi}$

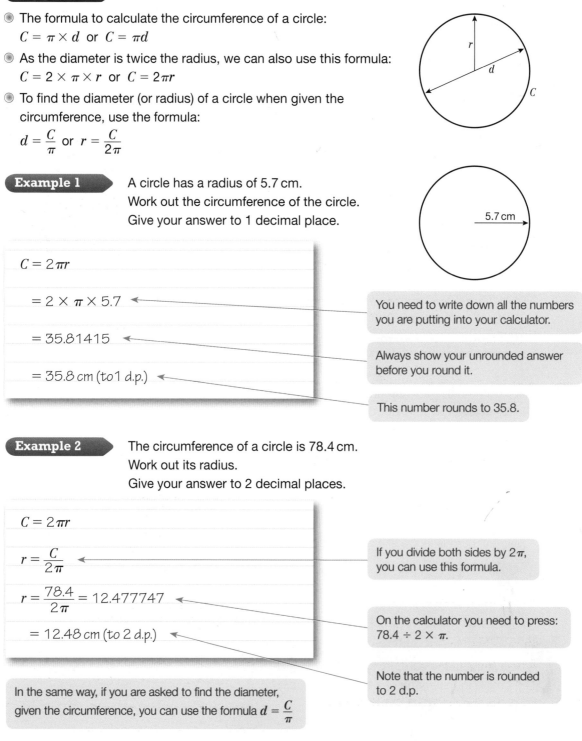

Example 1 A circle has a radius of 5.7 cm.
Work out the circumference of the circle.
Give your answer to 1 decimal place.

$C = 2\pi r$

$\quad = 2 \times \pi \times 5.7$ ← You need to write down all the numbers you are putting into your calculator.

$\quad = 35.81415$ ← Always show your unrounded answer before you round it.

$\quad = 35.8 \, \text{cm} \, (\text{to 1 d.p.})$ ← This number rounds to 35.8.

Example 2 The circumference of a circle is 78.4 cm.
Work out its radius.
Give your answer to 2 decimal places.

$C = 2\pi r$

$r = \dfrac{C}{2\pi}$ ← If you divide both sides by 2π, you can use this formula.

$r = \dfrac{78.4}{2\pi} = 12.477747$ ← On the calculator you need to press: $78.4 \div 2 \times \pi$.

$\quad = 12.48 \, \text{cm} \, (\text{to 2 d.p.})$ ← Note that the number is rounded to 2 d.p.

In the same way, if you are asked to find the diameter, given the circumference, you can use the formula $d = \dfrac{C}{\pi}$

Questions in this chapter are targeted at the grades indicated.

Give your answers to 1 decimal place in each of the following questions.

1 Work out the circumferences of circles with the following radii.
a 6.3 m   b 9.5 cm   c 4.2 cm   d 12.5 mm   e 29.4 cm

2 Work out the circumferences of circles with the following diameters.
a 6.9 cm   b 10.1 mm   c 5.3 cm
d 9.7 cm   e 5 m

Hint: Use the fomula $C = \pi d$

3 A circular pond has a radius of 1.8 metres. Work out the circumference of the pond.

4 A circular plate has a radius of 16 cm. Work out the circumference of the plate.

5 A penny-farthing bicycle has a large wheel and a small wheel. The large wheel has a diameter of 1.43 metres and the small wheel has a radius of 0.15 metres.

a Work out the circumference of the large wheel.
b Work out the circumference of the small wheel.
c Work out how many times the small wheel has to turn when the large wheel turns once.
Give your answers to 2 decimal places.

6 Work out the diameters of circles with the following circumferences.
a 45.6 m   b 20 cm   c 58.1 cm
d 37.2 mm   e 100 cm

Hint: Use $d = \dfrac{C}{\pi}$

7 Work out the radii of circles with the following circumferences.
a 30.4 cm   b 71.8 mm   c 64 cm   d 93.2 cm   e 49.5 m

8 A trundle wheel is used to measure a garden path.
The circumference of the trundle wheel is 188 cm.

Work out the diameter of the trundle wheel.

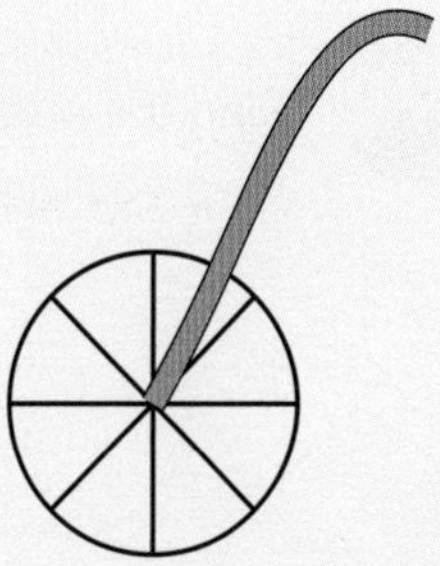

9 The diagram shows a shape made from a semicircle, a rectangle and an equilateral triangle.

The rectangle has length 18 cm and width 10 cm.
Work out the perimeter of the shape.

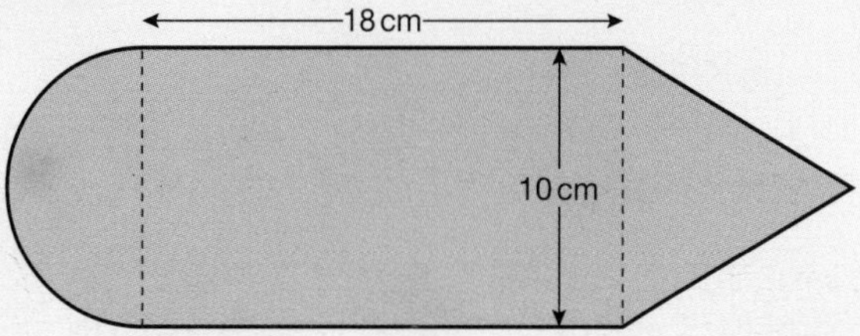

—18 cm—
10 cm

C

A02
A03
B

14.2 You can remember and use the formula to find the area of a circle

Key point

● The formula to find the area of a circle A is:
$A = \pi r^2$

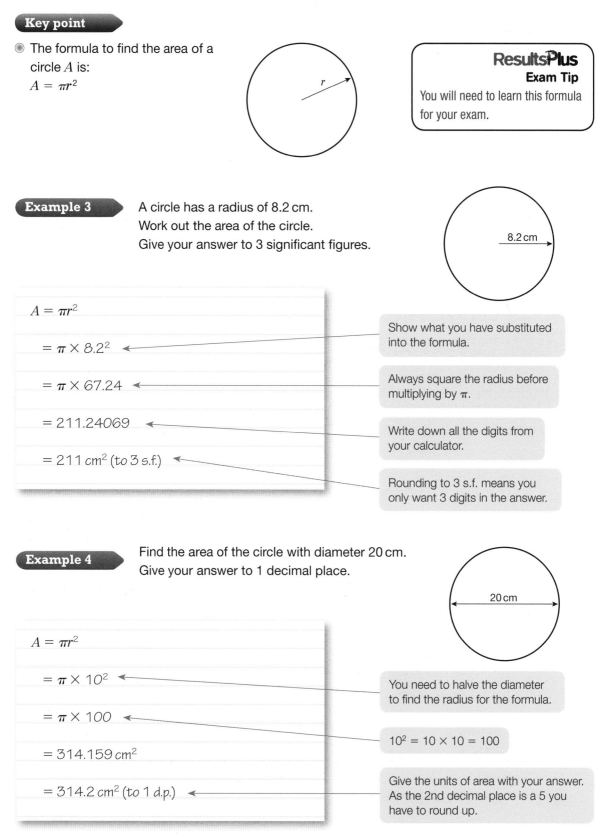

ResultsPlus
Exam Tip
You will need to learn this formula for your exam.

Example 3

A circle has a radius of 8.2 cm.
Work out the area of the circle.
Give your answer to 3 significant figures.

8.2 cm

$A = \pi r^2$

$= \pi \times 8.2^2$

$= \pi \times 67.24$

$= 211.24069$

$= 211 \text{ cm}^2 \text{ (to 3 s.f.)}$

Show what you have substituted into the formula.

Always square the radius before multiplying by π.

Write down all the digits from your calculator.

Rounding to 3 s.f. means you only want 3 digits in the answer.

Example 4

Find the area of the circle with diameter 20 cm.
Give your answer to 1 decimal place.

20 cm

$A = \pi r^2$

$= \pi \times 10^2$

$= \pi \times 100$

$= 314.159 \text{ cm}^2$

$= 314.2 \text{ cm}^2 \text{ (to 1 d.p.)}$

You need to halve the diameter to find the radius for the formula.

$10^2 = 10 \times 10 = 100$

Give the units of area with your answer. As the 2nd decimal place is a 5 you have to round up.

Exercise 14B

Give your answers to 3 significant figures in each of the following questions.

1. Work out the areas of circles with the following radii.

   a 5.1 m   b 3 cm   c 8.7 cm   d 15.2 mm   e 9.4 cm

2. Work out the areas of circles with the following diameters.

   a 30 cm   b 24.4 mm   c 7.4 cm   d 12.3 cm   e 8 m

3. A goat is tied to a post in the middle of a field covered in grass.
   He is tied so that he can eat the grass within 3.8 m of the post.
   Work out the area of grass from which he cannot eat.

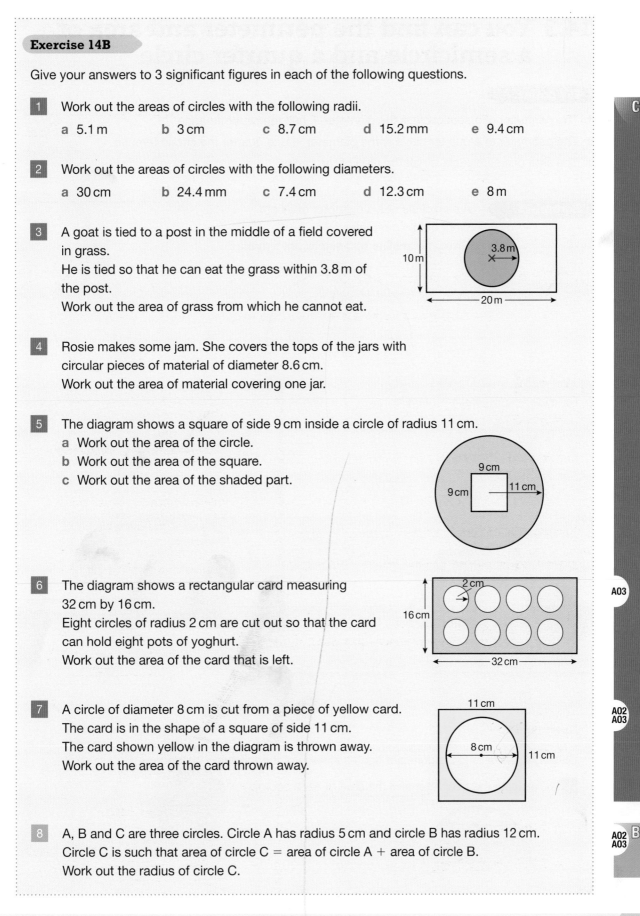

4. Rosie makes some jam. She covers the tops of the jars with circular pieces of material of diameter 8.6 cm.
   Work out the area of material covering one jar.

5. The diagram shows a square of side 9 cm inside a circle of radius 11 cm.
   a Work out the area of the circle.
   b Work out the area of the square.
   c Work out the area of the shaded part.

6. The diagram shows a rectangular card measuring 32 cm by 16 cm.
   Eight circles of radius 2 cm are cut out so that the card can hold eight pots of yoghurt.
   Work out the area of the card that is left.

7. A circle of diameter 8 cm is cut from a piece of yellow card.
   The card is in the shape of a square of side 11 cm.
   The card shown yellow in the diagram is thrown away.
   Work out the area of the card thrown away.

8. A, B and C are three circles. Circle A has radius 5 cm and circle B has radius 12 cm.
   Circle C is such that area of circle C = area of circle A + area of circle B.
   Work out the radius of circle C.

C

A03

A02
A03

A02
A03

B

14.3 You can find the perimeter and area of a semicircle and a quarter circle

Key points

- The perimeter of a semicircle is the diameter + half the circumference.
- The perimeter of a quarter circle is the diameter + one quarter the circumference.
- The area of a semicircle is half the area of the circle.

Example 5

A semicircle has a diameter of 24 cm.
Work out its perimeter.
Give your answer to 3 significant figures.

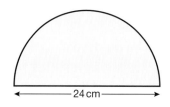

24 cm

Perimeter = arc length + diameter

$C = \pi \times d$
$C = \pi \times 24$ ←   *Show how to work out the whole circumference.*
  = 75.398 cm

Arc length = 75.398 ÷ 2   ←   *The semicircle is one half of the circle.*
          = 37.699 cm

Perimeter = 37.699 + 24   ←   *Show the examiner that you know that you must add 24 to the arc length.*
     = 61.699
     = 61.7 cm (to 3 s.f.)   ←   *Put the units with your answer.*

Exercise 14C

Give your answers to 3 significant figures in each of the following questions.

1 Calculate the perimeter and the area of each sector.

a

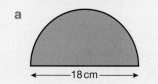

18 cm

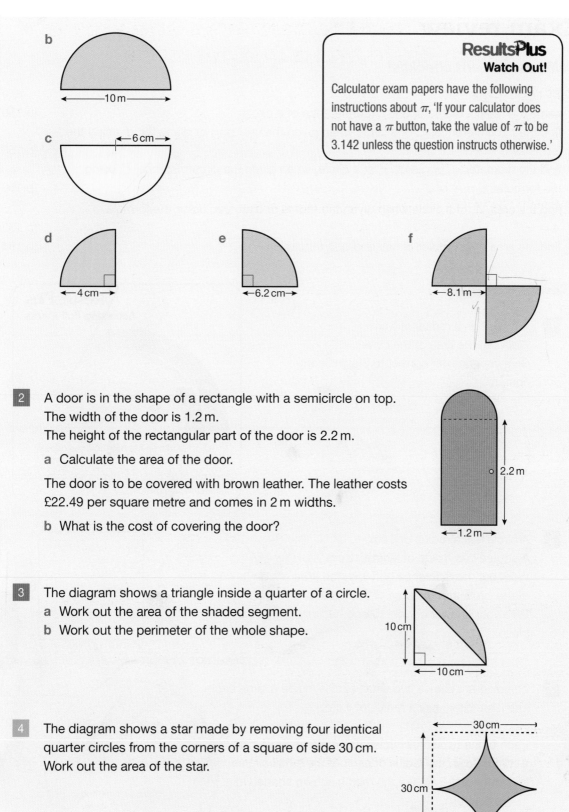

b

←10 m→

c

←6 cm→

ResultsPlus
Watch Out!
Calculator exam papers have the following instructions about π, 'If your calculator does not have a π button, take the value of π to be 3.142 unless the question instructs otherwise.'

d

←4 cm→

e

←6.2 cm→

f

←8.1 m→

2 A door is in the shape of a rectangle with a semicircle on top.
The width of the door is 1.2 m.
The height of the rectangular part of the door is 2.2 m.

a Calculate the area of the door.

The door is to be covered with brown leather. The leather costs £22.49 per square metre and comes in 2 m widths.

b What is the cost of covering the door?

2.2 m

←1.2 m→

A02
A03

3 The diagram shows a triangle inside a quarter of a circle.
a Work out the area of the shaded segment.
b Work out the perimeter of the whole shape.

10 cm

←10 cm→

A02

4 The diagram shows a star made by removing four identical quarter circles from the corners of a square of side 30 cm.
Work out the area of the star.

←30 cm→

30 cm

A02
A03

B

C

Exam review

Self-assessment checklist

I can:

- name the radius, diameter and circumference of a circle [p.150]
- find the circumference, C, of a circle when given the radius, r, or diameter, d, using the formulae $C = \pi d$ or $C = 2\pi r$ [p.150]
- find the diameter, d, or radius, r, of a circle, when given the circumference, C, using the formulae $d = \dfrac{C}{\pi}$ or $\dfrac{C}{2\pi}$ [p.150]
- find the area, A, of a circle when given the radius or diameter, using the formula $A = \pi r^2$ [p.152]
- find the area or perimeter of half and quarter circles. [p.154]

Exam practice

1 A circle has a radius of 5 cm.
Work out the area of the circle.
Give your answer correct to 3 significant figures.

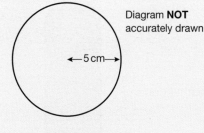

Diagram **NOT** accurately drawn

←—5 cm—→

ResultsPlus
Achieving Full Marks

■ C candidates
■ D candidates
100% 100%

To get full marks on this question, you need to remember the formula for the area of a circle, then substitute 5 into the formula and carry out the arithmetic correctly.

Nov 2009

2 A circle has a radius of 6 cm.
A square has a side of length 12 cm.
Work out the difference between the area of the circle and the area of the square.
Give your answer correct to one decimal place.

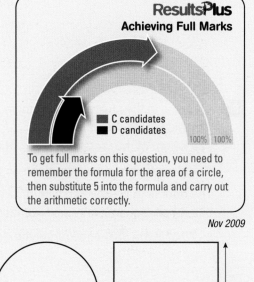

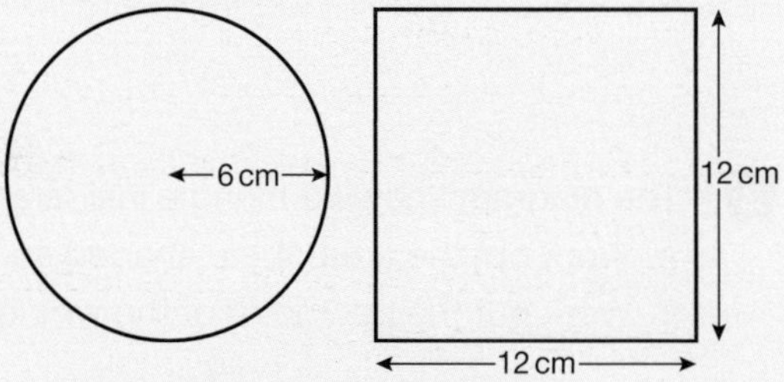

←6 cm→   12 cm

←————12 cm————→

Diagram **NOT** accurately drawn

Nov 2008

3 The diagram shows two small circles inside a large circle.
The large circle has a radius of 8 cm.

Each of the two small circles has a diameter of 4 cm.
a Write down the radius of each of the small circles.
b Work out the area of the region shown shaded in the diagram.
Give your answer correct to one decimal place.

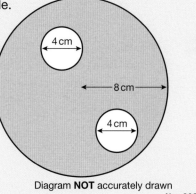

4 cm
←—8 cm—→
4 cm

Diagram **NOT** accurately drawn
Nov 2008

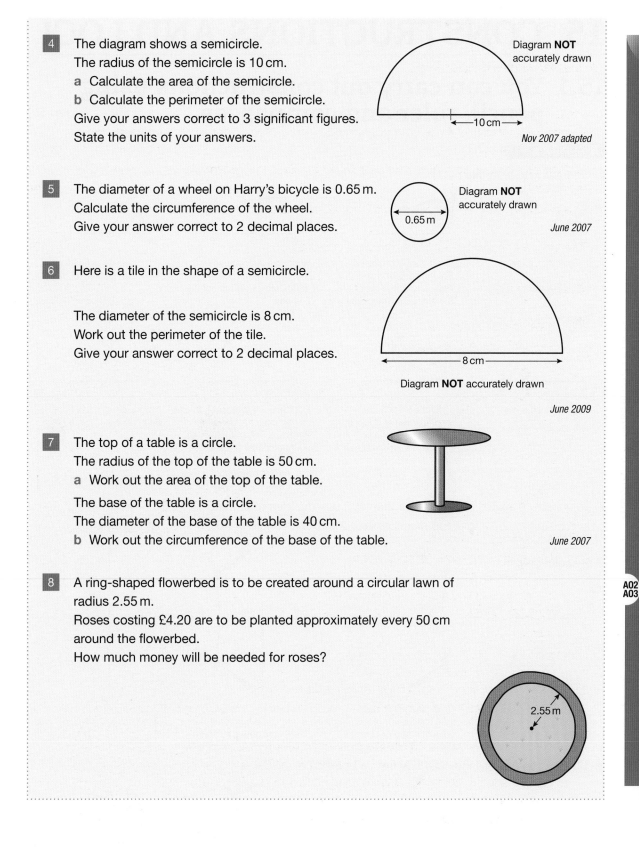

4 The diagram shows a semicircle.
The radius of the semicircle is 10 cm.
a Calculate the area of the semicircle.
b Calculate the perimeter of the semicircle.
Give your answers correct to 3 significant figures.
State the units of your answers.

Diagram **NOT** accurately drawn

←10 cm→

Nov 2007 adapted

5 The diameter of a wheel on Harry's bicycle is 0.65 m.
Calculate the circumference of the wheel.
Give your answer correct to 2 decimal places.

Diagram **NOT** accurately drawn

0.65 m

June 2007

6 Here is a tile in the shape of a semicircle.

The diameter of the semicircle is 8 cm.
Work out the perimeter of the tile.
Give your answer correct to 2 decimal places.

←—— 8 cm ——→

Diagram **NOT** accurately drawn

June 2009

7 The top of a table is a circle.
The radius of the top of the table is 50 cm.
a Work out the area of the top of the table.

The base of the table is a circle.
The diameter of the base of the table is 40 cm.
b Work out the circumference of the base of the table.

June 2007

8 A ring-shaped flowerbed is to be created around a circular lawn of
radius 2.55 m.
Roses costing £4.20 are to be planted approximately every 50 cm
around the flowerbed.
How much money will be needed for roses?

2.55 m

C

A02
A03

15 CONSTRUCTIONS AND LOCI

15.1 You can carry out constructions using pencil, ruler and compasses

Key Points

● Constructing an angle of 60°.

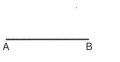 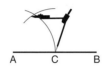 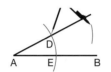

A B	A C B	A C B	A C B
Start with a line.	Open your compasses. Put the point at A and draw an arc that cuts the line. Label the point C.	Keeping your compasses the same width, put the point at C. Draw an arc to cut the first one.	Join up to get a 60° angle. This is an equilateral triangle.

● Bisecting an angle.

A B	A E B	A E B	A E B
Start with an angle.	Put the point of the compasses at A and draw an arc that cuts both lines. Label the points D and E.	Put the point at D and draw an arc between the two sides of the angle. Without adjusting your compasses, place the point at E and draw an arc to cut the first one. Label the point where they cross F.	Draw a straight line from F to A to bisect the angle.

● To construct angles of sizes other than 60°, use the idea of starting with 60°, or a multiple of 60°, and bisecting the angle. For example, to construct an angle of 30°, first construct an angle of 60° and then bisect it.

● Bisecting a line.

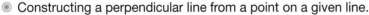

A B	A B	A B	A B
Start with a line.	Open your compasses to more than half the line length. Put the point at A and draw an arc above and below the line.	Keeping your compasses the same, put the point at B and draw arcs above and below the line to cross the other arcs.	Join the crosses to make a line. This line will bisect AB.

● Constructing a perpendicular line from a point on a given line.

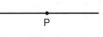 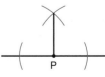

P	P	P	P
Start with a line and a point P on that line.	Put your compass on point P and draw arcs on the line either side of point P.	From each of the arcs drawn, use compasses to draw two intersecting arcs above the line.	Join the intersecting arcs to point P. This line is perpendicular to the given line at P.

Constructing a perpendicular line from a point to a given line.

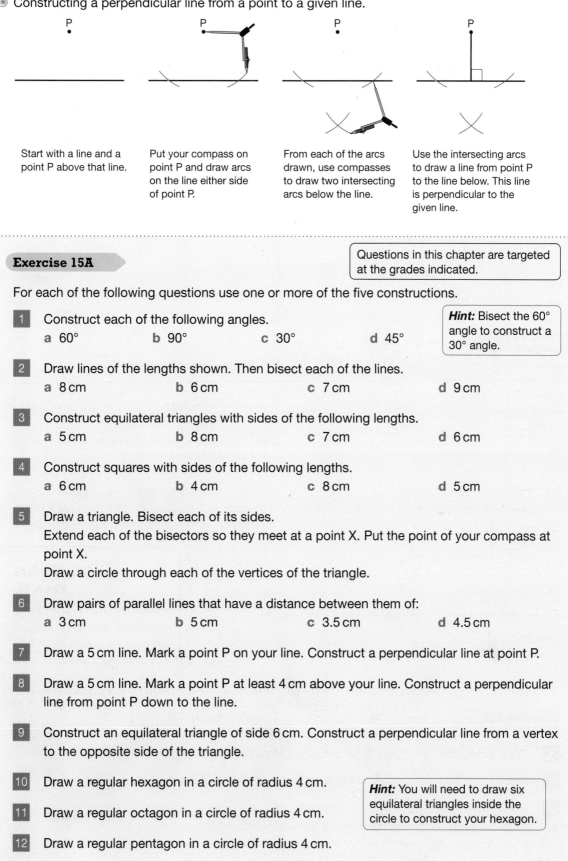

Start with a line and a point P above that line.

Put your compass on point P and draw arcs on the line either side of point P.

From each of the arcs drawn, use compasses to draw two intersecting arcs below the line.

Use the intersecting arcs to draw a line from point P to the line below. This line is perpendicular to the given line.

Exercise 15A

Questions in this chapter are targeted at the grades indicated.

For each of the following questions use one or more of the five constructions.

1   Construct each of the following angles.
    a 60°   **b** 90°   **c** 30°   **d** 45°

    Hint: Bisect the 60° angle to construct a 30° angle.

2   Draw lines of the lengths shown. Then bisect each of the lines.
    a 8 cm   **b** 6 cm   **c** 7 cm   **d** 9 cm

3   Construct equilateral triangles with sides of the following lengths.
    a 5 cm   **b** 8 cm   **c** 7 cm   **d** 6 cm

4   Construct squares with sides of the following lengths.
    a 6 cm   **b** 4 cm   **c** 8 cm   **d** 5 cm

5   Draw a triangle. Bisect each of its sides.
    Extend each of the bisectors so they meet at a point X. Put the point of your compass at point X.
    Draw a circle through each of the vertices of the triangle.

6   Draw pairs of parallel lines that have a distance between them of:
    a 3 cm   **b** 5 cm   **c** 3.5 cm   **d** 4.5 cm

7   Draw a 5 cm line. Mark a point P on your line. Construct a perpendicular line at point P.

8   Draw a 5 cm line. Mark a point P at least 4 cm above your line. Construct a perpendicular line from point P down to the line.

9   Construct an equilateral triangle of side 6 cm. Construct a perpendicular line from a vertex to the opposite side of the triangle.

10   Draw a regular hexagon in a circle of radius 4 cm.

     Hint: You will need to draw six equilateral triangles inside the circle to construct your hexagon.

11   Draw a regular octagon in a circle of radius 4 cm.

12   Draw a regular pentagon in a circle of radius 4 cm.

15.2 You can draw and interpret a locus as a set of points

Key Points

⦿ A locus is a set of points that obey a given rule. Loci is the plural of locus.

⦿ The locus of points which are the same distance (equidistant) from a single point is a circle.

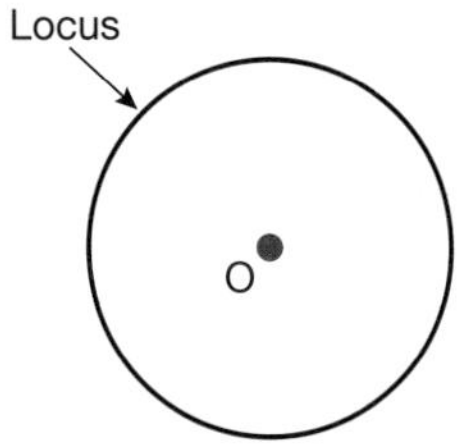

⦿ The locus of points that are the same distance from two points is a line that is the perpendicular bisector of the line joining the two points.

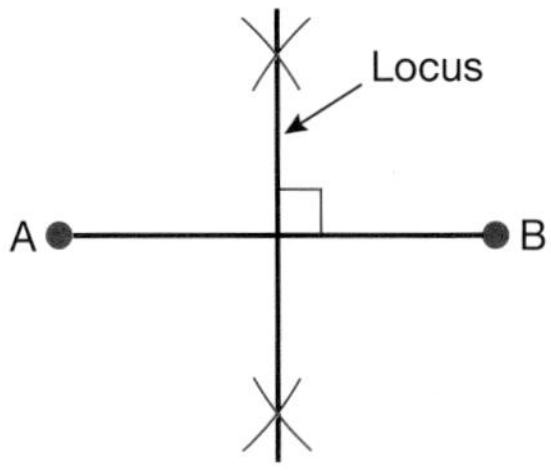

⦿ The locus of points the same distance from two lines is the bisector of the angle between the lines.

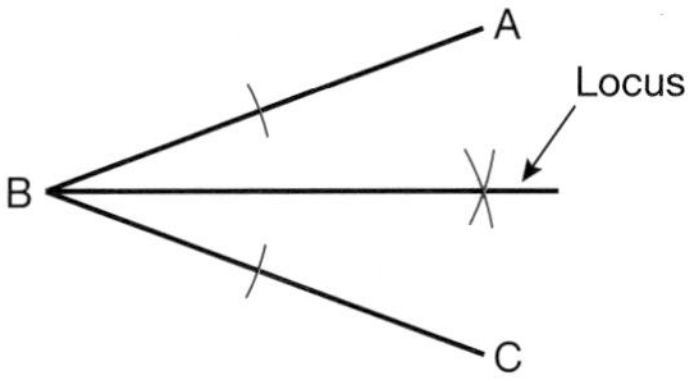

Example 1

Here is a line AB.
Draw the locus of points that are equidistant from the line AB.

A _____ B

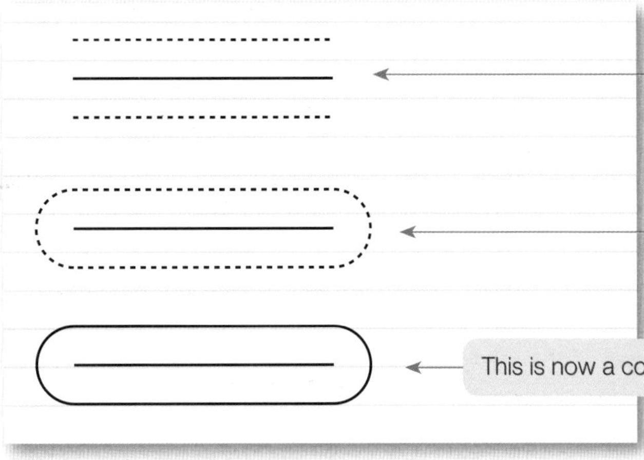

Points can be placed that are the same distance above and below the line. So parts of the locus are parallel lines above and below AB.

However, more points can be placed at an equal distance (radius) around the end points A and B. The loci of the points are semicircles at each end.

This is now a complete locus.

ResultsPlus
Exam Tip

Always remember to show your construction arcs when using constructions to draw loci.

Exercise 15B

C

A03
1 Draw a line of length 5 cm. Draw the locus of points that are 2 cm from this line.

A03
2 Plot a point P on your page. Draw the locus of points that are 4 cm from point P.

A03
3 Draw two points, A and B, 8 cm apart.
Draw the locus of points that are the same distance from point A and from point B.

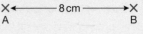

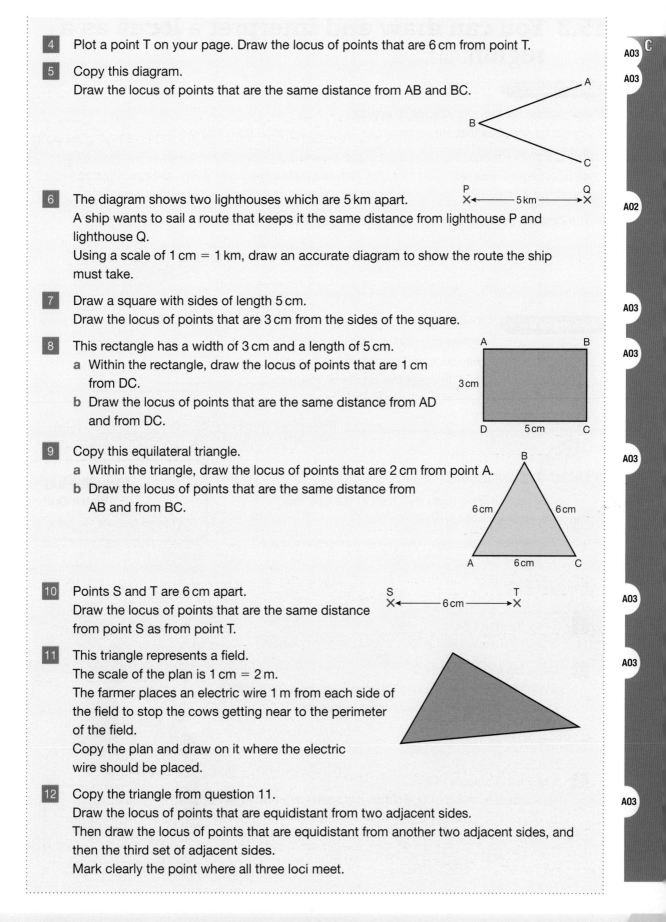

4   Plot a point T on your page. Draw the locus of points that are 6 cm from point T.

5   Copy this diagram.
Draw the locus of points that are the same distance from AB and BC.

6   The diagram shows two lighthouses which are 5 km apart.
A ship wants to sail a route that keeps it the same distance from lighthouse P and lighthouse Q.
Using a scale of 1 cm = 1 km, draw an accurate diagram to show the route the ship must take.

7   Draw a square with sides of length 5 cm.
Draw the locus of points that are 3 cm from the sides of the square.

8   This rectangle has a width of 3 cm and a length of 5 cm.
   a   Within the rectangle, draw the locus of points that are 1 cm from DC.
   b   Draw the locus of points that are the same distance from AD and from DC.

9   Copy this equilateral triangle.
   a   Within the triangle, draw the locus of points that are 2 cm from point A.
   b   Draw the locus of points that are the same distance from AB and from BC.

10   Points S and T are 6 cm apart.
Draw the locus of points that are the same distance from point S as from point T.

11   This triangle represents a field.
The scale of the plan is 1 cm = 2 m.
The farmer places an electric wire 1 m from each side of the field to stop the cows getting near to the perimeter of the field.
Copy the plan and draw on it where the electric wire should be placed.

12   Copy the triangle from question 11.
Draw the locus of points that are equidistant from two adjacent sides.
Then draw the locus of points that are equidistant from another two adjacent sides, and then the third set of adjacent sides.
Mark clearly the point where all three loci meet.

A03
A03
A02
A03
A03
A03
A03
A03
A03

15.3 You can draw and interpret a locus as a region

Key Points

⊙ Sometimes the locus is a region of space.
⊙ The locus of points that are no more than a given distance from a single point is the area within a circle.

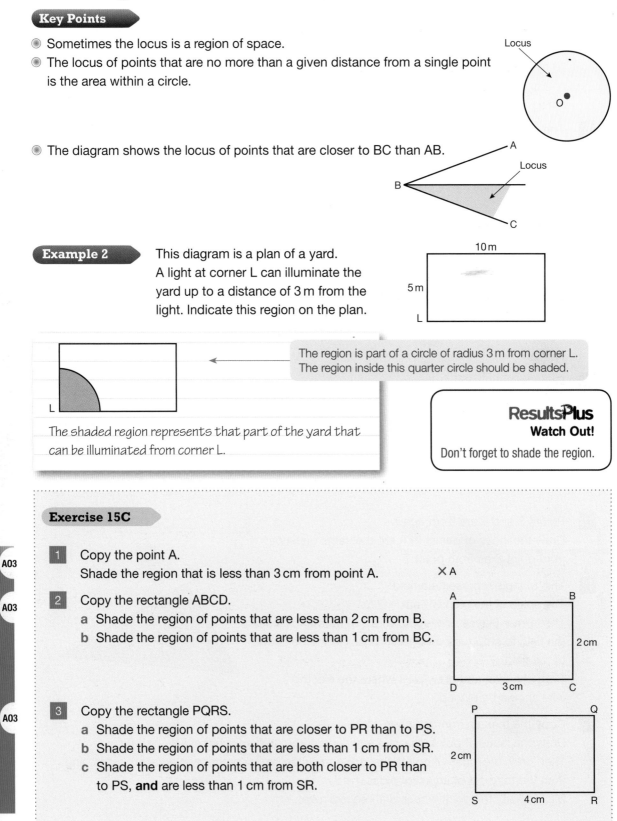

⊙ The diagram shows the locus of points that are closer to BC than AB.

Example 2   This diagram is a plan of a yard.
A light at corner L can illuminate the yard up to a distance of 3 m from the light. Indicate this region on the plan.

The region is part of a circle of radius 3 m from corner L.
The region inside this quarter circle should be shaded.

The shaded region represents that part of the yard that can be illuminated from corner L.

ResultsPlus
Watch Out!

Don't forget to shade the region.

Exercise 15C

1 Copy the point A.
Shade the region that is less than 3 cm from point A.

2 Copy the rectangle ABCD.
  a Shade the region of points that are less than 2 cm from B.
  b Shade the region of points that are less than 1 cm from BC.

3 Copy the rectangle PQRS.
  a Shade the region of points that are closer to PR than to PS.
  b Shade the region of points that are less than 1 cm from SR.
  c Shade the region of points that are both closer to PR than to PS, **and** are less than 1 cm from SR.

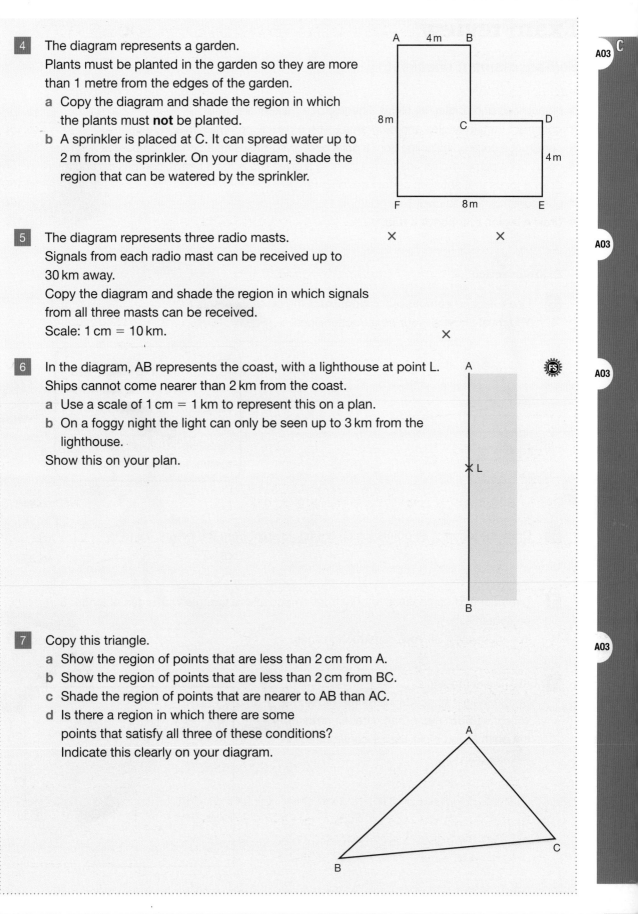

4 The diagram represents a garden.
Plants must be planted in the garden so they are more than 1 metre from the edges of the garden.

a Copy the diagram and shade the region in which the plants must **not** be planted.

b A sprinkler is placed at C. It can spread water up to 2 m from the sprinkler. On your diagram, shade the region that can be watered by the sprinkler.

5 The diagram represents three radio masts.
Signals from each radio mast can be received up to 30 km away.
Copy the diagram and shade the region in which signals from all three masts can be received.
Scale: 1 cm = 10 km.

6 In the diagram, AB represents the coast, with a lighthouse at point L.
Ships cannot come nearer than 2 km from the coast.

a Use a scale of 1 cm = 1 km to represent this on a plan.

b On a foggy night the light can only be seen up to 3 km from the lighthouse.
Show this on your plan.

7 Copy this triangle.

a Show the region of points that are less than 2 cm from A.

b Show the region of points that are less than 2 cm from BC.

c Shade the region of points that are nearer to AB than AC.

d Is there a region in which there are some points that satisfy all three of these conditions?
Indicate this clearly on your diagram.

Exam review

Self-assessment checklist

I can:

- bisect lines and angles by using a pencil, compasses and ruler   [p.158]
- construct certain angles and diagrams using a pencil, compasses and ruler   [p.158]
- construct a perpendicular line from a point on a given line using a pencil, compasses and ruler   [p.158]
- construct a perpendicular line from a point to a given line using a pencil, compasses and ruler   [p.158]
- draw a locus that satisfies certain conditions   [p.160]
- use constructions to draw loci   [p.160]
- draw a region that obeys a rule.   [p.162]

Exam practice

1. Use ruler and compasses to **construct** the bisector of this angle.
   You must show all your construction lines.

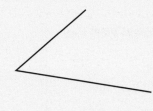

> **ResultsPlus**
> **Exam Tip**
>
> Use your compasses, ruler and pencil only. Do not use a protractor. Remember to leave in your construction arcs.

Nov 2008

2. Draw the locus of all points which are equidistant from the points A and B.

   A✗   ✗B   *Nov 2008*

3. Use ruler and compasses to construct an equilateral triangle with sides of length 6 centimetres.
   You must show all your construction lines.   *June 2008*

4. ABCD is a rectangle.
   Shade the set of points inside the rectangle which are **both** more than 4 centimetres from the point A and more than 1 centimetre from the line DC.

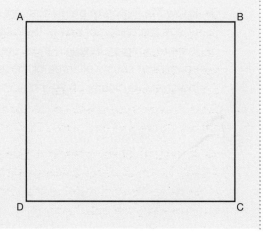

5 ABC is a triangle. Make an accurate copy of ABC.
Shade the region inside the triangle which is **both**
less than 4 centimetres from the point B
and closer to the line AC than the line BC.

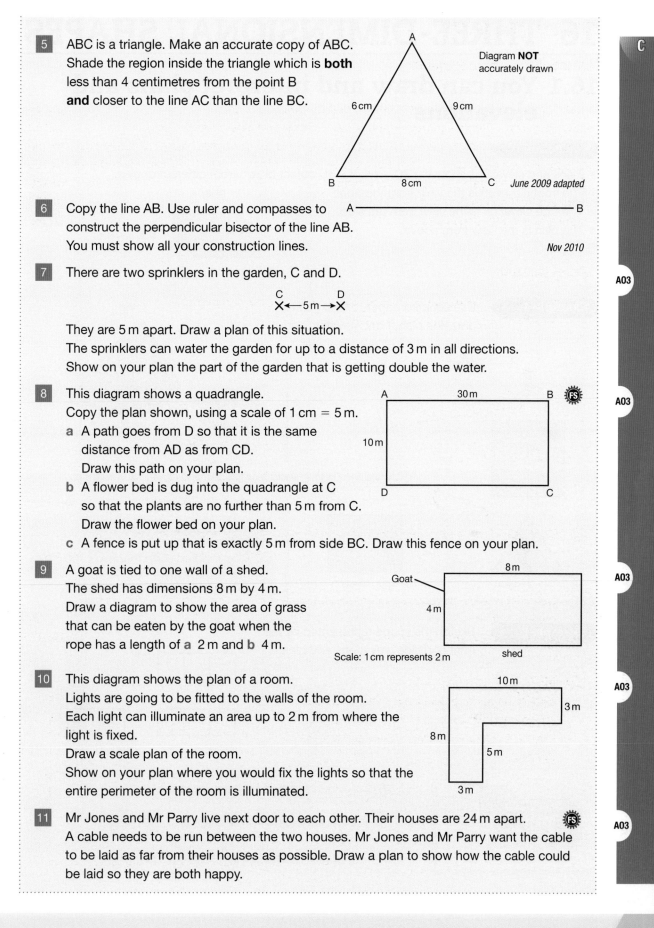

Diagram **NOT**
accurately drawn

6 cm   9 cm

B   8 cm   C   *June 2009 adapted*

6 Copy the line AB. Use ruler and compasses to
construct the perpendicular bisector of the line AB.
You must show all your construction lines.

A ——————————————————— B

Nov 2010

7 There are two sprinklers in the garden, C and D.

C   D
X ←—5 m—→ X

They are 5 m apart. Draw a plan of this situation.
The sprinklers can water the garden for up to a distance of 3 m in all directions.
Show on your plan the part of the garden that is getting double the water.

A03

8 This diagram shows a quadrangle.
Copy the plan shown, using a scale of 1 cm = 5 m.
 a A path goes from D so that it is the same
distance from AD as from CD.
Draw this path on your plan.
 b A flower bed is dug into the quadrangle at C
so that the plants are no further than 5 m from C.
Draw the flower bed on your plan.
 c A fence is put up that is exactly 5 m from side BC. Draw this fence on your plan.

A   30 m   B

10 m

D   C

A03

9 A goat is tied to one wall of a shed.
The shed has dimensions 8 m by 4 m.
Draw a diagram to show the area of grass
that can be eaten by the goat when the
rope has a length of **a** 2 m and **b** 4 m.

Goat

4 m

8 m

shed

Scale: 1 cm represents 2 m

A03

10 This diagram shows the plan of a room.
Lights are going to be fitted to the walls of the room.
Each light can illuminate an area up to 2 m from where the
light is fixed.
Draw a scale plan of the room.
Show on your plan where you would fix the lights so that the
entire perimeter of the room is illuminated.

10 m

3 m

8 m

5 m

3 m

A03

11 Mr Jones and Mr Parry live next door to each other. Their houses are 24 m apart.
A cable needs to be run between the two houses. Mr Jones and Mr Parry want the cable
to be laid as far from their houses as possible. Draw a plan to show how the cable could
be laid so they are both happy.

A03

16 THREE-DIMENSIONAL SHAPES

16.1 You can draw and interpret plans and elevations

Key Points

- Plans and elevations show the 2D view of a 3D object drawn from different angles.
- The front elevation is the view from the front.
- The side elevation is the view from the side.
- The plan is the view from above.

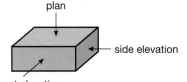

Example 1

Use squared paper to help you to draw the plan, front elevation and side elevation of this triangular prism.

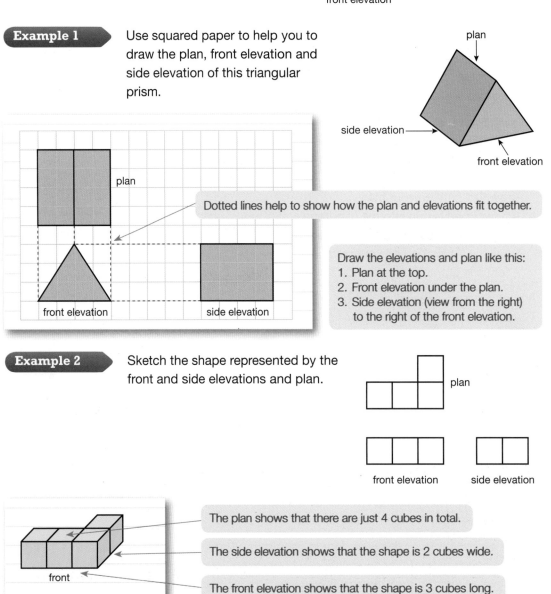

Dotted lines help to show how the plan and elevations fit together.

Draw the elevations and plan like this:
1. Plan at the top.
2. Front elevation under the plan.
3. Side elevation (view from the right) to the right of the front elevation.

Example 2

Sketch the shape represented by the front and side elevations and plan.

The plan shows that there are just 4 cubes in total.

The side elevation shows that the shape is 2 cubes wide.

The front elevation shows that the shape is 3 cubes long.

Exercise 16A

Questions in this chapter are targeted at the grades indicated.

D

A03

1 Use squared paper to make an accurate drawing of the plan, front elevation and side elevation for this cuboid.

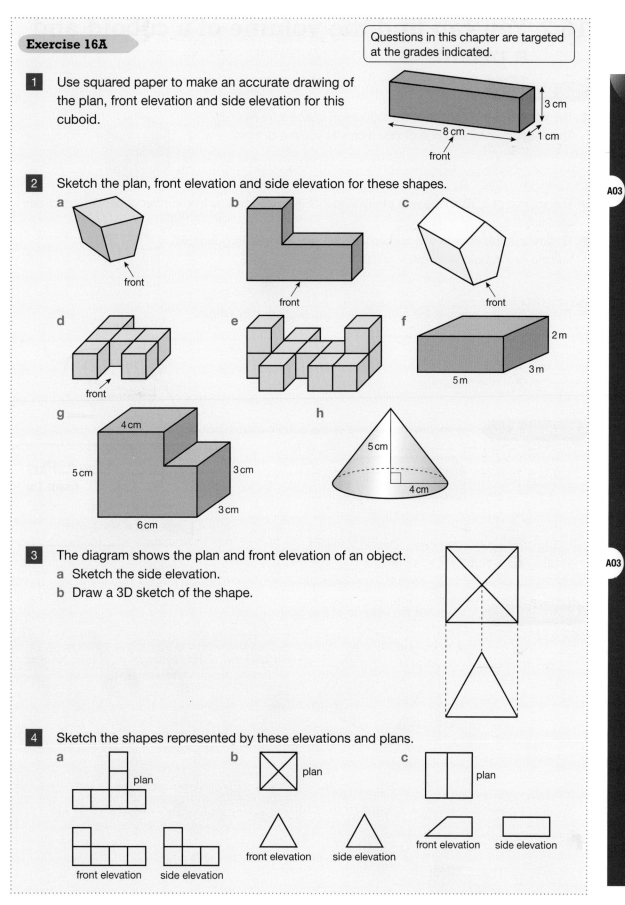

2 Sketch the plan, front elevation and side elevation for these shapes.

a   front

b   front

c   front

d   front

e

f   2 m   3 m   5 m

g   4 cm   5 cm   3 cm   3 cm   6 cm

h   5 cm   4 cm

A03

3 The diagram shows the plan and front elevation of an object.
   a Sketch the side elevation.
   b Draw a 3D sketch of the shape.

4 Sketch the shapes represented by these elevations and plans.

a   plan   front elevation   side elevation

b   plan   front elevation   side elevation

c   plan   front elevation   side elevation

167

16.2 You can find the volume of a cuboid and a prism

Key Points

⊙ The volume of a 3D shape is the amount of space it takes up.
The diagram shows a cube of side 1 cm. Its volume is 1 cm³.

⊙ The volume of a 3D shape with measurements in centimetres is the number of centimetre cubes it contains.

⊙ To work out the volume of a cuboid you can use the following formula.
Volume of a cuboid = length × width × height
$$= lwh$$

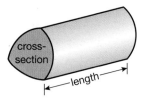

⊙ The volume of a prism is the area of the cross-section × its length.

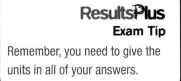

cross-section

length

Example 3 Work out the volume of the cuboid shown below.

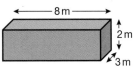

8 m
2 m
3 m

> **ResultsPlus**
> **Exam Tip**
> Remember, you need to give the units in all of your answers.

Volume of the cuboid = length × width × height
Volume = 8 × 3 × 2 m³ = 48 m³

Example 4 Work out the volume of this prism.

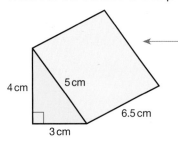

4 cm
5 cm
6.5 cm
3 cm

> The cross-section of the prism is a triangle.
> Remember: area of a triangle = $\frac{1}{2}$ × base × height.
> Here the base = 3 cm and height = 4 cm.

Area of cross-section = $\frac{1}{2}$ × 3 × 4 = 6 cm²
Volume of prism = 6 × 6.5 = 39 cm³

> Use volume of prism = area of cross-section × length.
> Here the area of cross-section = 6 cm² and length = 6.5 cm.

Exercise 16B

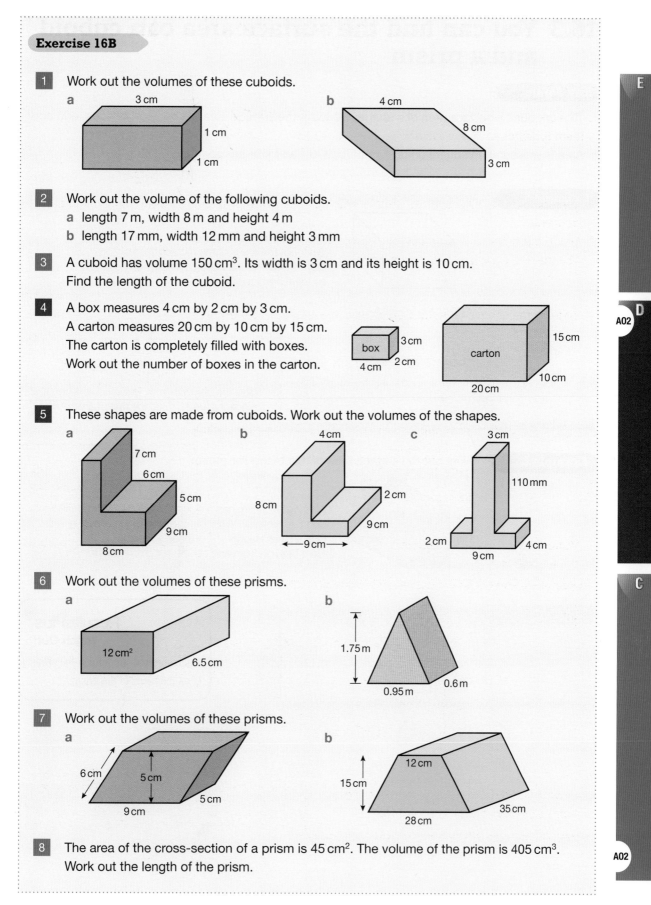

1   Work out the volumes of these cuboids.

    a   3 cm   1 cm   1 cm

    b   4 cm   8 cm   3 cm

2   Work out the volume of the following cuboids.
    a   length 7 m, width 8 m and height 4 m
    b   length 17 mm, width 12 mm and height 3 mm

3   A cuboid has volume 150 cm³. Its width is 3 cm and its height is 10 cm.
    Find the length of the cuboid.

4   A box measures 4 cm by 2 cm by 3 cm.
    A carton measures 20 cm by 10 cm by 15 cm.
    The carton is completely filled with boxes.
    Work out the number of boxes in the carton.

    box   3 cm   4 cm   2 cm

    carton   15 cm   10 cm   20 cm

5   These shapes are made from cuboids. Work out the volumes of the shapes.

    a   7 cm   6 cm   5 cm   9 cm   8 cm

    b   4 cm   2 cm   8 cm   9 cm   9 cm

    c   3 cm   110 mm   2 cm   4 cm   9 cm

6   Work out the volumes of these prisms.

    a   12 cm²   6.5 cm

    b   1.75 m   0.95 m   0.6 m

7   Work out the volumes of these prisms.

    a   6 cm   5 cm   5 cm   9 cm

    b   12 cm   15 cm   28 cm   35 cm

8   The area of the cross-section of a prism is 45 cm². The volume of the prism is 405 cm³.
    Work out the length of the prism.

16.3 You can find the surface area of a cuboid and a prism

> ### Key Points
> ● To work out the surface area of a shape, work out the surface area of each of the faces, and add them together.
> ● Area is measured in square units − mm², cm², m² and km² are common.

Example 5 Work out the surface area of this cuboid.

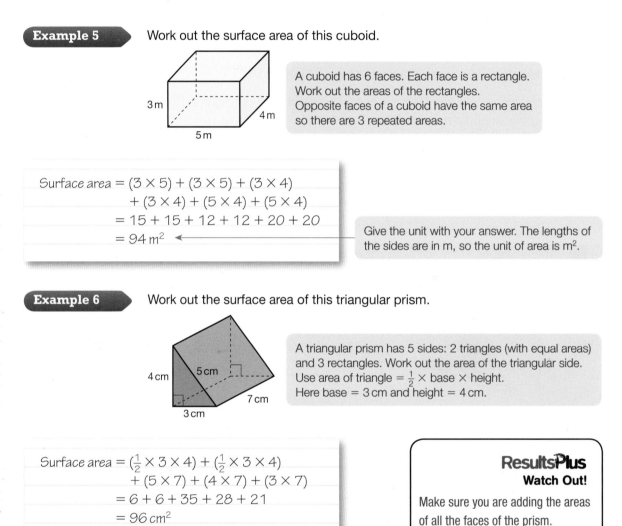

A cuboid has 6 faces. Each face is a rectangle. Work out the areas of the rectangles. Opposite faces of a cuboid have the same area so there are 3 repeated areas.

Surface area = $(3 \times 5) + (3 \times 5) + (3 \times 4)$
              $+ (3 \times 4) + (5 \times 4) + (5 \times 4)$
            $= 15 + 15 + 12 + 12 + 20 + 20$
            $= 94 \, m^2$ ◄

Give the unit with your answer. The lengths of the sides are in m, so the unit of area is m².

Example 6 Work out the surface area of this triangular prism.

A triangular prism has 5 sides: 2 triangles (with equal areas) and 3 rectangles. Work out the area of the triangular side. Use area of triangle = $\frac{1}{2} \times$ base $\times$ height. Here base = 3 cm and height = 4 cm.

Surface area = $(\frac{1}{2} \times 3 \times 4) + (\frac{1}{2} \times 3 \times 4)$
              $+ (5 \times 7) + (4 \times 7) + (3 \times 7)$
            $= 6 + 6 + 35 + 28 + 21$
            $= 96 \, cm^2$

ResultsPlus
Watch Out!

Make sure you are adding the areas of all the faces of the prism.

Exercise 16C

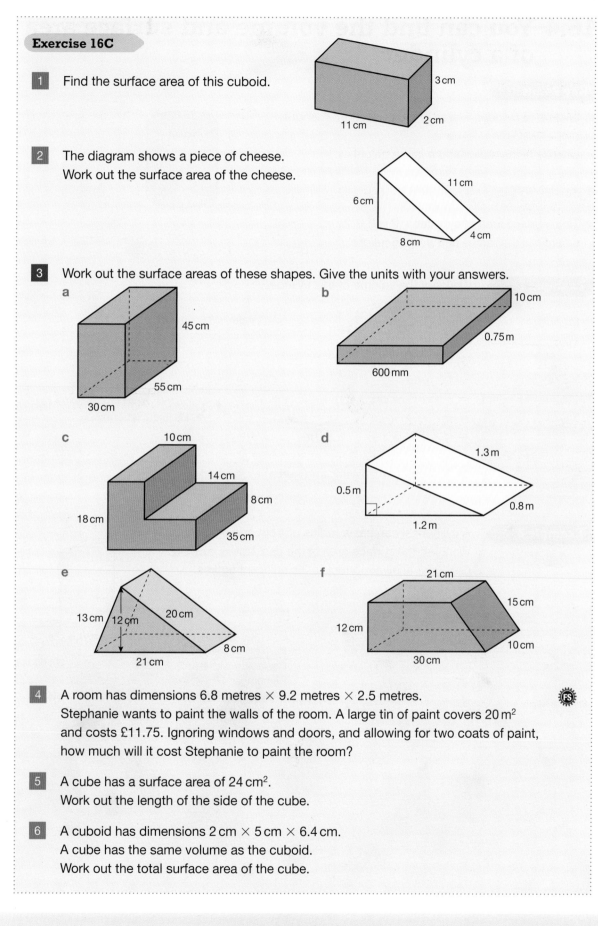

1 Find the surface area of this cuboid.

3 cm
11 cm
2 cm

2 The diagram shows a piece of cheese.
Work out the surface area of the cheese.

11 cm
6 cm
8 cm
4 cm

3 Work out the surface areas of these shapes. Give the units with your answers.

a
45 cm
55 cm
30 cm

b
10 cm
0.75 m
600 mm

c
10 cm
14 cm
8 cm
18 cm
35 cm

d
1.3 m
0.5 m
0.8 m
1.2 m

e
13 cm 12 cm
20 cm
8 cm
21 cm

f
21 cm
15 cm
12 cm
10 cm
30 cm

4 A room has dimensions 6.8 metres × 9.2 metres × 2.5 metres.
Stephanie wants to paint the walls of the room. A large tin of paint covers 20 m²
and costs £11.75. Ignoring windows and doors, and allowing for two coats of paint,
how much will it cost Stephanie to paint the room?

5 A cube has a surface area of 24 cm².
Work out the length of the side of the cube.

6 A cuboid has dimensions 2 cm × 5 cm × 6.4 cm.
A cube has the same volume as the cuboid.
Work out the total surface area of the cube.

16.4 You can find the volume and surface area of a cylinder

Key Points

● Volume of cylinder = area of cross-section × length
$$= \pi r^2 h$$
where r is the radius and h is the height.

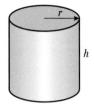

● Total surface area of cylinder $= 2\pi rh + 2\pi r^2$,
where r is the radius and h is the height.

Example 7 — Work out the volume of this cylinder.

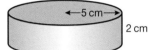

5 cm

2 cm

A cylinder is a prism with a circular cross-section.

Volume of a cylinder = Area of the circular end × height
$$= \pi \times r^2 \times h$$
$$= \pi \times 5 \times 5 \times 2 \quad = 50\pi$$
$$= 157.0796327$$
$$= 157 \text{ cm}^3 \text{ (to 3 significant figures)}$$

Put in the values you know for the radius and the height.

Use the π button on your calculator.

Example 8 — A cylindrical can has a radius of 4 cm and a height of 12 cm.
Work out the surface area of the can. Use $\pi = 3.142$.
Give your answer correct to 3 significant figures.

4 cm

12 cm

Surface area $= 2 \times \pi \times 4 \times 12 + 2 \times \pi \times 4^2$
$$= 2 \times 3.142 \times 4 \times 12 +$$
$$2 \times 3.142 \times 4 \times 4$$
$$= 301.632 + 100.544$$
$$= 402.176$$
$$= 402 \text{ cm}^2 \text{ (3 s.f.)}$$

Use total surface area of cylinder $= 2\pi rh + 2\pi r^2$.
Here $r = 4$ cm and $h = 12$ cm.
Replace π with 3.142.
Remember $4^2 = 4 \times 4$.
Write down all the figures on your calculator display.
Give your final answer correct to 3 significant figures.
Remember to give the units with your answer.

Exercise 16D

In this exercise give your answers to 3 significant figures. Do not forget to give the units.

1 Find the volume of these cylinders.

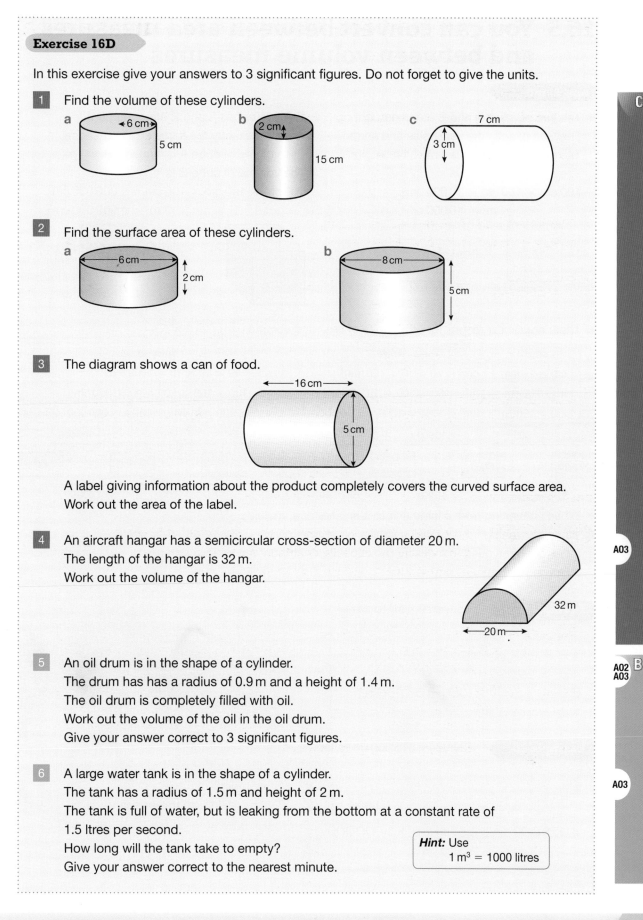

a
◄6 cm►
5 cm

b
2 cm
15 cm

c
7 cm
3 cm

2 Find the surface area of these cylinders.

a
6 cm
2 cm

b
8 cm
5 cm

3 The diagram shows a can of food.

16 cm
5 cm

A label giving information about the product completely covers the curved surface area.
Work out the area of the label.

4 An aircraft hangar has a semicircular cross-section of diameter 20 m.
The length of the hangar is 32 m.
Work out the volume of the hangar.

32 m
20 m

5 An oil drum is in the shape of a cylinder.
The drum has has a radius of 0.9 m and a height of 1.4 m.
The oil drum is completely filled with oil.
Work out the volume of the oil in the oil drum.
Give your answer correct to 3 significant figures.

6 A large water tank is in the shape of a cylinder.
The tank has a radius of 1.5 m and height of 2 m.
The tank is full of water, but is leaking from the bottom at a constant rate of
1.5 ltres per second.
How long will the tank take to empty?
Give your answer correct to the nearest minute.

Hint: Use
$1 \, m^3 = 1000$ litres

C

A03

A02
A03
B

A03

16.5 You can convert between area measures and between volume measures

- The two squares A and B are congruent. They are exactly the same size and shape. The area of square A is $1\,m \times 1\,m = 1\,m^2$. The area of square B is $100\,cm \times 100\,cm = 10\,000\,cm^2$.

$$1\,m^2 = 10\,000\,cm^2$$

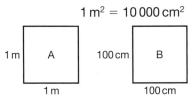

- The two cubes A and B are congruent. They are exactly the same size and shape. The volume of cube A is $1\,m \times 1\,m \times 1\,m = 1\,m^3$. The volume of cube B is $100\,cm \times 100\,cm \times 100\,cm = 1\,000\,000\,cm^3$.

$$1\,m^3 = 1\,000\,000\,cm^3$$

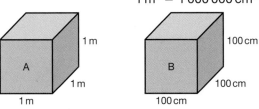

- There are similar results for other units of area and volume.

Length	Area	Volume
$1\,cm = 10\,mm$	$1\,cm^2 = 10 \times 10 = 100\,mm^2$	$1\,cm^3 = 10 \times 10 \times 10 = 1000\,mm^3$
$1\,m = 100\,cm$	$1\,m^2 = 100 \times 100 = 10\,000\,cm^2$	$1\,m^3 = 100 \times 100 \times 100 = 1\,000\,000\,cm^3$
$1\,km = 1000\,m$	$1\,km^2 = 1000 \times 1000 = 1\,000\,000\,m^2$	$1\,km^3 = 1000 \times 1000 \times 1000 = 1\,000\,000\,000\,m^3$

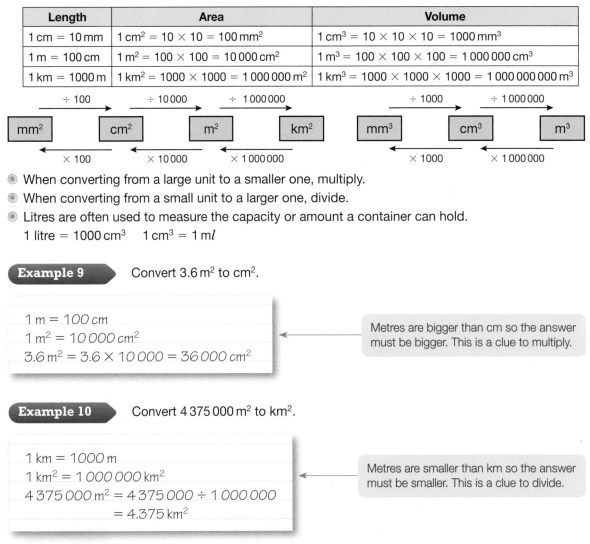

- When converting from a large unit to a smaller one, multiply.
- When converting from a small unit to a larger one, divide.
- Litres are often used to measure the capacity or amount a container can hold.

$$1\,litre = 1000\,cm^3 \qquad 1\,cm^3 = 1\,ml$$

Example 9 Convert $3.6\,m^2$ to cm^2.

$1\,m = 100\,cm$
$1\,m^2 = 10\,000\,cm^2$
$3.6\,m^2 = 3.6 \times 10\,000 = 36\,000\,cm^2$

> Metres are bigger than cm so the answer must be bigger. This is a clue to multiply.

Example 10 Convert $4\,375\,000\,m^2$ to km^2.

$1\,km = 1000\,m$
$1\,km^2 = 1\,000\,000\,km^2$
$4\,375\,000\,m^2 = 4\,375\,000 \div 1\,000\,000$
$\qquad\qquad = 4.375\,km^2$

> Metres are smaller than km so the answer must be smaller. This is a clue to divide.

Example 11　a Convert 7 m³ to cm³.　　b Convert 500 000 cm³ to m³.

1 m = 100 cm
1 m³ = 1 000 000 cm³
a 7 × 1 000 000 = 7 000 000 cm³
b 500 000 ÷ 1 000 000 = 0.5 m³

ResultsPlus
Exam Tip
Remember that to change from a larger unit to a smaller unit, you multiply.

Example 12　a Convert 2.5 litres to cm³.　　b Convert 5000 cm³ to litres.

1 litre = 1000 cm³
a 2.5 × 1000 = 2500 cm³
b 5000 ÷ 1000 = 5 litres

Exercise 16E

1　Convert to cm².
　a 3 m²　　　　b 4.5 m²　　　　c 300 mm²　　　　d 34 mm²

2　Convert to m².
　a 6 km²　　　　b 0.4 km²　　　　c 20 000 cm²　　　　d 3450 cm²

3　Convert to cm³.
　a 4 m³　　　　b 4.5 ml　　　　c 400 mm³　　　　d 3 litres

4　Convert to litres.
　a 400 ml　　　　b 5600 cm³　　　　c 1 m³　　　　d 3500 mm³

5　Dave is tiling the wall in a bathroom.
　The wall is 3 m long and is to be tiled to a height of 1.5 m.
　The tiles are square with length 15 cm. How many tiles are needed?

6　The diagram shows a cuboid.
　Work out the volume of the cuboid in
　a cm³
　b mm³.

4 cm
3 cm
12 cm

7　The diagram shows a wall with a window in it.
　Work out the shaded area.

4.5 m
180 cm
75 cm
2.9 m

8　The petrol tank of a car holds 42 litres of fuel. How many cm³ is this?

9　A bottle of medicine holds 0.5 litres.
　How many 5 cm³ doses are contained in the bottle?

10　A swimming pool has length 50 m, width 9 m and depth 1.5 m.
　How much water does it hold? Give your answer in litres.

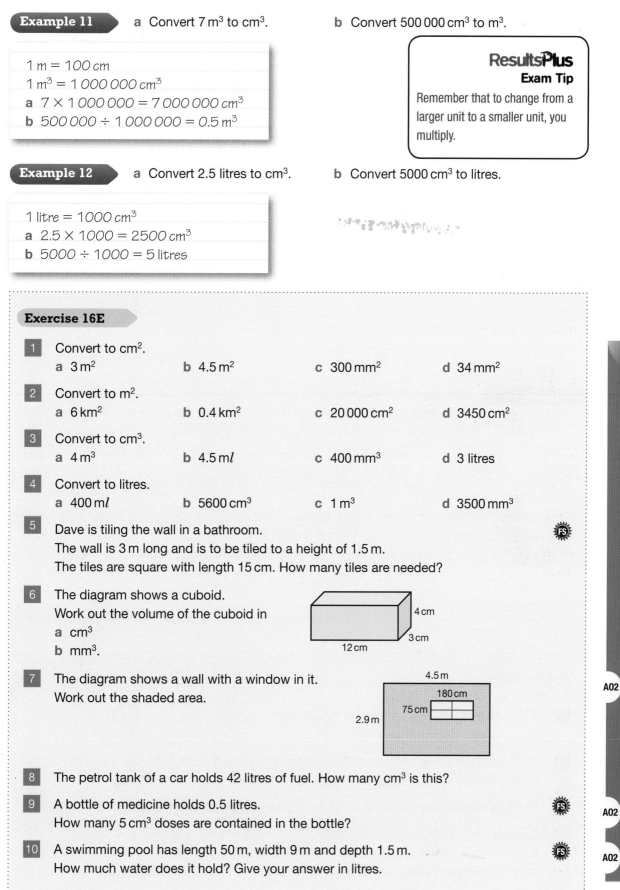

C

A02

A02

A02

16.6 You can solve problems with density

Key Points

◉ Density is a compound measure. To solve a density problem, use the following equations:

density $= \dfrac{\text{mass}}{\text{volume}}$

mass $=$ density $\times$ volume

volume $= \dfrac{\text{mass}}{\text{density}}$

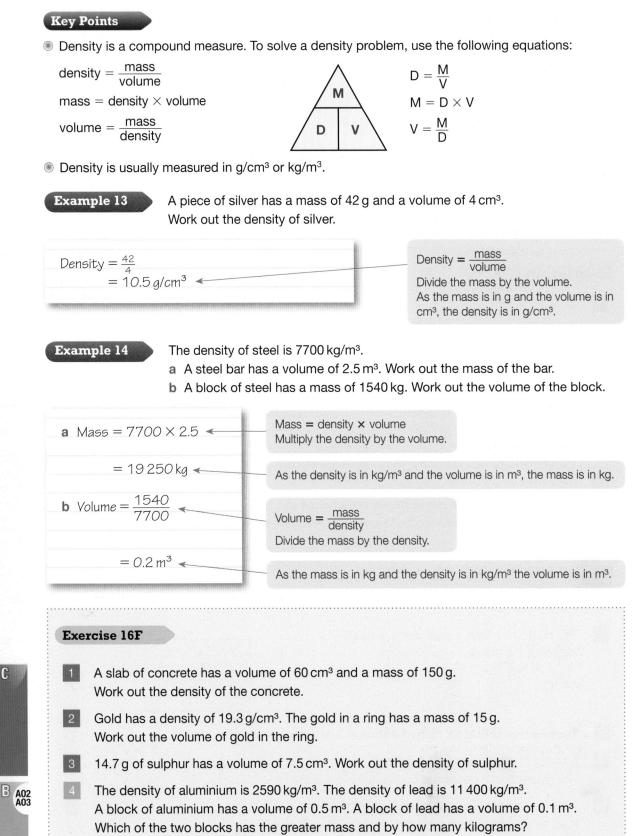

$D = \dfrac{M}{V}$

$M = D \times V$

$V = \dfrac{M}{D}$

◉ Density is usually measured in g/cm³ or kg/m³.

Example 13 A piece of silver has a mass of 42 g and a volume of 4 cm³.
Work out the density of silver.

Density $= \dfrac{42}{4}$
$= 10.5 \text{ g/cm}^3$

Density $= \dfrac{\text{mass}}{\text{volume}}$
Divide the mass by the volume.
As the mass is in g and the volume is in cm³, the density is in g/cm³.

Example 14 The density of steel is 7700 kg/m³.
a A steel bar has a volume of 2.5 m³. Work out the mass of the bar.
b A block of steel has a mass of 1540 kg. Work out the volume of the block.

a Mass $= 7700 \times 2.5$

$= 19\,250 \text{ kg}$

b Volume $= \dfrac{1540}{7700}$

$= 0.2 \text{ m}^3$

Mass = density × volume
Multiply the density by the volume.

As the density is in kg/m³ and the volume is in m³, the mass is in kg.

Volume $= \dfrac{\text{mass}}{\text{density}}$
Divide the mass by the density.

As the mass is in kg and the density is in kg/m³ the volume is in m³.

Exercise 16F

1 A slab of concrete has a volume of 60 cm³ and a mass of 150 g.
Work out the density of the concrete.

2 Gold has a density of 19.3 g/cm³. The gold in a ring has a mass of 15 g.
Work out the volume of gold in the ring.

3 14.7 g of sulphur has a volume of 7.5 cm³. Work out the density of sulphur.

4 The density of aluminium is 2590 kg/m³. The density of lead is 11 400 kg/m³.
A block of aluminium has a volume of 0.5 m³. A block of lead has a volume of 0.1 m³.
Which of the two blocks has the greater mass and by how many kilograms?

C

B A02
A03

Exam review

Self-assessment checklist

I can:
- draw and interpret plans and elevations [p.166]
- find the volume, V, of a cuboid, when given the length, l, width, w, and height, h, using the formula $V = lwh$ [p.168]
- find the volume, V, of a prism, using the formula V = area of cross-section × length [p.168]
- find the surface area of a prism by finding the total area of all the faces [p.170]
- find the volume, V, of a cylinder, when given the radius, r, and height, h, using the formula $V = \pi r^2 h$ [p.172]
- find the surface area, S, of a cylinder, when given the radius, r, and height, h, using the formula $S = 2\pi rh + \pi r^2 h$ [p.172]
- convert between measures of area [p.174]
- convert between measures of volume [p.174]
- solve density problems using the formula density $= \dfrac{\text{mass}}{\text{volume}}$. [p.176]

Exam practice

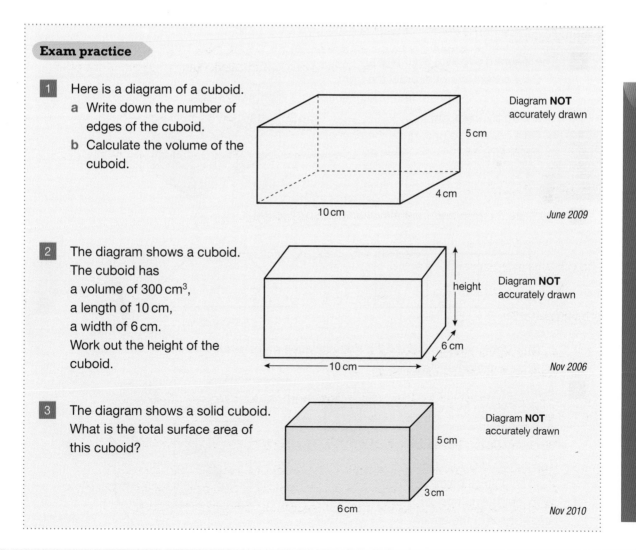

1 Here is a diagram of a cuboid.
   a Write down the number of edges of the cuboid.
   b Calculate the volume of the cuboid.

Diagram **NOT** accurately drawn

5 cm
4 cm
10 cm

June 2009

E

2 The diagram shows a cuboid.
   The cuboid has
   a volume of 300 cm³,
   a length of 10 cm,
   a width of 6 cm.
   Work out the height of the cuboid.

height
Diagram **NOT** accurately drawn
6 cm
10 cm

Nov 2006

3 The diagram shows a solid cuboid.
   What is the total surface area of this cuboid?

Diagram **NOT** accurately drawn
5 cm
3 cm
6 cm

Nov 2010

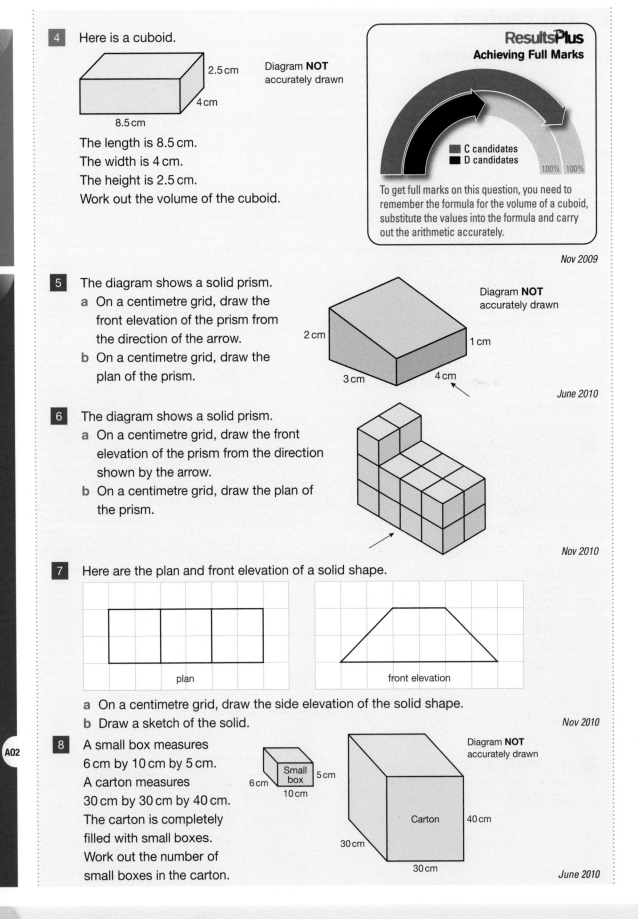

4 Here is a cuboid.

Diagram **NOT** accurately drawn

2.5 cm
4 cm
8.5 cm

The length is 8.5 cm.
The width is 4 cm.
The height is 2.5 cm.
Work out the volume of the cuboid.

ResultsPlus
Achieving Full Marks

■ C candidates
■ D candidates
100% 100%

To get full marks on this question, you need to remember the formula for the volume of a cuboid, substitute the values into the formula and carry out the arithmetic accurately.

Nov 2009

5 The diagram shows a solid prism.
a On a centimetre grid, draw the front elevation of the prism from the direction of the arrow.
b On a centimetre grid, draw the plan of the prism.

Diagram **NOT** accurately drawn

2 cm
1 cm
3 cm
4 cm

June 2010

6 The diagram shows a solid prism.
a On a centimetre grid, draw the front elevation of the prism from the direction shown by the arrow.
b On a centimetre grid, draw the plan of the prism.

Nov 2010

7 Here are the plan and front elevation of a solid shape.

plan

front elevation

a On a centimetre grid, draw the side elevation of the solid shape.
b Draw a sketch of the solid.

Nov 2010

8 A small box measures 6 cm by 10 cm by 5 cm.
A carton measures 30 cm by 30 cm by 40 cm.
The carton is completely filled with small boxes.
Work out the number of small boxes in the carton.

Diagram **NOT** accurately drawn

Small box
6 cm
5 cm
10 cm

Carton
40 cm
30 cm
30 cm

June 2010

9 The diagram represents a solid made from 5 identical cubes.
On a copy of the grid, draw the view of the solid from direction A.

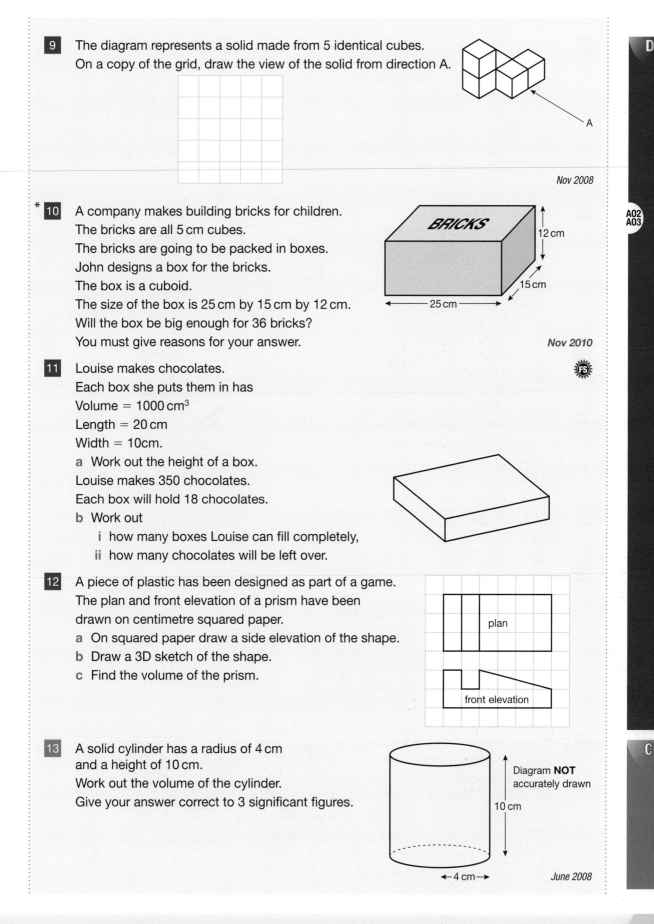

Nov 2008

* 10 A company makes building bricks for children.
The bricks are all 5 cm cubes.
The bricks are going to be packed in boxes.
John designs a box for the bricks.
The box is a cuboid.
The size of the box is 25 cm by 15 cm by 12 cm.
Will the box be big enough for 36 bricks?
You must give reasons for your answer.

Nov 2010

11 Louise makes chocolates.
Each box she puts them in has
Volume = 1000 cm³
Length = 20 cm
Width = 10cm.
a Work out the height of a box.
Louise makes 350 chocolates.
Each box will hold 18 chocolates.
b Work out
  i how many boxes Louise can fill completely,
  ii how many chocolates will be left over.

12 A piece of plastic has been designed as part of a game.
The plan and front elevation of a prism have been
drawn on centimetre squared paper.
a On squared paper draw a side elevation of the shape.
b Draw a 3D sketch of the shape.
c Find the volume of the prism.

13 A solid cylinder has a radius of 4 cm
and a height of 10 cm.
Work out the volume of the cylinder.
Give your answer correct to 3 significant figures.

Diagram **NOT**
accurately drawn

June 2008

179

14 An oil drum is in the shape of a cylinder.
The lid has been removed.
Calculate the surface area of the oil
drum without the lid.

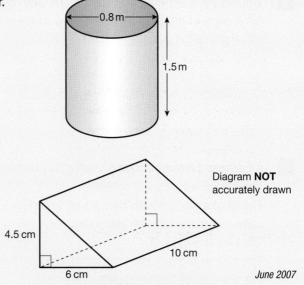

15 Here is a triangular prism.
Calculate the volume of the prism.

Diagram **NOT**
accurately drawn

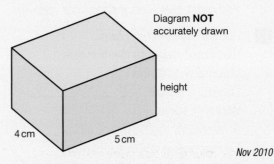

4.5 cm

10 cm

6 cm

June 2007

16 This cuboid has a width of 4 cm and
a length of 5 cm.
The volume of the cuboid is 60 cm³.
a Work out the height of the cuboid.
The cuboid is a solid made from copper.
The mass of the cuboid is 534 g.
b Work out the density of copper.

Diagram **NOT**
accurately drawn

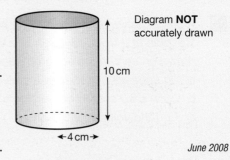

height

4 cm

5 cm

Nov 2010

17 The density of iron is 7850 kg/m³.
Work out the mass of 4 m³ of iron.

June 2010

18 A solid cylinder has a radius of 4 cm and
a height of 10 cm.
a Work out the volume of the cylinder.
Give your answer correct to 3 significant figures.
The cylinder is made from wood.
The density of the wood is 0.6 grams per cm³.
b Work out the mass of the cylinder.
Give your answer correct to 3 significant figures.

Diagram **NOT**
accurately drawn

10 cm

◄4 cm►

June 2008

19 The solid shape, shown in the diagram,
is made by cutting a hole all the way
through a wooden cube.
The cube has edges of length 5 cm.
The hole has a square cross section of side 3 cm.
a Work out the volume of wood in the solid shape.
The mass of the solid shape is 64 grams.
b Work out the density of the wood.

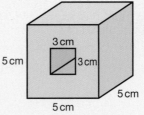

Diagram **NOT**
accurately drawn

3 cm

5 cm   3 cm

5 cm

5 cm

March 2009

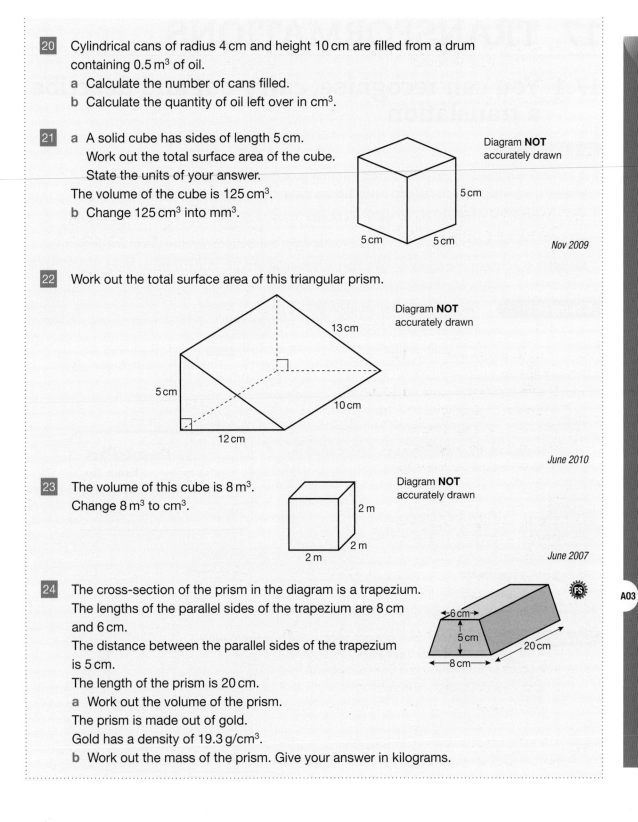

20 Cylindrical cans of radius 4 cm and height 10 cm are filled from a drum containing $0.5\,m^3$ of oil.

a Calculate the number of cans filled.

b Calculate the quantity of oil left over in cm^3.

21 a A solid cube has sides of length 5 cm.
Work out the total surface area of the cube.
State the units of your answer.
The volume of the cube is $125\,cm^3$.
b Change $125\,cm^3$ into mm^3.

Diagram **NOT** accurately drawn

5 cm
5 cm   5 cm

Nov 2009

22 Work out the total surface area of this triangular prism.

Diagram **NOT** accurately drawn

13 cm

5 cm

10 cm

12 cm

June 2010

23 The volume of this cube is $8\,m^3$.
Change $8\,m^3$ to cm^3.

Diagram **NOT** accurately drawn

2 m
2 m
2 m

June 2007

24 The cross-section of the prism in the diagram is a trapezium.
The lengths of the parallel sides of the trapezium are 8 cm and 6 cm.
The distance between the parallel sides of the trapezium is 5 cm.
The length of the prism is 20 cm.

a Work out the volume of the prism.

The prism is made out of gold.
Gold has a density of $19.3\,g/cm^3$.

b Work out the mass of the prism. Give your answer in kilograms.

6 cm
5 cm
20 cm
8 cm

A03

181

17 TRANSFORMATIONS

17.1 You can recognise, carry out and describe a translation

Key Points

⊚ A translation is a sliding movement made from one or more moves.
  In a simple translation you need to describe the distance and direction of each move.

⊚ You can describe a translation by using a column vector, e.g. $\binom{3}{2}$.

  The top number describes the movement to the right, the bottom number the movement up.

  Negative signs mean the opposite direction: left instead of right, down instead of up, e.g. $\binom{-2}{-3}$.

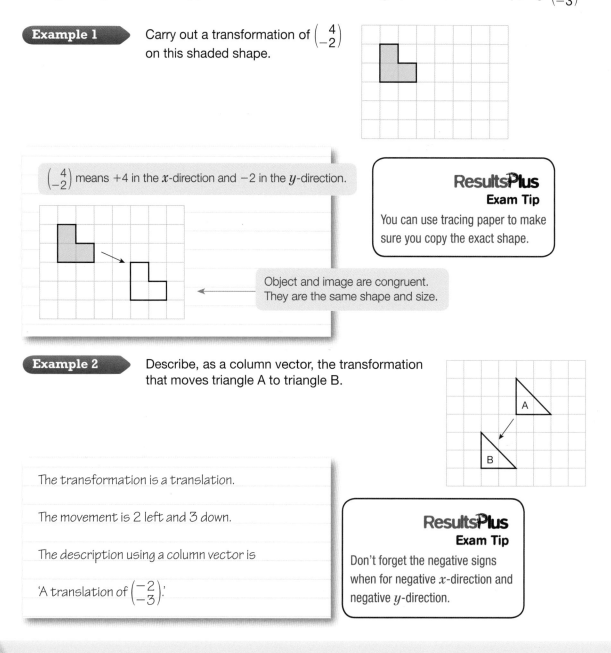

Example 1 Carry out a transformation of $\binom{4}{-2}$ on this shaded shape.

$\binom{4}{-2}$ means +4 in the x-direction and −2 in the y-direction.

Object and image are congruent. They are the same shape and size.

ResultsPlus
Exam Tip

You can use tracing paper to make sure you copy the exact shape.

Example 2 Describe, as a column vector, the transformation that moves triangle A to triangle B.

The transformation is a translation.

The movement is 2 left and 3 down.

The description using a column vector is

'A translation of $\binom{-2}{-3}$.'

ResultsPlus
Exam Tip

Don't forget the negative signs when for negative x-direction and negative y-direction.

C

Exercise 17A

Questions in this chapter are targeted at the grades indicated.

1 Copy each shape and carry out the translation described.

a $\begin{pmatrix} 1 \\ 2 \end{pmatrix}$
b $\begin{pmatrix} 3 \\ -1 \end{pmatrix}$
c $\begin{pmatrix} -1 \\ -3 \end{pmatrix}$

2 Carry out these translations on the shaded shape.

a $\begin{pmatrix} 2 \\ 3 \end{pmatrix}$ Label the shape A.

b $\begin{pmatrix} 3 \\ 2 \end{pmatrix}$ Label the shape B.

c $\begin{pmatrix} -1 \\ 2 \end{pmatrix}$ Label the shape C.

d $\begin{pmatrix} 4 \\ -2 \end{pmatrix}$ Label the shape D.

e $\begin{pmatrix} -3 \\ 0 \end{pmatrix}$ Label the shape E.

f $\begin{pmatrix} 3 \\ -2 \end{pmatrix}$ Label the shape F.

3 Describe, as a column vector, each transformation given below.

a
b
c

4 Describe, using a column vector, the transformation that moves the following shapes.

a A to B   b C to B   c B to D
d D to B   e B to A   f A to C

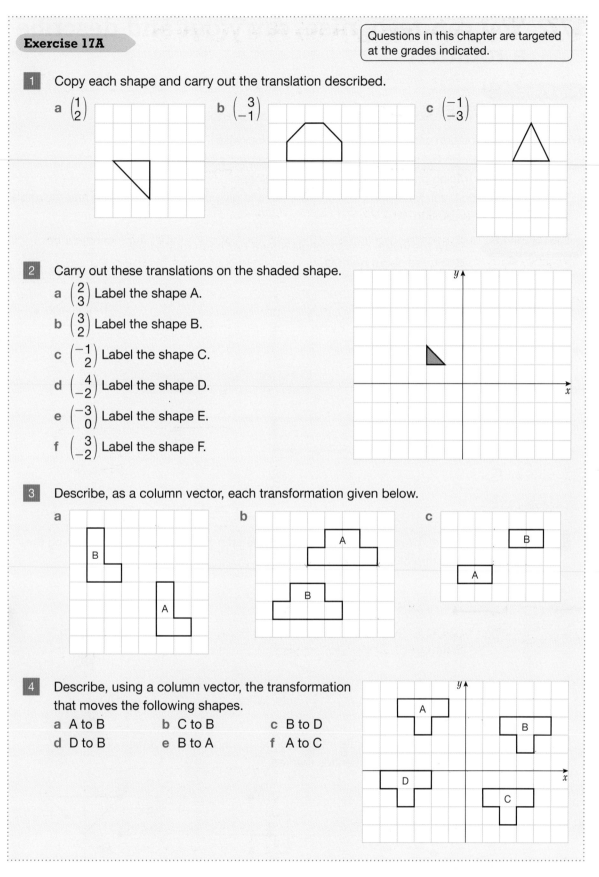

183

17.2 You can recognise, carry out and describe a rotation

Key Points

◉ A rotation can be described as a fraction of a turn, or as an angle of turn.

◉ The direction of rotation can be clockwise 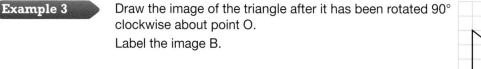 or anticlockwise.

◉ The point about which the shape is turned is called the centre of rotation.

◉ It is useful to use tracing paper to assist in rotating a shape.

◉ To decribe a rotation, you must use the word rotation and give the centre of rotation and the angle and direction of the rotation.

Example 3

Draw the image of the triangle after it has been rotated 90° clockwise about point O.

Label the image B.

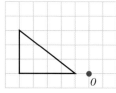

Object and image are congruent.
They are the same shape and size.

Exercise 17B

D

1 Copy each diagram. Draw the image of each shape after the rotation requested, using the point shown as centre of rotation.

a

b

c

90° turn
anticlockwise

¼ turn
clockwise

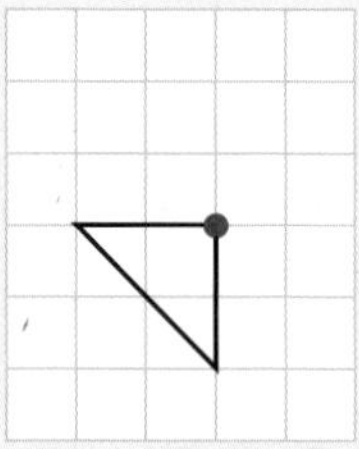

180° turn

2 Copy each diagram. Draw separate images for each shape after a rotation of 90° anticlockwise about each of the centres marked.

a

b

c

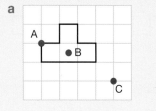

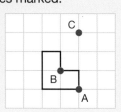

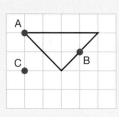

3 Copy the diagram. Draw separate images for each shape after the rotation requested, using the given point as centre of rotation.

a A rotation of A clockwise 90° about (1, 0)

b A rotation of B 90° clockwise about (−1, 2)

c A rotation of C 180° about (2, −2)

d A rotation of A anticlockwise 90° about (1, −1)

e A rotation of B 180° about (0, 3)

f A rotation of C clockwise 90° about (2, 2)

Example 4 Describe fully the transformation that maps shape A onto shape B.

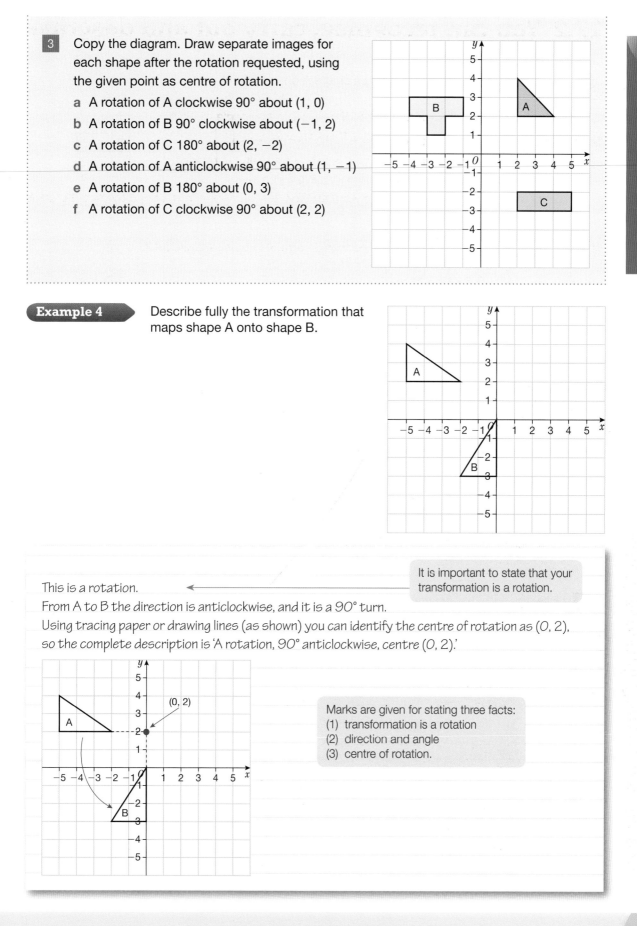

This is a rotation. ← It is important to state that your transformation is a rotation.

From A to B the direction is anticlockwise, and it is a 90° turn.

Using tracing paper or drawing lines (as shown) you can identify the centre of rotation as (0, 2), so the complete description is 'A rotation, 90° anticlockwise, centre (0, 2)'.

Marks are given for stating three facts:
(1) transformation is a rotation
(2) direction and angle
(3) centre of rotation.

Exercise 17C

1. Describe fully the rotation that maps shape A onto shape B.

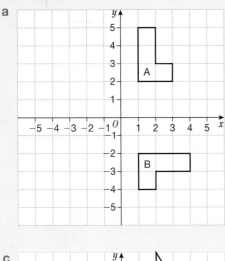

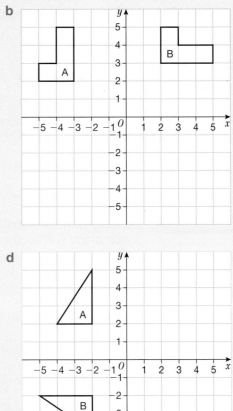

2. Describe fully the transformation that maps shape A onto shape B.

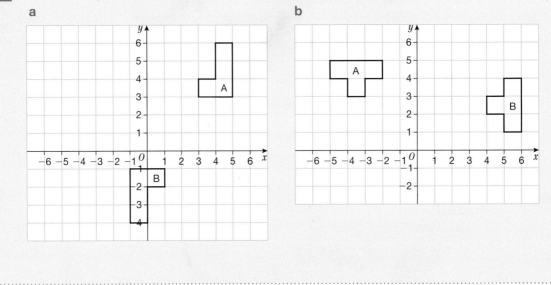

17.3 You can recognise, carry out and describe a reflection

Key Points

◉ Images of a shape that are formed by reflecting a given shape about a line of reflection (or mirror line) are called reflections of the shape.

◉ The reflection can sometimes be given on a coordinate grid.

◉ The line of reflection can be given as the equation of a line.

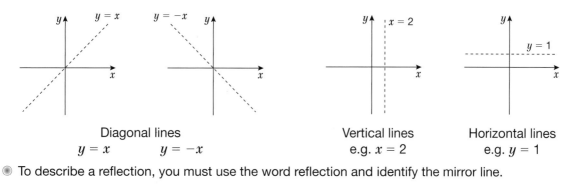

Diagonal lines
$y = x$ $y = -x$

Vertical lines
e.g. $x = 2$

Horizontal lines
e.g. $y = 1$

◉ To describe a reflection, you must use the word reflection and identify the mirror line.

Example 5　Draw the image of this shape after it has been reflected in the mirror line.

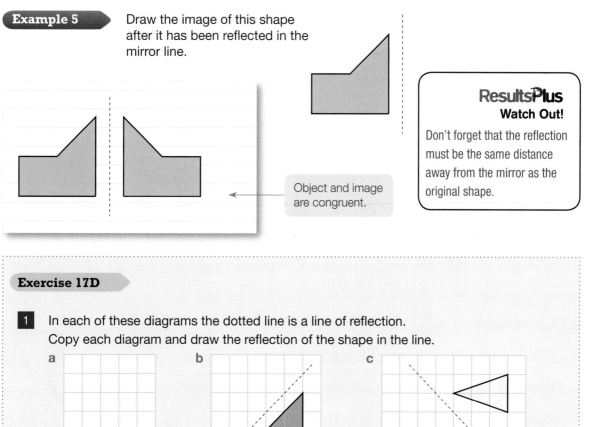

Object and image are congruent.

ResultsPlus
Watch Out!

Don't forget that the reflection must be the same distance away from the mirror as the original shape.

Exercise 17D

1　In each of these diagrams the dotted line is a line of reflection.
Copy each diagram and draw the reflection of the shape in the line.

a

b

c

F

2 **a** Reflect shape A in the x-axis. **b** Reflect shape B in the y-axis.

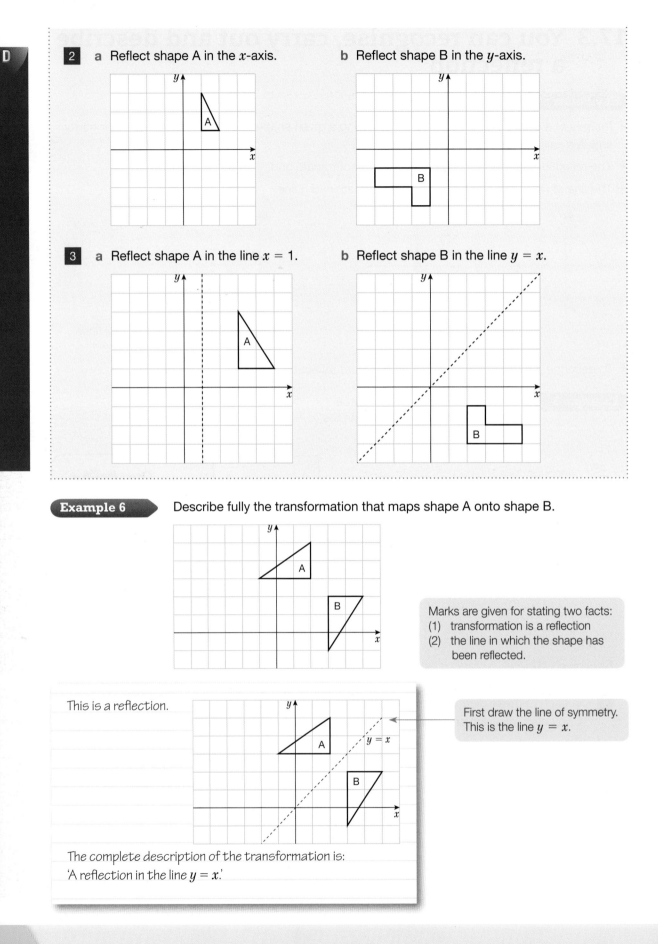

3 **a** Reflect shape A in the line $x = 1$. **b** Reflect shape B in the line $y = x$.

Example 6 Describe fully the transformation that maps shape A onto shape B.

Marks are given for stating two facts:
(1) transformation is a reflection
(2) the line in which the shape has been reflected.

This is a reflection.

First draw the line of symmetry. This is the line $y = x$.

The complete description of the transformation is:
'A reflection in the line $y = x$.'

Exercise 17E

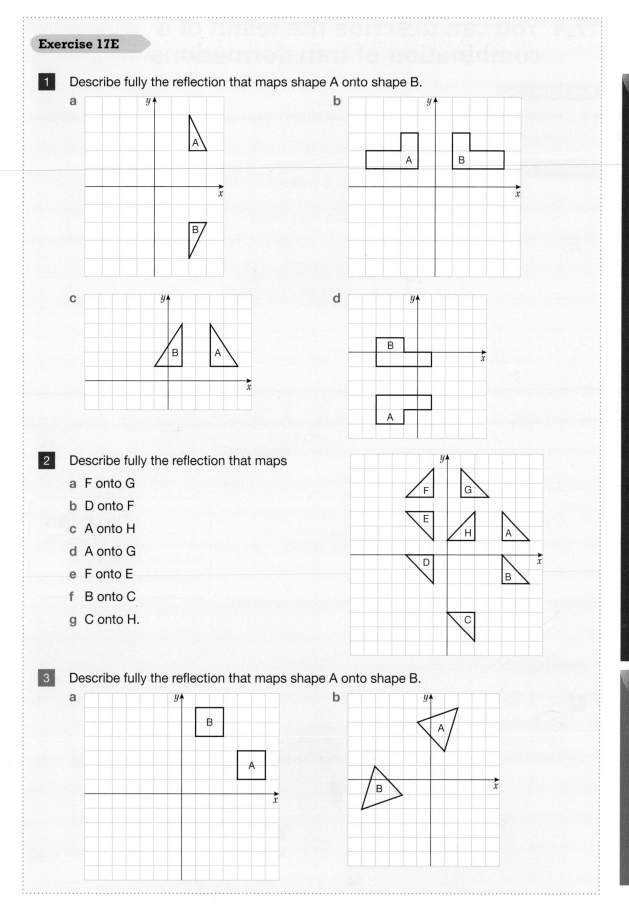

1 Describe fully the reflection that maps shape A onto shape B.

a

b

c

d

2 Describe fully the reflection that maps

a F onto G

b D onto F

c A onto H

d A onto G

e F onto E

f B onto C

g C onto H.

3 Describe fully the reflection that maps shape A onto shape B.

a

b

17.4 You can describe the result of a combination of transformations

Key Point

It is sometimes possible to find a single transformation that has the same effect as a combination of two transformations.

Example 7

Shape A is transformed by a reflection in the y-axis to image B. Image B is reflected in the x-axis to image C.
What single transformation maps shape A onto shape C?

Make sure you draw all the images carefully, and label them if asked.

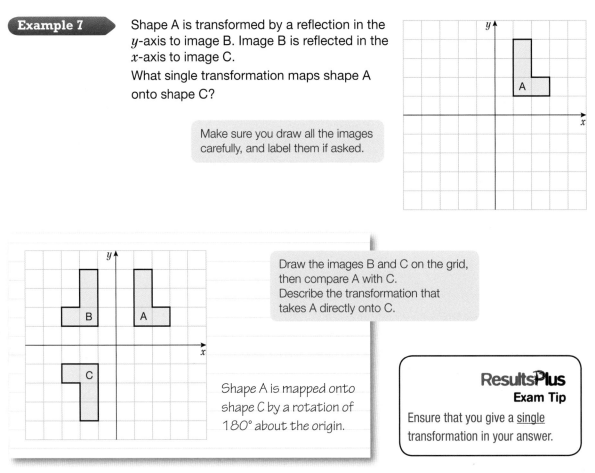

Draw the images B and C on the grid, then compare A with C.
Describe the transformation that takes A directly onto C.

Shape A is mapped onto shape C by a rotation of 180° about the origin.

ResultsPlus
Exam Tip

Ensure that you give a single transformation in your answer.

Exercise 17F

C

1　Copy the diagram.
　a Reflect the shape in the x-axis.
　b Reflect the image in the line $y = 2$.
　c Describe the single transformation that is equivalent to **a** followed by **b**.

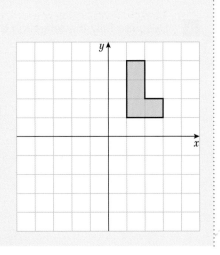

2 Copy the diagram.

  a Reflect the shape in the line $y = x$.

  b Rotate the image 90° anticlockwise about the origin.

  c Describe the single transformation that is equivalent to **a** followed by **b**.

3 Copy the diagram.

  a Reflect the shape A in the y-axis.
     Label the image B.

  b Reflect the image B in the x-axis.
     Label this image C.

  c Describe the single transformation that maps A onto C.

4 Copy the diagram.

  a Rotate the shape A 90° clockwise, centre (3, 3).
     Label the image B.

  b Rotate the image B 180°, centre (6, 3).
     Label this image C.

  c Describe the single transformation that maps A onto C.

5 Triangle P has been rotated 180° about the point (1, 1) to give triangle Q.

  a Rotate triangle Q 180° about the point (3, −1).
     Label the triangle R.

  b Describe the single transformation that takes triangle P to triangle R.

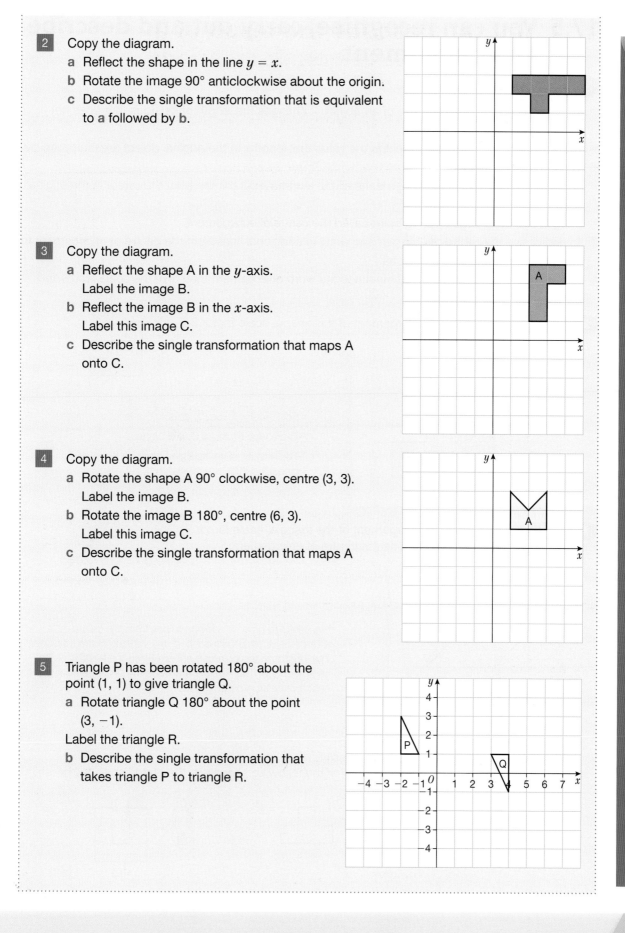

191

17.5 You can recognise, carry out and describe an enlargement

Key Points

- An enlargement changes the size of an object. It changes the length of its sides, but does not change its shape.
- The scale factor of the enlargement is the value that lengths in the original object are multiplied by to get the lengths in the image.
  For example, a scale factor of $1\frac{1}{2}$ means all the lengths are $1\frac{1}{2}$ times what they were in the original shape.
- Shapes can be enlarged from a point called the centre of enlargement.
- To find or use the centre of enlargement, draw in additional lines from the centre of enlargement to the vertices of the shape or shapes.
- To describe an enlargement, you must use the word enlargement then give the scale factor and the centre of enlargement.

Example 8 Draw an enlargement of this shape, scale factor 2.

Scale factor 2 means double the lengths of sides.

The shape must be drawn bigger.

The lengths of all the sides must be twice as long, since this is scale factor 2.

Object and image are similar.

Example 9 Draw an enlargement of the triangle, scale factor 2, using point A as the centre of enlargement.

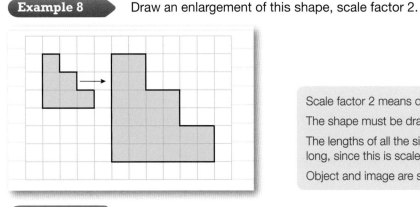

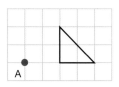

It is useful to draw in additional lines from the centre of enlargement, which will connect the vertices of the triangles. The lengths in the enlargement are twice the lengths of the original shape. The vertices are twice the distance from the centre of enlargement.

Exercise 17G

D

1 Copy the diagrams and enlarge each of the following shapes by the stated scale factor (sf).

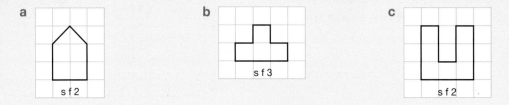

a s f 2

b s f 3

c s f 2

D

2 Copy each diagram onto squared paper. Enlarge each of these shapes by the stated scale factor (sf), from the given point of enlargement.

a

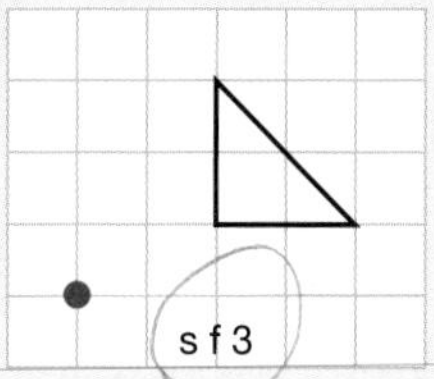

s f 3

b

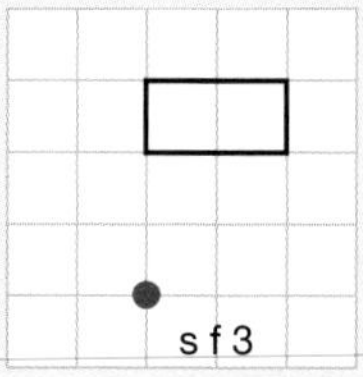

s f 3

c

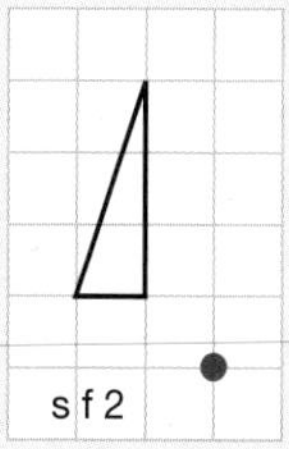

s f 2

3 Copy each diagram onto squared paper. For each diagram draw two images, one from each of the points of enlargement given.

a

A (0, 0)
B (3, −1)

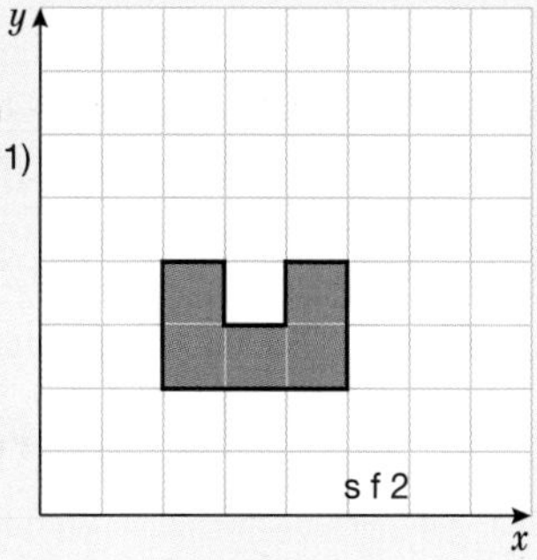

s f 2

b

C (0, 0)
D (−2, 1)

s f 3

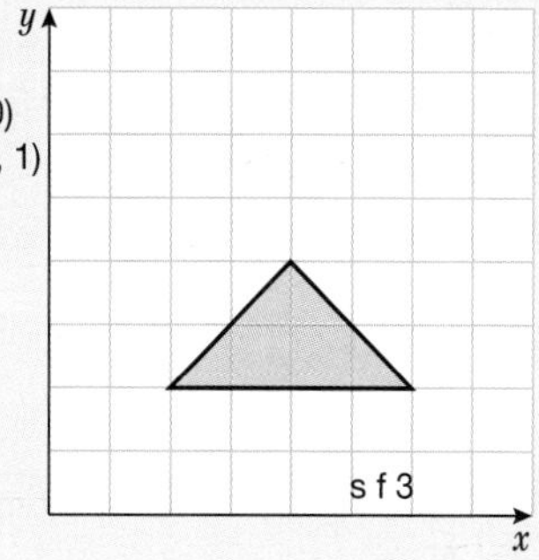

> **Example 10** Describe fully the transformation that maps shape A onto shape B.

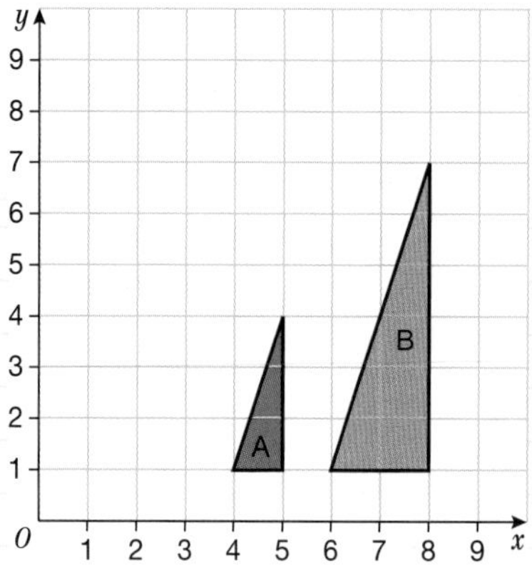

This is an enlargement.

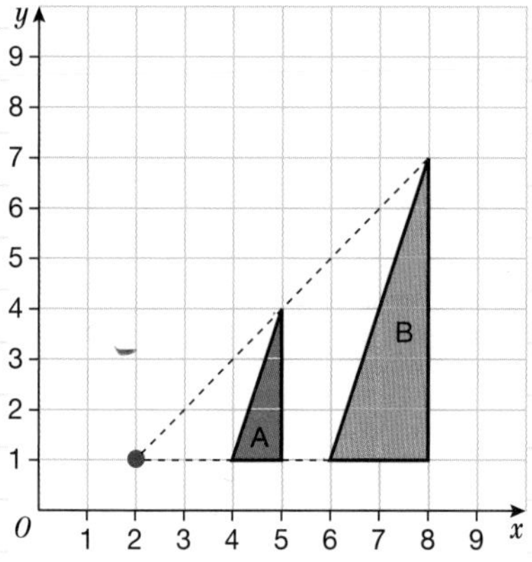

By comparing the lengths of the sides, you can tell that the sides on shape B are twice the lengths of the sides on shape A.

By joining up the vertices (see the dotted lines) you can extend these lines so they meet at the centre of enlargement (2, 1).
So the transformation is
'An enlargement of scale factor 2, centre (2, 1).'

ResultsPlus
Exam Tip

Marks are given for stating three facts.
(1) transformation is an enlargement
(2) the scale factor
(3) the centre of enlargement

Example 11

Describe fully the transformation which maps triangle A onto triangle B.

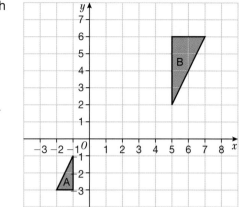

The lengths of the sides of triangle B are twice those of triangle A. This means that the transformation is an enlargement.

To find the centre of enlargement, join each corner (vertex) of triangle A to the corresponding vertex of triangle B.

The centre of enlargement C is the point where these lines cross.

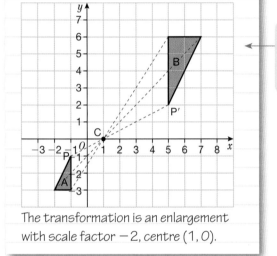

The transformation is an enlargement with scale factor −2, centre (1, 0).

Notice that point C is between the object A and the image B. From C to P' is twice the distance from C to P but in the opposite direction.
The scale factor of the enlargement is −2.

ResultsPlus

Watch Out!

When a shape is enlarged by a negative scale factor, the image is on the opposite side of the centre of enlargement to the object.

Exercise 17H

C A03

1 On a copy of the diagram complete the following enlargements.

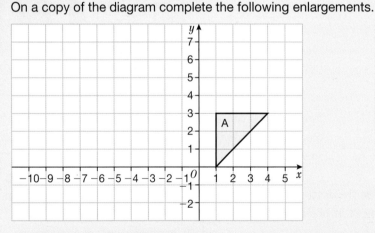

a Enlarge triangle A with a scale factor of −2, centre (0, 0). Label this new triangle B.

b Enlarge triangle A with a scale factor of −$\frac{1}{3}$, centre (1, 6). Label this new triangle C.

c Find the scale factor of the enlargement that maps triangle C onto triangle B.

2 Describe fully the transformation that maps shape A onto shape B.

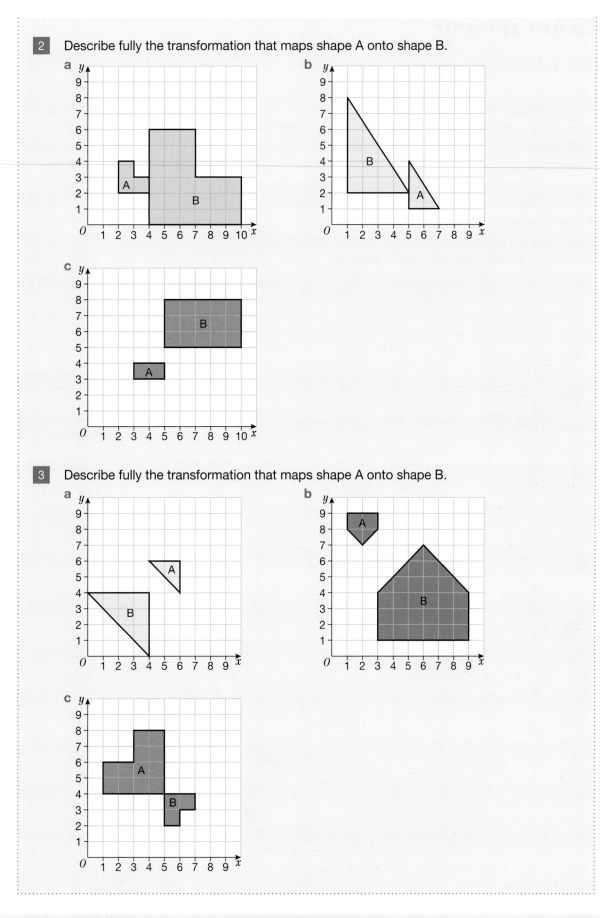

3 Describe fully the transformation that maps shape A onto shape B.

Exam review

Self-assessment checklist

I can:

- recognise and carry out a translation [p.182]
- describe a translation, giving a vector to describe the horizontal and vertical movement of the shape [p.182]
- recognise and carry out a rotation [p.184]
- describe a rotation, giving both the angle and direction through which the shape has been rotated and the coordinates of the centre of rotation [p.184]
- recognise and carry out a reflection [p.187]
- describe a reflection, giving the equation of the mirror line [p.187]
- carry out a combination of transformations [p.190]
- recognise and carry out an enlargement [p.192]
- describe an enlargement, giving both the scale factor of the enlargement and the coordinates of the centre of enlargement. [p.192]

Exam practice

1 On a copy of the grid, enlarge the shape with a scale factor of 2.

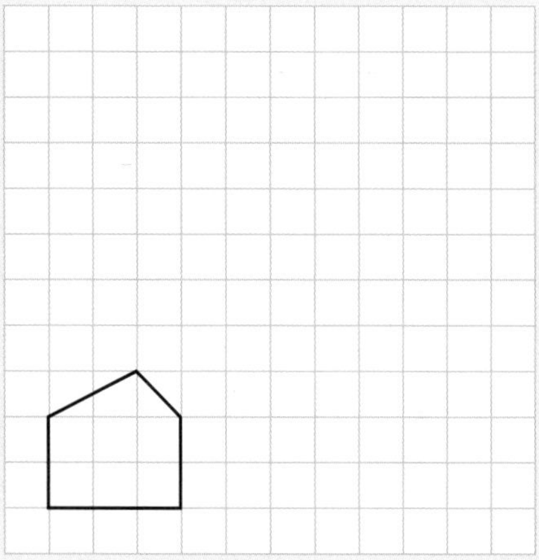

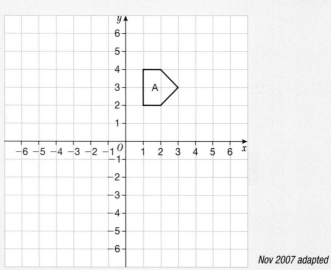

Nov 2008

2 **a** Reflect Shape **A** in the y-axis. Label your new shape **B**.

b Translate Shape **A** by the vector $\begin{pmatrix} 3 \\ -2 \end{pmatrix}$

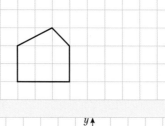

Nov 2007 adapted

196

3   Triangle **T** has been drawn on the grid.

a On a copy of the grid, reflect triangle **T** in the y-axis. Label the new triangle **A**.

b On a copy of the grid, rotate triangle **T** by a half turn, centre O. Label the new triangle **B**.

c Describe fully the single transformation which maps triangle **T** onto triangle **C**.

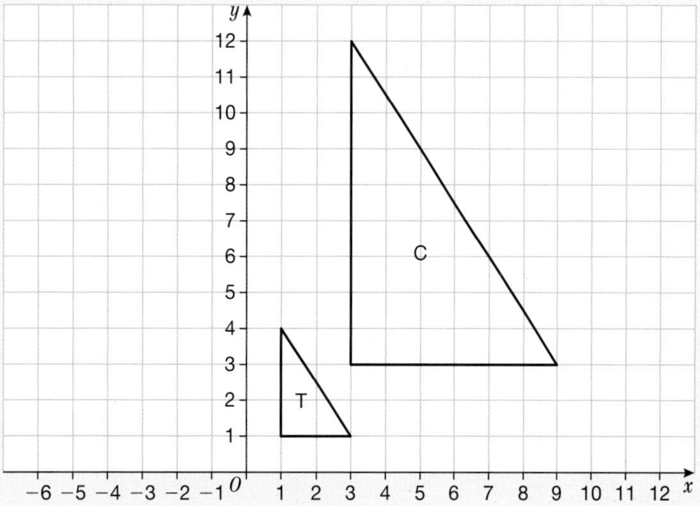

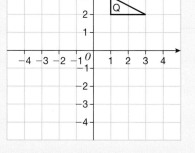

June 2007 adapted

4

Triangle **Q** has been drawn on a grid.
On a copy of the grid, rotate triangle **Q** 90° clockwise, centre O.

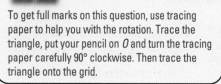

ResultsPlus
Achieving Full Marks

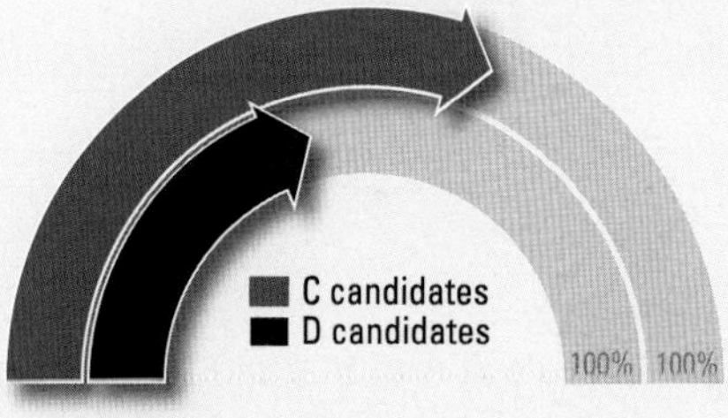

■ C candidates
■ D candidates

100%   100%

To get full marks on this question, use tracing paper to help you with the rotation. Trace the triangle, put your pencil on O and turn the tracing paper carefully 90° clockwise. Then trace the triangle onto the grid.

Nov 2009

5   Describe fully the single transformation that maps triangle **A** onto triangle **B**.

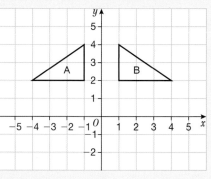

June 2009

6 **a** Reflect the shaded shape in the line $y = x$.

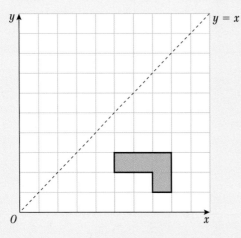

b On a copy of the grid, enlarge the shaded shape by a scale factor of 3, centre O.

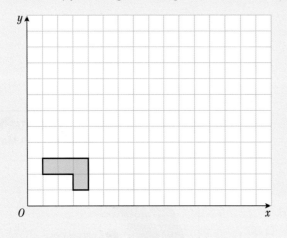

7 Triangle **A** and triangle **B** are drawn on the grid.

a Describe fully the single transformation which maps triangle **A** onto triangle **B**.

b Translate triangle **A** by the vector $\begin{pmatrix} 3 \\ 0 \end{pmatrix}$. Label the new triangle **C**.

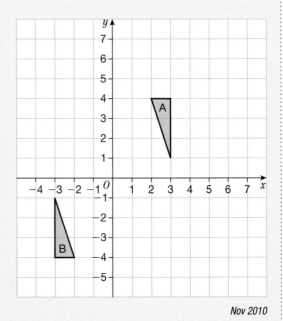

Nov 2010

8 Describe fully the single transformation which maps shape **P** onto shape **Q**.

June 2010

9 Triangle **T** has been drawn on the grid.
Rotate triangle **T** 180° about the point (1, 0).
Label the new triangle **A**.

June 2010

10 Describe fully the single transformation that maps triangle **A** onto triangle **B**.

Nov 2009

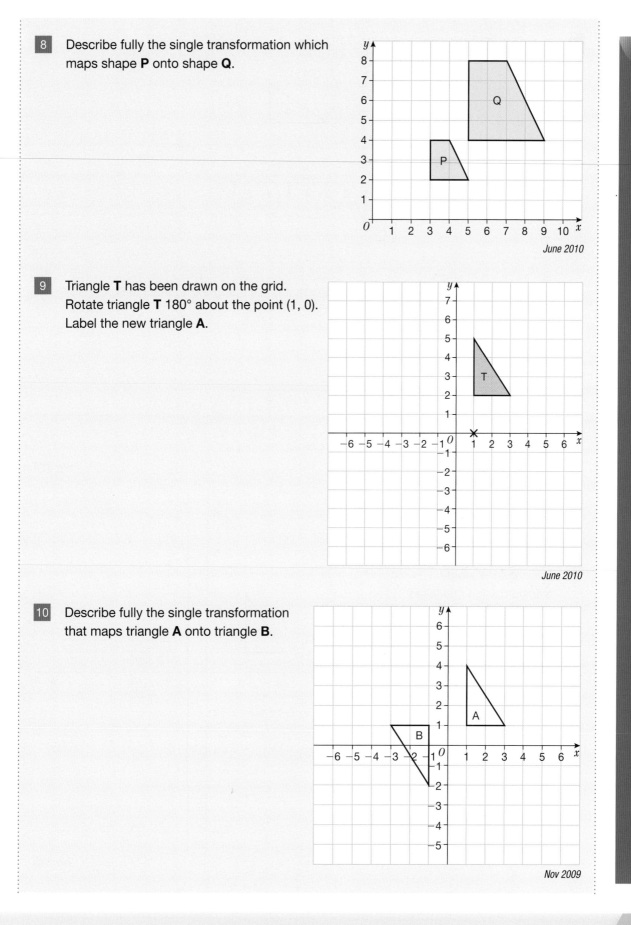

11 **a** On a copy of the grid, reflect triangle **P** in the line $x = 2$.

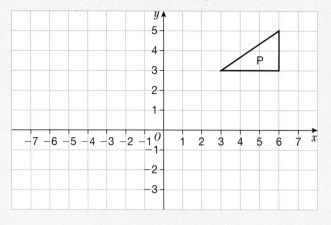

b Describe fully the **single** transformation that takes triangle **Q** to triangle **R**.

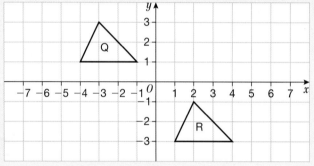

Nov 2006

12 Triangle **A** is reflected in the x-axis to give triangle **B**. Triangle **B** is reflected in the line $x = 1$ to give triangle **C**. Describe the **single** transformation that takes triangle **A** to triangle **C**.

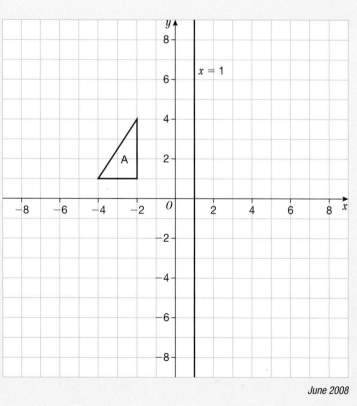

June 2008

18 PYTHAGORAS' THEOREM AND TRIGONOMETRY

18.1 You can remember and use Pythagoras' Theorem

Key Points

- For a right-angled triangle
  $$c^2 = a^2 + b^2 \quad \text{or} \quad a^2 + b^2 = c^2$$
  so $a^2 = c^2 - b^2 \quad \text{or} \quad b^2 = c^2 - a^2$

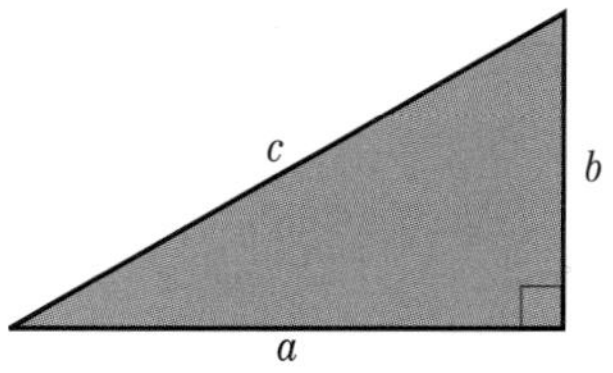

- To find the length of the hypotenuse (c):
  square each of the other sides (a) and (b), add the squares and then square root the sum.

- To find the length of one of the shorter sides (a or b):
  square each of the other sides (c) and (a or b), subtract the squares and then square root the sum.

Example 1   Find the length of AC in this right-angled triangle.

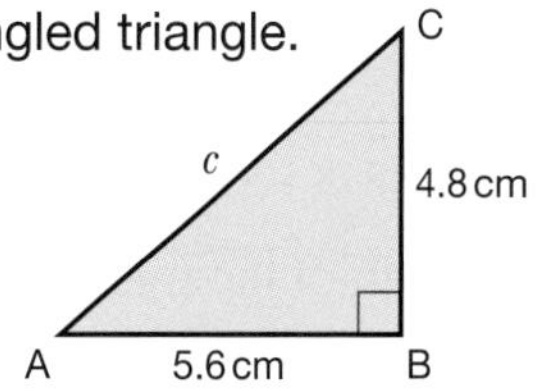

ResultsPlus
Exam Tip

You will need to learn Pythagoras' Theorem for your exam.

AC is the hypotenuse.

$c^2 = a^2 + b^2$ ←   Write down the statement.

$c^2 = 5.6^2 + 4.8^2$ ←   Put in the values 5.6 and 4.8.

$c^2 = 31.36 + 23.04$ ←   Square the 5.6 and 4.8.   Use the $\boxed{x^2}$ key.

$c^2 = 54.4$ ←   Add 31.36 and 23.04.

$c = \sqrt{54.4}$
$c = 7.375635566 \, \text{cm}$ ←   Square root the 54.4 to give 7.38 as the answer.   Use the $\boxed{\sqrt{x}}$ key.
$c = 7.38 \, \text{cm}$ (written to 3 significant figures)

Exercise 18A

Questions in this chapter are targeted at the grades indicated.

1   Calculate the length of the hypotenuse in these right-angled triangles.

a

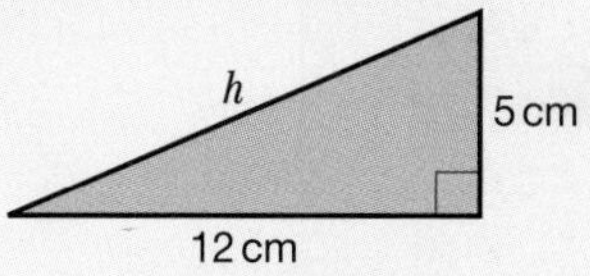

b

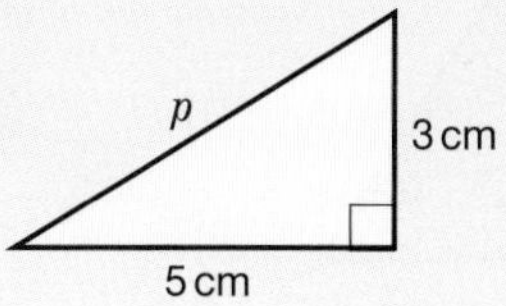

c

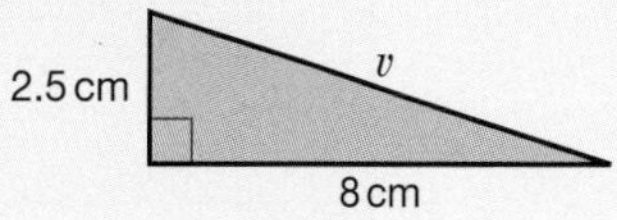

C

Example 2

Find the length of BC in this right-angled triangle.

AC is the hypotenuse.

BC is one of the shorter sides.

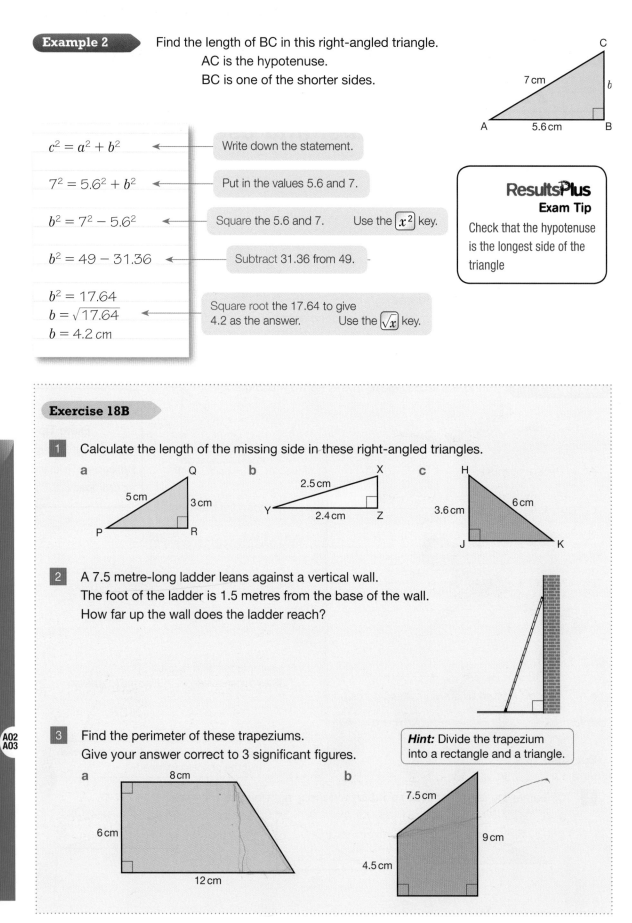

$c^2 = a^2 + b^2$ ← Write down the statement.

$7^2 = 5.6^2 + b^2$ ← Put in the values 5.6 and 7.

$b^2 = 7^2 - 5.6^2$ ← Square the 5.6 and 7. Use the x^2 key.

$b^2 = 49 - 31.36$ ← Subtract 31.36 from 49.

$b^2 = 17.64$
$b = \sqrt{17.64}$ ← Square root the 17.64 to give 4.2 as the answer. Use the $\sqrt{x}$ key.
$b = 4.2\ cm$

ResultsPlus
Exam Tip

Check that the hypotenuse is the longest side of the triangle

Exercise 18B

1   Calculate the length of the missing side in these right-angled triangles.

a

5 cm
3 cm

b

2.5 cm
2.4 cm

c

3.6 cm
6 cm

2   A 7.5 metre-long ladder leans against a vertical wall.
The foot of the ladder is 1.5 metres from the base of the wall.
How far up the wall does the ladder reach?

A02
A03

3   Find the perimeter of these trapeziums.
Give your answer correct to 3 significant figures.

Hint: Divide the trapezium into a rectangle and a triangle.

a

8 cm
6 cm
12 cm

b

7.5 cm
9 cm
4.5 cm

18.2 You can find the length of a line segment

Key Points

◉ To find the distance between two points on a coordinate grid:
  ◉ subtract the x-coordinates and square
  ◉ subtract the y-coordinates and square
  ◉ add the results
  ◉ square root the answer.

Example 3   Find the length of the line segment ST.

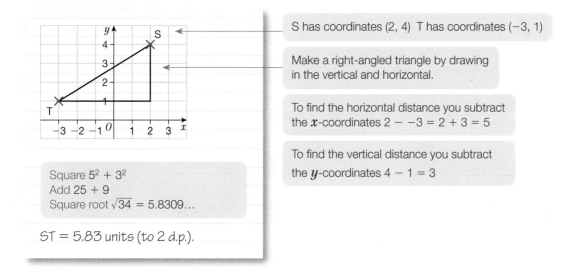

S has coordinates (2, 4) T has coordinates (−3, 1)

Make a right-angled triangle by drawing in the vertical and horizontal.

To find the horizontal distance you subtract the x-coordinates $2 - -3 = 2 + 3 = 5$

To find the vertical distance you subtract the y-coordinates $4 - 1 = 3$

Square $5^2 + 3^2$
Add $25 + 9$
Square root $\sqrt{34} = 5.8309\ldots$

$ST = 5.83$ units (to 2 d.p.).

Exercise 18C

1   Work out the lengths of each of these line segments.

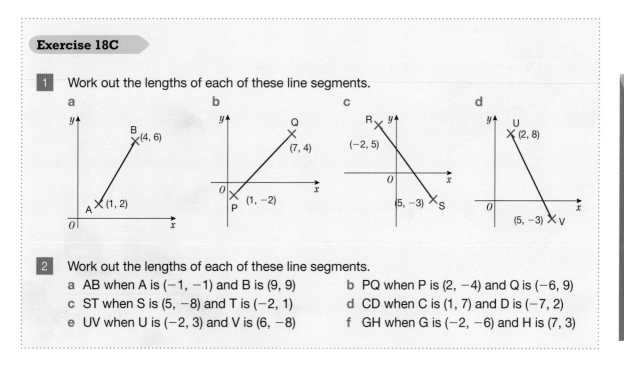

2   Work out the lengths of each of these line segments.
   a   AB when A is (−1, −1) and B is (9, 9)   b   PQ when P is (2, −4) and Q is (−6, 9)
   c   ST when S is (5, −8) and T is (−2, 1)   d   CD when C is (1, 7) and D is (−7, 2)
   e   UV when U is (−2, 3) and V is (6, −8)   f   GH when G is (−2, −6) and H is (7, 3)

18.3 You can use trigonometry to find the size of angles in right-angled triangles

Key Points

- The hypotenuse (hyp) of a right-angled triangle is the longest side of the triangle and is opposite the right angle.
  The side opposite an angle is called the opposite side (opp).
  The side next to this angle is called the adjacent side (adj).

$$\sin x° = \frac{\text{opp}}{\text{hyp}} \qquad \cos x° = \frac{\text{adj}}{\text{hyp}} \qquad \tan x° = \frac{\text{opp}}{\text{adj}}$$

SOHCAHTOA might help you remember these results.

Sin Opp Hyp Cos Adj Hyp Tan Opp Adj

- To answer questions involving trigonometry you must be able to use your calculator correctly.
  To find angles, you need to be able to use Sin⁻¹, Cos⁻¹ and Tan⁻¹.

Example 4 Work out the size of each of the marked angles.
Give each answer correct to one decimal place.

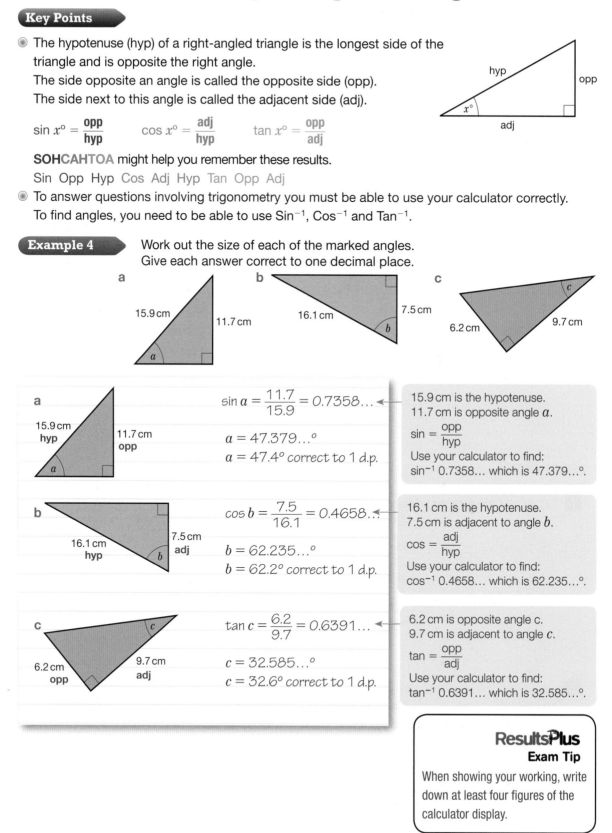

a

$$\sin a = \frac{11.7}{15.9} = 0.7358...$$

$$a = 47.379...°$$
$$a = 47.4° \text{ correct to 1 d.p.}$$

15.9 cm is the hypotenuse.
11.7 cm is opposite angle a.
$$\sin = \frac{\text{opp}}{\text{hyp}}$$
Use your calculator to find:
sin⁻¹ 0.7358... which is 47.379...°.

b

$$\cos b = \frac{7.5}{16.1} = 0.4658...$$

$$b = 62.235...°$$
$$b = 62.2° \text{ correct to 1 d.p.}$$

16.1 cm is the hypotenuse.
7.5 cm is adjacent to angle b.
$$\cos = \frac{\text{adj}}{\text{hyp}}$$
Use your calculator to find:
cos⁻¹ 0.4658... which is 62.235...°.

c

$$\tan c = \frac{6.2}{9.7} = 0.6391...$$

$$c = 32.585...°$$
$$c = 32.6° \text{ correct to 1 d.p.}$$

6.2 cm is opposite angle c.
9.7 cm is adjacent to angle c.
$$\tan = \frac{\text{opp}}{\text{adj}}$$
Use your calculator to find:
tan⁻¹ 0.6391... which is 32.585...°.

ResultsPlus
Exam Tip

When showing your working, write down at least four figures of the calculator display.

B

Exercise 18D

1 Work out the size of each of the marked angles. Give each answer correct to one decimal place.

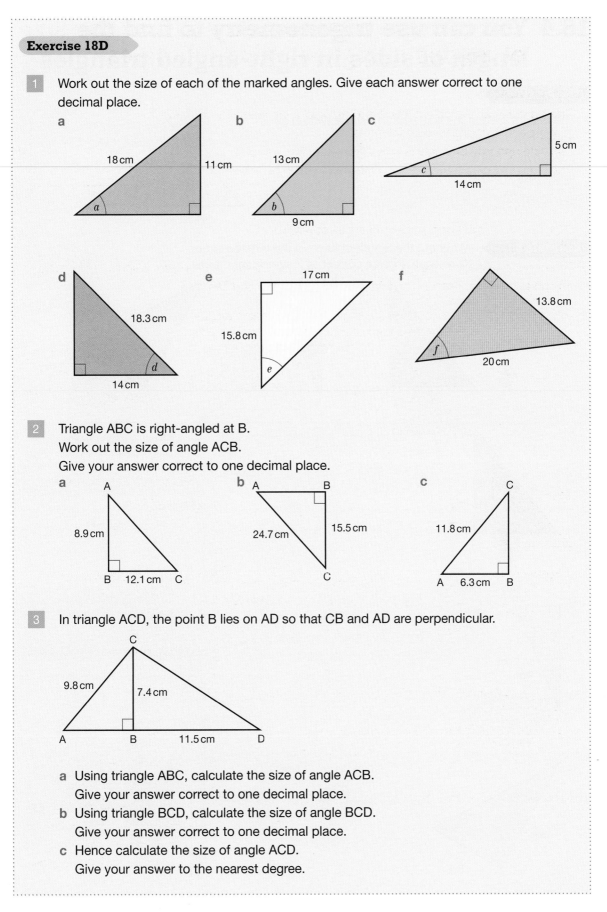

2 Triangle ABC is right-angled at B.
Work out the size of angle ACB.
Give your answer correct to one decimal place.

3 In triangle ACD, the point B lies on AD so that CB and AD are perpendicular.

a Using triangle ABC, calculate the size of angle ACB.
Give your answer correct to one decimal place.
b Using triangle BCD, calculate the size of angle BCD.
Give your answer correct to one decimal place.
c Hence calculate the size of angle ACD.
Give your answer to the nearest degree.

18.4 You can use trigonometry to find the length of sides in right-angled triangles

Key Point

- The results used in the last section can be written as

  $opp = hyp \times \sin x°$

  $adj = hyp \times \cos x°$

  $opp = adj \times \tan x°$

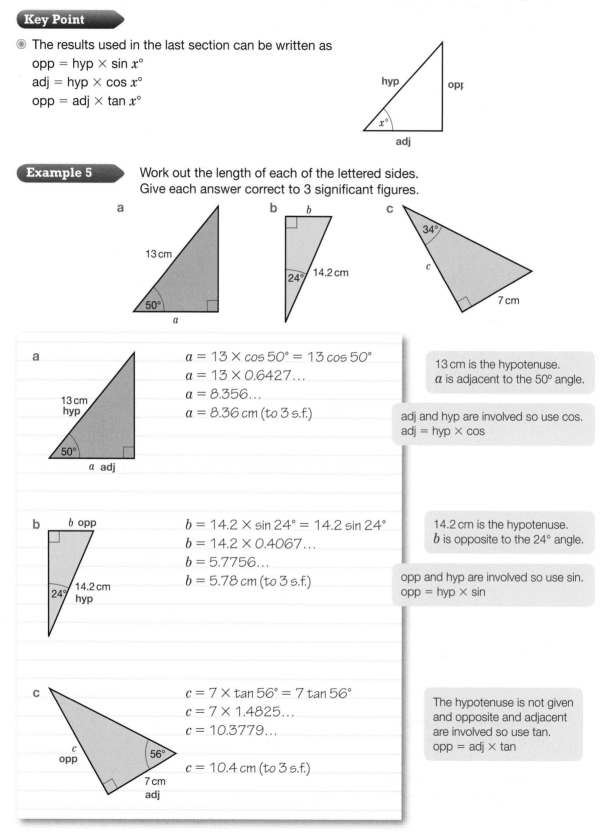

Example 5   Work out the length of each of the lettered sides.
Give each answer correct to 3 significant figures.

a

$a = 13 \times \cos 50° = 13 \cos 50°$

$a = 13 \times 0.6427...$

$a = 8.356...$

$a = 8.36\,cm$ (to 3 s.f.)

> 13 cm is the hypotenuse.
> a is adjacent to the 50° angle.

> adj and hyp are involved so use cos.
> adj = hyp × cos

b

$b = 14.2 \times \sin 24° = 14.2 \sin 24°$

$b = 14.2 \times 0.4067...$

$b = 5.7756...$

$b = 5.78\,cm$ (to 3 s.f.)

> 14.2 cm is the hypotenuse.
> b is opposite to the 24° angle.

> opp and hyp are involved so use sin.
> opp = hyp × sin

c

$c = 7 \times \tan 56° = 7 \tan 56°$

$c = 7 \times 1.4825...$

$c = 10.3779...$

$c = 10.4\,cm$ (to 3 s.f.)

> The hypotenuse is not given and opposite and adjacent are involved so use tan.
> opp = adj × tan

Exercise 18E

1 Work out the length of each marked side.
Give each answer correct to three significant figures.

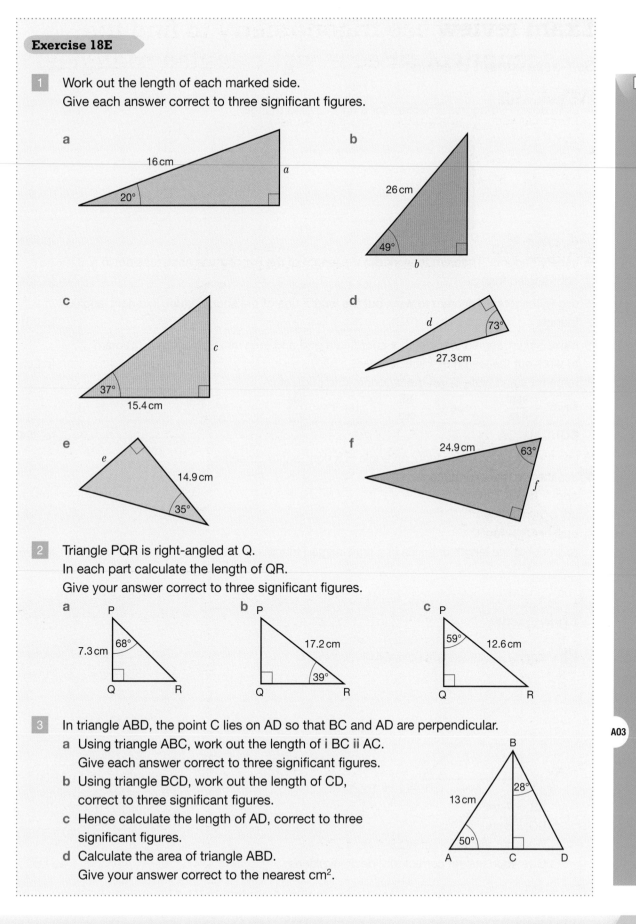

a

16 cm

a

20°

b

26 cm

49°

b

c

c

37°

15.4 cm

d

d

73°

27.3 cm

e

e

14.9 cm

35°

f

24.9 cm

63°

f

2 Triangle PQR is right-angled at Q.
In each part calculate the length of QR.
Give your answer correct to three significant figures.

a

P

68°

7.3 cm

Q   R

b

P

17.2 cm

39°

Q   R

c

P

59° 12.6 cm

Q   R

3 In triangle ABD, the point C lies on AD so that BC and AD are perpendicular.
   a Using triangle ABC, work out the length of **i** BC **ii** AC.
   Give each answer correct to three significant figures.
   b Using triangle BCD, work out the length of CD,
   correct to three significant figures.
   c Hence calculate the length of AD, correct to three
   significant figures.
   d Calculate the area of triangle ABD.
   Give your answer correct to the nearest cm².

B

28°

13 cm

50°

A   C   D

A03

Exam review

Self-assessment checklist

I can:

- write down Pythagoras' Theorem for a right-angled triangle

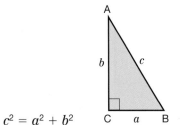

$c^2 = a^2 + b^2$ [p.201]

- use Pythagoras' Theorem to work out the length of the hypotenuse (longest side) in a right-angled triangle [p.201]

- use Pythagoras' Theorem to work out the length one of the shorter sides in a right-angled triangle [p.201]

- make a right-angled triangle on a coordinate grid and then use Pythagoras' Theorem to work out the length of a line segment [p.203]

- remember and write down the trigonometric (trig) ratios

  $\sin x° = \dfrac{\text{opp}}{\text{hyp}}$ $\qquad \cos x° = \dfrac{\text{adj}}{\text{hyp}}$ $\qquad \tan x° = \dfrac{\text{opp}}{\text{adj}}$

  SOHCAHTOA [p.204]

- use the trig ratios to work out an angle in a right-angled triangle

- use the trig ratios in the form
  opp = hyp × sin $x°$
  adj = hyp × cos $x°$
  opp = adj × tan $x°$
  to work out the length of a side in a right-angled triangle. [p.206]

Exam practice

 1 ABC is a right-angled triangle.

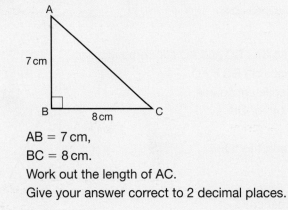

AB = 7 cm,
BC = 8 cm.
Work out the length of AC.
Give your answer correct to 2 decimal places. *June 2008*

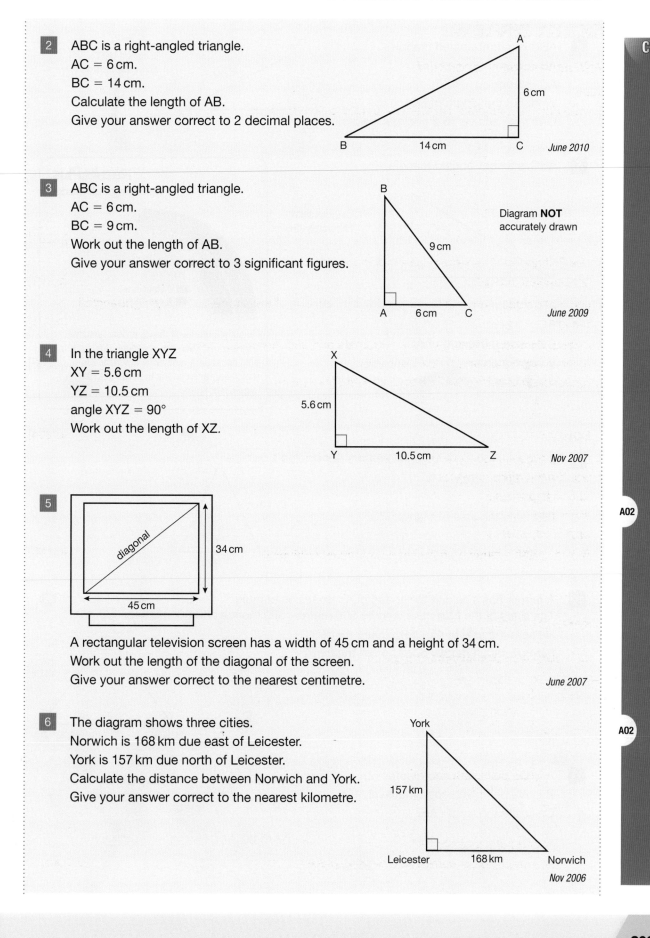

2 ABC is a right-angled triangle.
   AC = 6 cm.
   BC = 14 cm.
   Calculate the length of AB.
   Give your answer correct to 2 decimal places.

   A

   6 cm

   B   14 cm   C   *June 2010*

3 ABC is a right-angled triangle.
   AC = 6 cm.
   BC = 9 cm.
   Work out the length of AB.
   Give your answer correct to 3 significant figures.

   B

   Diagram **NOT**
   accurately drawn

   9 cm

   A   6 cm   C   *June 2009*

4 In the triangle XYZ
   XY = 5.6 cm
   YZ = 10.5 cm
   angle XYZ = 90°
   Work out the length of XZ.

   X

   5.6 cm

   Y   10.5 cm   Z   *Nov 2007*

5
   diagonal

   34 cm

   45 cm

   A rectangular television screen has a width of 45 cm and a height of 34 cm.
   Work out the length of the diagonal of the screen.
   Give your answer correct to the nearest centimetre.   *June 2007*

   A02

6 The diagram shows three cities.
   Norwich is 168 km due east of Leicester.
   York is 157 km due north of Leicester.
   Calculate the distance between Norwich and York.
   Give your answer correct to the nearest kilometre.

   York

   A02

   157 km

   Leicester   168 km   Norwich

   Nov 2006

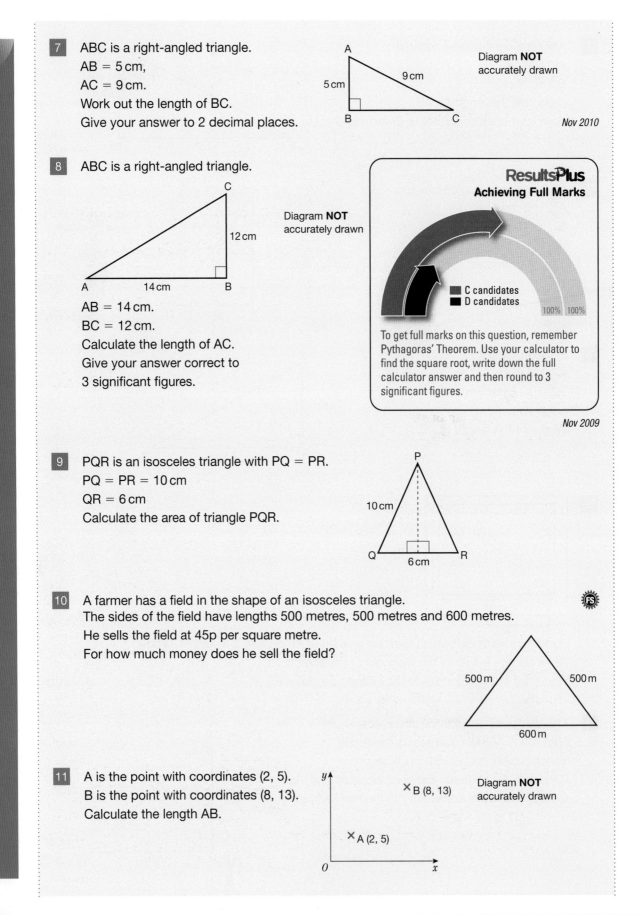

7 ABC is a right-angled triangle.
AB = 5 cm,
AC = 9 cm.
Work out the length of BC.
Give your answer to 2 decimal places.

A

9 cm

5 cm

B C

Diagram **NOT** accurately drawn

Nov 2010

8 ABC is a right-angled triangle.

C

12 cm

A 14 cm B

Diagram **NOT** accurately drawn

AB = 14 cm.
BC = 12 cm.
Calculate the length of AC.
Give your answer correct to
3 significant figures.

ResultsPlus
Achieving Full Marks

■ C candidates
■ D candidates
100% 100%

To get full marks on this question, remember Pythagoras' Theorem. Use your calculator to find the square root, write down the full calculator answer and then round to 3 significant figures.

Nov 2009

9 PQR is an isosceles triangle with PQ = PR.
PQ = PR = 10 cm
QR = 6 cm
Calculate the area of triangle PQR.

P

10 cm

Q 6 cm R

10 A farmer has a field in the shape of an isosceles triangle.
The sides of the field have lengths 500 metres, 500 metres and 600 metres.
He sells the field at 45p per square metre.
For how much money does he sell the field?

500 m 500 m

600 m

11 A is the point with coordinates (2, 5).
B is the point with coordinates (8, 13).
Calculate the length AB.

y

×B (8, 13)

×A (2, 5)

0 x

Diagram **NOT** accurately drawn

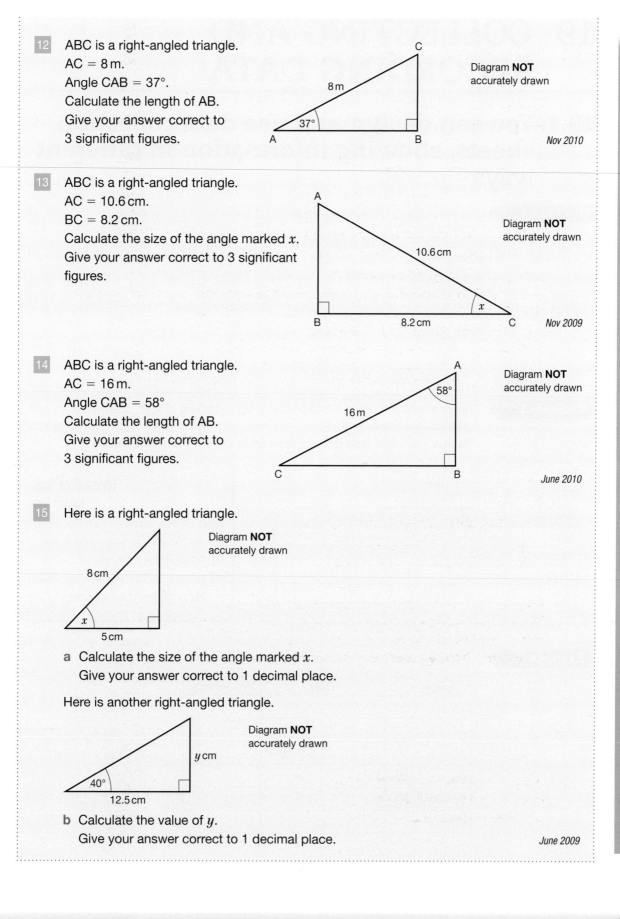

12 ABC is a right-angled triangle.
AC = 8 m.
Angle CAB = 37°.
Calculate the length of AB.
Give your answer correct to
3 significant figures.

Diagram **NOT** accurately drawn

8 m

37°

A   B

C

Nov 2010

13 ABC is a right-angled triangle.
AC = 10.6 cm.
BC = 8.2 cm.
Calculate the size of the angle marked x.
Give your answer correct to 3 significant
figures.

A

10.6 cm

Diagram **NOT** accurately drawn

B   8.2 cm   C

x

Nov 2009

14 ABC is a right-angled triangle.
AC = 16 m.
Angle CAB = 58°
Calculate the length of AB.
Give your answer correct to
3 significant figures.

A

58°

16 m

Diagram **NOT** accurately drawn

C   B

June 2010

15 Here is a right-angled triangle.

Diagram **NOT** accurately drawn

8 cm

x

5 cm

a Calculate the size of the angle marked x.
Give your answer correct to 1 decimal place.

Here is another right-angled triangle.

Diagram **NOT** accurately drawn

y cm

40°

12.5 cm

b Calculate the value of y.
Give your answer correct to 1 decimal place.

June 2009

19 COLLECTING AND RECORDING DATA

19.1 You can design and use data collection sheets, showing information in different ways

Key Points

- When collecting data by observation a data collection sheet is used.
- If data is numerical, and widely spread, you can group the data into class intervals. These class intervals do not have to be the same size.
- When dealing with continuous data you need to make sure the intervals do not overlap, i.e. ensure your class intervals use the $<$ and $\leqslant$ signs correctly.

  for example, the class interval for the variable w (weight) could be of the form:

  $500\,g \leqslant w < 550\,g$

  This means that w is greater than or equal to 500 g but less than 550 g.

Example 1

Katya wants to find information about the numbers of men, women, boys and girls using a sports hall.

Design a suitable data collection sheet to collect the information.

People	Tally	Frequency
Men		
Women		
Boys		
Girls		

ResultsPlus
Exam Tip

Three aspects are required in this answer.
(i) Tally heading or tally marks shown
(ii) Frequency or total column
(iii) Heading for the type of person or a list of the four required types

Example 2

The tally chart below shows the age at marriage of a sample of men.

Age, a	Tally	Frequency
$16 < a \leqslant 20$	||	
$20 < a \leqslant 30$	⦀⦀ ⦀⦀ |||	
$30 < a \leqslant 40$	⦀⦀ ⦀⦀ ⦀⦀ ⦀⦀ ⦀⦀	
$40 < a \leqslant 50$	⦀⦀ ||	
$50 < a \leqslant 60$	|||	
$60 < a$	|	

a Fill in the frequency column.
b Write down the most popular age range in which men get married.
c Work out how many men in total there were in the sample.

a

Age, a	Tally	Frequency
$16 < a \leqslant 20$	||	2
$20 < a \leqslant 30$	ЖЖ |||	13
$30 < a \leqslant 40$	ЖЖ ЖЖ ЖЖ	25
$40 < a \leqslant 50$	Ж ||	7
$50 < a \leqslant 60$	|||	3
$60 < a$			1

Add together the tallies:
5 + 5 + 3 = 13.

Look for the class with the highest frequency.

b $30 < a \leqslant 40$ **c** 51

Add together all of the frequencies:
2 + 13 + 25 + 7 + 3 + 1 = 51.

Exercise 19A

Questions in this chapter are targeted at the grades indicated.

1 A road traffic controller keeps a record of the types of vehicle using a busy junction during a two-minute rush-hour period. This data is listed below:

Car	Car	Bus	Car	Car	Car		HGV	Bike	Car	Car	Car	Bus
Bus	HGV	Car	Car	Car	Motorbike	Bike	Car	Car	Bus	Car	HGV
Bus	Car	Car	Car	Car	Bike		HGV	Car	Car	Car	Car	Bike

a Draw a tally chart to show this data.
b Write down the name of the least common type of vehicle.
c Write down the name of the most common type of vehicle.

2 Ouzma wants to find out the method of transport people use to travel to a shopping centre. Design a suitable data collection sheet she could use to collect this information.

3 A shopkeeper asks 30 people entering her shop how many DVDs they have bought in the last three months. The responses are shown below:

3	5	8	9	2	7	4	10	12	3
6	2	4	9	12	13	1	7	7	11
14	3	6	5	8	1	2	7	4	3

Draw and complete a data collection sheet showing this information.
Use equal class intervals starting with the class 0–3.

4 A gardener weighs 24 tomatoes produced from plants in his greenhouse.
The weights, in grams, are shown below:

60.5	65	64.5	59	67	61.5	67	69	58	59.3	57.2	67
68.5	63	64.2	69	57	57.8	62.4	65.5	67	58	70	75

Weight (w)	Tally	Frequency
$57 \leqslant w < 60$		
$60 \leqslant w < 63$		
$63 \leqslant w < 66$		
$66 \leqslant w < 69$		
$69 \leqslant w$		

a Copy and complete the data collection sheet for this data.
b Write down the most common class.   **c** Write down the least common class.

F

A02

D

19.2 You can design and criticise questions relating to questionnaires

⦿ A questionnaire is a list of questions designed to collect data. There are two types of question used in questionnaires.
   ⦾ An open question is one that has no suggested answers.
   ⦾ A closed question is one that has a set of answers to choose from, usually in the form of response boxes.
⦿ It is important that the information in the response boxes:
   ⦾ does not overlap
   ⦾ is exhaustive (i.e. covers all possible answers)
   ⦾ relates to the question.
⦿ A small, carefully chosen number of people can be used to represent the population being surveyed. These chosen individuals are called a sample and the investigation is called a sample survey.
⦿ The sample must be representative of all the people being investigated. If it isn't, it is biased.

Example 3   Here is an example of part of a well-designed questionnaire.

1. Tick one box to indicate your age group.

    ☐   ☐   ☐   ☐   ☐
    Under 21   21 to 30   31 to 40   41 to 50   Over 50

    > These are response boxes. The categories do not overlap.

2. How often have you visited the dentist in the last 4 years? Tick one box.

    ☐   ☐   ☐   ☐   ☐
    Never   1 or 2 times   3 or 4 times   5 or 6 times   More than 6 times

    > This allows for other answers.

3. Do you agree or disagree that people who visit a dentist regularly have fewer fillings in their teeth?

    ☐   ☐
    Agree   Disagree

    > 'Agree' or 'Disagree' makes the question unbiased.

    > These options are specific, unlike 'often' or 'sometimes' which are ambiguous.

Example 4   Anil wants to find out how many DVDs people buy.
He uses this question on a questionnaire.
'How many DVDs do you buy?'

    ☐   ☐   ☐   ☐
    1–5   5–10   10–15 15–20

Write down two things wrong with this question.

> **ResultsPlus**
> **Exam Tip**
> In an exam it is common to find that the question does not give a time frame.

Errors include:
The response boxes overlap, e.g. 1–5 and 5–10.
The response boxes are not exhaustive, e.g. no place for 0 or over 20.
There is no time period in which the DVDs are bought, e.g. each week or each month.

Exercise 19B

1 A local council wants to know whether or not the residents would like a new swimming pool in the town. It is decided to use a questionnaire. The following questions are suggested.

A: What do you think about the idea of a new pool being built?

B: Do you want a new pool?   Yes/No

C: Where should we build a new pool?

D: Is a pool a good idea?   Yes/No

Which of the above are open questions and which are closed?

2 The management of a theme park have made some changes to the amusements. They want to use a questionnaire to find out what people think about the changes. The following questions are suggested. Write down what is wrong with each of them and design a new question for each that is more suitable.

 a What do you think of the new amusements?

   Very good ☐   Good ☐   Satisfactory ☐

 b How much money would you normally expect to pay for each amusement?

   £5–£7 ☐   £7–£8 ☐   More than £8 ☐

 c How often do you visit the park each year?

   Often ☐   Not very often ☐

3 200 students in Year 11 took a mathematics test.

Kamini wants to find out whether students in Year 11 like mathematics.

For her sample she asks the 20 students who got the highest marks in the test.

This is **not** a good sample to use.

 a Write down **one** reason why.

She uses this question on her questionnaire.

'What do you think of mathematics?'

Excellent ☐   Very good ☐   Good ☐

 b Write down **one** thing that is wrong with this question.

4 Fred is going to take a survey of the magazines read by students.

He wants to design a questionnaire.

 a Design a suitable question that he could use to find out what types of magazine students read.

Fred put the question below on his questionnaire.

'How many magazines have you read?'

A few ☐   A lot ☐

 b Design a better question.

You should include some response boxes.

*****5** A supermarket manager wants to find out if people like the new layout. She decides to use a questionnaire. Write down a suitable question she could use.

19.3 You can design and use two-way tables

- Sometimes we collect two pieces of information, for example gender and eye-colour. To record this we would use a two-way table. A two-way table shows the frequency with which data falls into two different categories.

	Blue	Brown	Green	Total
Boys	6	14	5	25
Girls	4	16	5	25
Total	10	30	10	50

This is the number of boys with brown eyes.

This is the number of girls with brown eyes.

This the total number with brown eyes.

This is the total number of boys and girls.

- Sometimes a table is incomplete and has to be filled in before you can answer a question.

Example 5

Students in Year 11 were asked to choose their favourite drink from a choice of three. Below are the boys' and girls' responses.

Girls

Tea	Coffee	Coffee	Tea	Soft
Tea	Coffee	Tea	Coffee	Tea
Soft	Soft	Tea	Tea	Soft
Coffee	Coffee	Soft	Soft	Coffee

Boys

Coffee	Coffee	Tea	Soft	Tea
Tea	Tea	Soft	Coffee	Coffee
Soft	Tea	Tea	Coffee	Coffee
Soft	Tea	Coffee	Coffee	Coffee

a Show all of this information in a suitable table.

b Write down the drink that was chosen most by girls.

c Write down the drink that was chosen most by boys.

d Write down the drink that was chosen by most of the students.

a

	Tea	Coffee	Soft drink	Total
Boys	7	9	4	20
Girls	7	7	6	20
Total	14	16	10	40

The most suitable table is a two-way table. Count up the number of boys that chose tea and enter it here. Do the same for the other drinks and the girls' drinks.

Total the rows and columns.

b Tea and coffee. ← Look for the highest number in the girls' row.

c Coffee ← Look for the highest number in the boys' row.

d Coffee ← Look for the drink which has the highest total.

Example 6

The following two-way table gives information about people's hair and eye colour.

a Complete the table.

b Which eye colour was most frequent?

c Which eye colour was least frequent?

		Eye colour			
		Brown	Green	Blue	Total
Hair colour	Brown/Black	4	4		16
	Fair	3		4	
	Ginger		1	1	4
	Total	9	8		30

a

		Eye colour			
		Brown	Green	Blue	Total
Hair colour	Brown/ Black	4	4	8	16
	Fair	3	3	4	10
	Ginger	2	1	1	4
	Total	9	8	13	30

b Blue

c Green

ResultsPlus
Exam Tip

Look for rows with only one number missing and fill these in first. The numbers in each row must add up to the row total and the same goes for columns.

The number of people with blue eyes and black hair $= 16 - 4 - 4 = 8$

The number of people with brown eyes and ginger hair $= 4 - 1 - 1 = 2$

The number of people with green eyes and fair hair $= 8 - 4 - 1 = 3$

The total number of people with fair hair $= 3 + 3 + 4 = 10$

The total number of people with blue eyes $= 30 - 8 - 9 = 13$

Exercise 19C

1 A teacher is working out a timetable for Class 10B. Of the 30 students in class 10B:

seven want to do Art and Music

twelve want to do Drama and PE

five want to do Music and PE

six want to do Drama and Art.

	Music	Drama	Total
Art			
PE			
Total			30

Copy and complete the two-way table to show these data.

2 A number of men and women were asked which type of crisps they liked best. A total of twelve people said Plain, of which seven were men. Six women liked Salt and Vinegar. Fourteen men and twelve women liked Cheese and Onion. There were 28 men in total.

a Draw and complete a table of the data.

b How many people liked Salt and Vinegar crisps best?

c How many people were asked altogether?

3 In a supermarket survey 30 men and 30 women were asked whether they preferred orange juice or grapefruit juice. 22 men preferred orange juice. 12 women preferred grapefruit juice.

a Draw up a two-way table to show this information.

b How many people liked orange juice best?

4 A factory employs 12 supervisors, of which 2 are female; 14 office staff, of which 3 are male; and 120 shop floor workers, of which 38 are female.

a Work out the total number of female employees.

b Work out the total number of employees.

E

A02 C

A03

Exam review

Self-assessment checklist

I can:

- design and use data collection sheets [p.212]
- understand and use a tally [p.212]
- group data into class intervals [p.212]
- collect data by using a questionnaire [p.214]
- criticise questions for a questionnaire [p.214]
- design and use two-way tables [p.216]
- use information to complete a two-way table. [p.216]

Exam practice

D

1 James wants to find out how many text messages people send.
He uses this question on a questionnaire.

'How many text messages do you send?'

1 to 10 ☐   11 to 20 ☐   21 to 30 ☐   more than 30 ☐

a Write down **two** things wrong with this question.

James asks 10 students in his class to complete his questionnaire.

b Give **one** reason why this may not be a suitable sample. *March 2009*

2 Poppy wants to find out how much time people use their computer for.
She uses this questionnaire.

> For how much time do you use your computer?
>
> 0–1 hours ☐   3–4 hours ☐
>
> 1–2 hours ☐   4–5 hours ☐
>
> 2–3 hours ☐   5–6 hours ☐

a Write down **two** things that are wrong with this question.

Poppy gives her questionnaire to all the students in her class. Her sample is biased.

b Give **one** reason why. *Nov 2008*

C

A03

3 Naomi wants to find out how often adults go to the cinema.
She uses this question on a questionnaire.

> 'How many times do you go to the cinema?'
>
> ☐   ☐   ☐
>
> Not very often   Sometimes   A lot

a Write down **two** things wrong with this question.
b Design a better question for her questionnaire to find out how often adults go to the cinema. You should include some response boxes. *Nov 2008*

* 4 Valerie is the manager of a supermarket.
She wants to find out how often people shop at her supermarket.
She will use a questionnaire.
Design a suitable question for Valerie to use on her questionnaire.
You must include some response boxes.

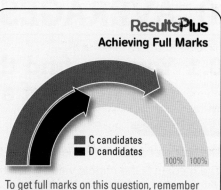

ResultsPlus
Achieving Full Marks

■ C candidates
■ D candidates
100% 100%

To get full marks on this question, remember to give a time period, such as number of times per month, and make sure that response boxes do not overlap. Only *one* box could be selected by anyone answering the question.

June 2008

* 5 Angela asked 20 people in which country they spent their last holiday.
Here are their answers.

France	Spain	Italy	England	Spain	England
France	Spain	Italy	France	England	Spain
Spain	Italy	Spain	France	England	Spain
France	Italy

Design **and** complete a suitable data collection sheet that Angela could have used to show this information.

March 2004

6 Write down, with reasons, whether or not each of the following is biased.

a A call centre manager wants to know how easy it is to use the staff reference sheets when answering a call. He asks all the people working on the night shift.

b A mobile phone company wants to find out what people think about their new pricing contract. The company randomly selects 10% to ask.

c A town council poses the question 'Do you agree that we are doing a good job in the area of recycling?'

7 120 children went on a school activities day. Some children went bowling.
Some children went to the cinema. The rest of the children went skating.
66 of these children were girls.
28 of the 66 girls went bowling.
36 children went to the cinema.
20 of the children who went to the cinema were girls.
15 boys went skating.
Work out the number of children who went bowling.

Hint: Display this information in a two-way table.

Nov 2010

8 80 children went on a school trip.
They went to London or to York.
23 boys and 19 girls went to London.
14 boys went to York.

	London	York	Total
Boys			
Girls			
Total			

a Use this information to complete the two-way table.
One of these 80 children is chosen at random.

b What is the probability that this child went to London?

March 2009

20 AVERAGES AND RANGE

20.1 You can find the mode, median, mean and range of a set of data

Key Points

- The mode of a set of data is the value that occurs most frequently.
- The median is the middle value when the data are ordered.
- If there are two middle values in a set of data, the median is halfway between them.
- The mean of a set of data is the sum of the values divided by the total number of values.

  $$\text{mean} = \frac{\text{sum of the values}}{\text{number of values}}$$

- The mean can be worked out using the statistical functions on a scientific calculator. The method for inputting the data will vary between different scientific calculators, and the instruction leaflet will explain how to enter and process the statistical data.
- The range of a set of data is the difference between the highest value and the lowest value. The range tells you how spread out the data are.

  Range = highest value − lowest value

Example 1

Find
a the mode b the median c the mean d the range of the numbers
2, 4, 6, 6, 8, 9, 8, 5 and 6.

a Mode = 6 ← 6 occurs three times, 8 occurs just two times and the other numbers appear only once.

b 2 4 5 6 6 6 8 8 9 ← Arrange the numbers in order, smallest to largest.

The median is 6 ← The middle value is 6. There are four numbers less than 6 and four numbers greater than 6.

c 2 + 4 + 6 + 6 + 8 + 9 + 8 + 5 + 6 = 54 ← Total up the values.

Mean = $\frac{54}{9}$ = 6 ← Divide by the number of values to get the mean.

d Range = 9 − 2 = 7 ← Subtract the lowest value from the highest value.

Example 2

The weekly consumptions of electricity, in units, during an 8-week period were 340, 350, 340, 355, 340, 345, 340 and 450 units.

Find a the mode b the median c the mean d the range.

a The mode is 340 units ← 340 occurs four times, each of the other values occurs once.

b 340 340 340 **340** **345** 350 355 450 ← There are two middle values: 340 and 345.

The median is 342.5 units. ← Halfway between is 342.5.

220

c The total of all values = 340 + 340 + 340 + 340 + 345 + 350
    + 355 + 450 = 2860 ← Find the total sum.

Mean = $\frac{2860}{8}$ = 357.5 units ← Divide by the number values.

d Range = 450 − 340 = 110 ← Find the difference between the largest and smallest values.

ResultsPlus
Watch Out!
Some students use the term average – make sure you specify mean, mode or median.

Exercise 20A

Questions in this chapter are targeted at the grades indicated.

1 During a football season a school team played 30 matches.
They scored the following numbers of goals in each game.

1	6	7	2	3	3	0	6	3	2
0	1	5	3	0	2	1	4	0	6
2	5	1	0	2	2	4	0	1	2

Find
a the mode   b the median   c the mean
d the range, of the number of goals scored.

2 The heights, in centimetres, of 11 members of a cricket team were

172   174   190   190   185   186   182   189   190   185   192

a Find the mode.   b Work out the median height.
c Work out the mean height.   d Find the range.

3 The numbers of emails received by a sample of six people during one week were

44   72   107   155   214   197

a Find the mode.   b Work out the median number of emails.
c Work out the mean number of emails.   d Find the range.

4 The number of school meals bought by 10 children in one week were

2   4   3   5   5   4   2   5   5   5

a Work out the mean number of meals.
The school has 250 children.
b Work out an estimate for the number of school meals they should provide each day.

A03

5 A restaurant records the number of diners it has every day for a week. The numbers are as follows.

28   40   28   38   110   170   33

a Write down the mode.
b Work out the median number of diners.
c Work out the mean number of diners.
d The manager wishes to sell the restaurant. What average is he likely to use when talking to prospective buyers? Give a reason for your answer.

Hint: Which average gives the best impression of the restaurant?

A03   D

20.2 You can construct and interpret a stem and leaf diagram

Key Points

⦿ A stem and leaf diagram makes it easy to find the mode, median and range of a set of data.
⦿ A stem and leaf diagram should always have a key.
⦿ From a stem and leaf diagram, you can find statistics about the data.
  The lower quartile (LQ) is the value of a quarter of the way through the data, the median is halfway through the data, and the upper quartile (UQ) is three-quarters of the way through the data.
⦿ The interquartile range (IQR) is the difference between the upper and lower quartiles.
  IQR = UQ − LQ

Example 3

Here are the times, in minutes, taken by 15 people to complete a crossword puzzle:
20, 35, 40, 42, 32, 15, 22, 30, 28, 34, 40, 43, 28, 41, 25
  a Write these data as an ordered stem and leaf diagram.
  b Write down the mode of these data.
  c Find the median of these data.
  d Work out the range of these data.
  e Find the lower and upper quartiles and interquartile range.

a

Stem	Leaf				
1	5				
2	0	2	8	8	5
3	5	2	0	4	
4	0	2	0	3	1

Key 1|5 stands for 15

1	5				
2	0	2	5	8	8
3	0	2	4	5	
4	0	0	1	2	3

Key 1|5 stands for 15

> The digit that each number begins with is called the stem.

> The following digit is called the leaf.

> Under stem, write the numbers 1 to 4.

> Opposite each stem, write the leaves. Don't worry about the order. This gives you an unordered stem and leaf diagram.

> Write the numbers in each leaf in order from smallest to largest.

ResultsPlus
Exam Tip
The key is worth **1 mark**.

  b There are two modes: 28 and 40. ◄──── Each appears twice, the others only once.

  c The median is 32. ◄──── 32 is the middle value (8th value of 15).

  d The range is 43 − 15 = 28 ◄──── The range is the difference between the largest and smallest values.
  The largest value is the last number in the last leaf. The smallest value is the first number in the first leaf.

  e LQ = 25   UQ = 40
   IQR = 40 − 25 = 15

> LQ = $\frac{16}{4}$th value = 4th value
>
> UQ = 3 × $\frac{16}{4}$th value = 12th value
> You can find the values by counting in from each end.

C

1. Nassim records the number of emails he receives every day for 35 days.
The data he collects are shown in the stem and leaf diagram.

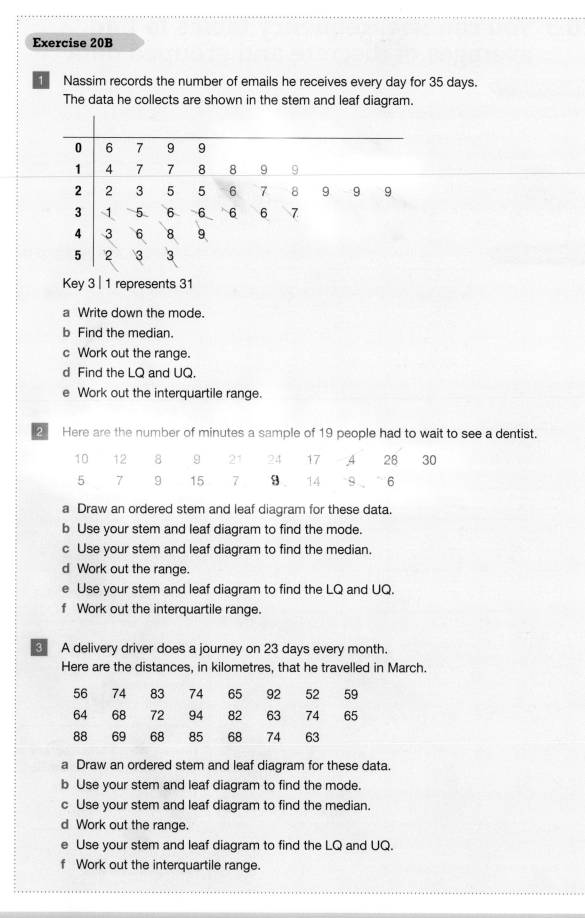

0	6	7	9	9					
1	4	7	7	8	8	9	9		
2	2	3	5	5	6	7	8	9	9	9
3	1	5	6	6	6	6	7		
4	3	6	8	9					
5	2	3	3						

Key 3 | 1 represents 31

a Write down the mode.

b Find the median.

c Work out the range.

d Find the LQ and UQ.

e Work out the interquartile range.

2. Here are the number of minutes a sample of 19 people had to wait to see a dentist.

10	12	8	9	21	24	17	4	28	30
5	7	9	15	7	9	14	9	6	

a Draw an ordered stem and leaf diagram for these data.

b Use your stem and leaf diagram to find the mode.

c Use your stem and leaf diagram to find the median.

d Work out the range.

e Use your stem and leaf diagram to find the LQ and UQ.

f Work out the interquartile range.

3. A delivery driver does a journey on 23 days every month.
Here are the distances, in kilometres, that he travelled in March.

56	74	83	74	65	92	52	59
64	68	72	94	82	63	74	65
88	69	68	85	68	74	63	

a Draw an ordered stem and leaf diagram for these data.

b Use your stem and leaf diagram to find the mode.

c Use your stem and leaf diagram to find the median.

d Work out the range.

e Use your stem and leaf diagram to find the LQ and UQ.

f Work out the interquartile range.

20.3 You can use frequency tables to find averages of discrete and grouped data

Key Points

- For discrete data in a frequency table:

  mean $= \dfrac{\sum f \times x}{\sum f}$ where f is the frequency, x is the variable and $\sum$ means 'the sum of'.

- For grouped data you do not know the exact data in each class interval, you cannot give an exact value for the mode or the median and can only estimate the mean value.
- The class interval with the highest frequency is called the modal class.
- You can only write down the class interval in which the median falls.

Example 4   The table shows information about the number of children in a sample of families.

Number of children in family	1	2	3	4	5
Frequency	3	11	9	5	6

a Write down the mode.

b Find the median.

c Work out the mean.

a The mode is 2 children. ← 2 has the highest frequency, which is 11.

b

Number of children in family x	Frequency f	Frequency × number of children $f \times x$
1	3	3
2	11	22
3	9	27
4	5	20
5	6	30
Total	34	102

There are 11 families with 2 children in each so the number of children is $11 \times 2 = 22$ children.

The total number of families is 34 $(= \Sigma f)$.

The total number of children is the sum of all the $f \times x$ values $(\Sigma f \times x)$.

The total frequency is 34 so the median will be between the 17th and 18th values. ← There will be 16 values either side.

There are 3 families with 1 child in them.

3 lies between the 14th and 23rd values.

There are $3 + 11 = 14$ families with 2 or 1 children.

There are $3 + 11 + 9 = 23$ families with 3, 2 or 1 children.

The 17th and 18th values must both be 3.

The median is 3.

ResultsPlus
Exam Tip

Divide by total frequency **not** number of intervals.

c The mean is $\dfrac{102}{34} = 3$ children. ←

Mean $= \dfrac{\text{Total number of children}}{\text{Total number of families}} = \dfrac{\Sigma f \times x}{\Sigma f}$

Example 5

The frequency table gives information about the number of letters, l, in a sample of people's surnames.

    a Find the modal class.

    b Find the class into which the median falls.

Class interval	Frequency
3 to 5	1
6 to 8	3
9 to 11	5
12 to 14	4
15 to 17	2

a The modal class is 9 to 11. ←

b There are 15 names in total so the median will be the 8th value.
There are $3 + 1 = 4$ names that are less than 9 letters long
and $5 + 3 + 1 = 9$ names that are less than 12 letters long,
so the median is in the class interval 9–11.

Look for the class with the highest frequency.

Exercise 20C

1 A council wanted to provide extra parking on an estate.

They asked a sample of households how many cars they had.

The results are shown in the frequency table.

    a Write down the mode.

    b Find the median number of cars.

    c Work out the mean number of cars.

    d Recommend the number of extra parking places they should provide.
       You must explain your answer.

Number of cars	Frequency
0	0
1	10
2	7
3	6
4	2

2 A sample of a tomato crop was taken and each tomato was weighed.

The weights to the nearest 5 g are shown in the frequency table.

    a Write down the mode of these data.

    b Find the median weight of the tomatoes.

    c Work out the mean weight of the tomatoes.

Weight of tomatoes	Frequency
55	2
60	5
65	10
70	6
75	2

3 A group of students were asked how many times they visited a library in a term. The results are shown in the frequency table.

Class interval	0 to 2	3 to 5	6 to 8	9 to 11
Frequency	0	6	10	6

Hint: This is discrete data.

    a Write down the modal class.

    b Find the class into which the median falls.

4 The frequency table gives the diameter, d in mm, of 48 balls of lead used in a quality control investigation.

    a Write down the modal class.

    b Find the class into which the median falls.

Hint: This is continuous data.

Class interval	Frequency
$0.7 \leqslant d < 0.9$	2
$0.9 \leqslant d < 1.1$	4
$1.1 \leqslant d < 1.3$	16
$1.3 \leqslant d < 1.5$	12
$1.5 \leqslant d < 1.7$	14

20.4 You can estimate the mean of grouped data

Key Point

◉ An estimate for the mean of grouped data can be found by using the midpoint of the class interval

and the formula $\dfrac{\sum fx}{\sum f}$ where f is the frequency and x is the class midpoint.

Example 6   Work out an estimate for the mean length (number of letters) of the people's surnames given in Example 5.

Class interval	Frequency f	Class midpoint x	$f \times x$
3 to 5	1	4	4
6 to 8	3	7	21
9 to 11	5	10	50
12 to 14	4	13	52
15 to 17	2	16	32
Totals	15		159

ResultsPlus
Exam Tip

Remember to use the class midpoint when estimating the average.

The middle value of the class 3–5 is 4.

The middle value of the class 6–8 is 7. The three people in the class 6–8 might not all have surnames 7 letters long. This is why it is an estimated mean.

$$\text{Estimated mean} = \frac{\sum f \times x}{\sum f} = \frac{159}{15} = 10.6$$

You can now use the formula.

Exercise 20D

1 A store is worried about the reliability of its lift. It records the number of times it breaks down each week over a period of 28 weeks.
The results are shown in the frequency table.
Find an estimate for the mean number of breakdowns.

Class interval	Frequency f
0 to 1	20
2 to 3	3
4 to 5	4
6 to 7	1

2 Emma recorded the length of time (t), in minutes, each of her business phone calls took over a period of one month.
The results are shown in the frequency table.
Find an estimate for the mean time for her business phone calls.

Hint: Find the class midpoints for continuous data in the same way as for grouped discrete data.

Class interval	Frequency
$0 \leqslant t < 5$	9
$5 \leqslant t < 10$	10
$10 \leqslant t < 15$	9
$15 \leqslant t < 20$	7
$20 \leqslant t < 25$	5

3 The following group frequency table shows the ages of members of an aerobics class.

Age range (years)	16–25	26–35	36–45	46–55	56–65	66–75
Frequency	4	10	12	4	8	2

Work out an estimate for the mean age of the members.

Exam review

Self-assessment checklist

I can:
- find the mode, median, mean and range of a set of data [p.220]
- construct and interpret a stem and leaf diagram [p.222]
- use frequency tables to find averages of discrete and continuous data [p.224]
- estimate the mean from grouped data. [p.226]

Exam practice

1 Peter rolled a 6-sided dice ten times.
Here are his scores.

3   2   4   6   3   3   4   2   5   4

  a Work out the median of his scores.
  b Work out the mean of his scores.
  c Work out the range of his scores.

> *Hint:* The median is the middle value when written in order.

> *Hint:* The mean is the sum of the values divided by the number of values.

> *Hint:* The range = highest value − lowest value

June 2007

2 Here are the weights, in kg, of 8 people.

63   65   65   70   72   86   90   97

  a Write down the mode of the 8 weights.   b Work out the range of the weights.   *June 2007*

3 Jason collected some information about the heights of 19 plants.
This information is shown in the stem and leaf diagram.

```
1 | 1  2  3  4
2 | 3  3  5  9  9            Key:
3 | 0  2  2  6  6  7         4|8 means 48 mm
4 | 1  1  4  8
```

Find the median. *Nov 2008*

4 Five positive numbers have a mode of 5, a median of 5 and a mean of 4.
Write down as many possible combinations of five numbers that give these statistics as you can.

5 The stem and leaf diagram shows the ages, in years, of all the workers in a small factory.

```
2 | 0  2  2  5  7
3 | 3  4  4  4  4  5              Key:
4 | 5  6  6  6  6  8  9  9  9     4|5 represents 45 years
5 | 2  4  4  6  7  9
6 | 0  2  5
```

  a Work out the number of workers.
  b Write down the mode.
  c Find the median.
  d Work out the range.

> *Hint:* Remember the numbers in the stem represent 20, 30, 40, 50 and 60.

6 A group of girls went to a college dance. They each bought a new dress.
The costs of the dresses were

£22   £22   £22   £28   £32   £36   £40   £40   £45   £180

  a Write down the mode.

  b Find the median price.

  c Work out the mean price.

  d Which of the three averages worked out in parts **a**, **b** and **c** best describes the
price the girls paid? Give a reason for your answer.

7 Samples of apples were taken from two trees. One was an eating apple tree and
the other was a cooking apple tree.
The weights, in grams, of the apples were

Eating apple	135	135	140	138	142	150	132
Cooking apple	140	136	150	160	138	162	150

> **Hint:** Compare the median and means, and compare the ranges.

  a Find the means and ranges for these data.

  b Compare the frequency distributions of the weights of
the two types of apple.

8 Zoe recorded the weights, in kilograms, of 15 people.
Here are her results.

87   51   46   77   74   58   68   78
48   63   52   64   79   60   66

  a Copy and complete the ordered stem and
leaf diagram to show these results.

  b Write down the number of people with a
weight of more than 70 kg.

  c Work out the range of the weights.

4	
5	
6	
7	
8	

March 2009

9 Zoe recorded the heart rate of each of 15 people.
She showed her results in a stem and leaf diagram.

```
5 | 8  9
6 | 0  1  4  6  6  7        Key:
7 | 2  3  6  8  9           5|8 means 58 beats per minute
8 | 1  4
```

  a Find the median heart rate.

  b Work out the range of the heart rates.

Zoe then asked the 15 people to walk up some stairs.
Zoe recorded the heart rates again.
She used the results to work out the median and the range.

Median	78
Range	37

  c Compare the heart rates of the people before they walked up the stairs with
their heart rates after they walked up the stairs.

Nov 2010

10 Zach has 10 CDs.
The table gives some information about
the number of tracks on each CD.
a Write down the mode.
b Work out the mean.

Number of tracks	Frequency	
11	1	
12	3	
13	0	
14	2	
15	4	

June 2009

11 Here are the ages, in years, of 15 teachers.

| *Hint:* Draw an **un**ordered stem and leaf diagram first. |

35 52 42 27 36
23 31 41 50 34
44 28 45 45 53

Draw an ordered stem and leaf diagram to show this information.
You must include a key. *May 2008 adapted*

12 Ali found out the number of rooms in each of 40 houses in a town.
He used the information to complete the frequency table.

Number of rooms x	Frequency f	
4	4	
5	7	
6	10	
7	12	
8	5	
9	2	

Hint: Work out frequency (f) × number of rooms (x) in the blank column.

Ali said that the mode is 9. Ali is wrong.
a Explain why.
b Calculate the mean number of rooms. *Nov 2007*

13 A group of university students did a maths test. The table shows their scores.

Males	42	22	65	42	70	50	45
Females	25	90	55	26	95	50	87

Using your understanding of averages and range, compare the males' and the females' scores.

*14 Class 5A take six maths tests every year, each one out of 100. Meena has a mean score of 64 marks per test for the first five tests of the year. Her parents have promised her a bicycle if she can achieve a mean score of 70.
What mark would she have to get in the sixth test to achieve this mean score?

D

A03

A03

* **15** A small factory pays salaries to 8 workers, a manager and an owner.
The salaries they earn are shown in the table.

	Salary
Workers	£10 000
Manager	£40 000
Owner	£180 000

Depending on the average you use, the average wage of people in the factory is vastly different.
If you were negotiating for a higher salary for the workers, which average would you use?
If you were negotiating for the management to keep the salaries low, which average would you use?
Explain your answers.

16 Here are the amounts in £, spent by some shoppers at a supermarket.

37	56	23	40	38	56
31	48	25	49	32	46

Draw an ordered stem and leaf diagram for these amounts.
You must include a key.

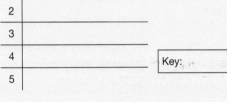

Key:

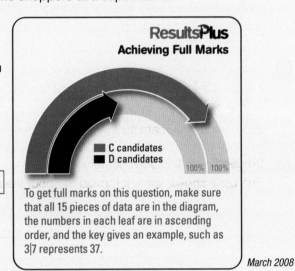

ResultsPlus
Achieving Full Marks

■ C candidates
■ D candidates   100% 100%

To get full marks on this question, make sure that all 15 pieces of data are in the diagram, the numbers in each leaf are in ascending order, and the key gives an example, such as 3|7 represents 37.

March 2008

17 The hourly wages, in pounds, of the employees in a factory were recorded.
The results are shown in the frequency table.

Hourly wage £s	7 to 9	10 to 12	13 to 15	16 to 18	19 to 21
Frequency	5	20	20	10	5

Hint: Use the mid-interval values.

a Write down the modal class of these data.
b Find the class interval that contains the median hourly wage.
c Estimate the mean hourly wage.

18 Oliver measured the heights (h), in cm, of the leek plants in his garden.
Here are his results.

a Write down the modal class.
b Find the class into which the median height falls.
c Work out an estimate for the mean height of the leeks.

Class interval	Frequency
$25 \leqslant h < 27$	5
$27 \leqslant h < 29$	10
$29 \leqslant h < 31$	13
$31 \leqslant h < 33$	15
$33 \leqslant h < 35$	7

19 Josh asked 30 students how many minutes they each took to get to school.
The table shows some information about his results.

Time (t minutes)	Frequency
$0 < t \leqslant 10$	6
$10 < t \leqslant 20$	11
$20 < t \leqslant 30$	8
$30 < t \leqslant 40$	5

Work out an estimate for the mean number of minutes taken by the 30 students. *Nov 2008*

20 Vanessa made 80 phone calls last month.
The table gives information about the length of the calls.

Length of call (t minutes)	Frequency	
$0 < t \leqslant 10$	20	
$10 < t \leqslant 20$	32	
$20 < t \leqslant 30$	14	
$30 < t \leqslant 40$	9	
$40 < t \leqslant 50$	5	

Work out an estimate for the mean length of the calls. *March 2008*

21 80 people work in Joe's factory.
The table shows some information about the annual pay of these 80 workers.

Annual pay (£x)	Number of workers
$10\,000 < x \leqslant 14\,000$	32
$14\,000 < x \leqslant 16\,000$	24
$16\,000 < x \leqslant 18\,000$	16
$18\,000 < x \leqslant 20\,000$	6
$20\,000 < x \leqslant 40\,000$	2

a Write down the modal class interval.
b Find the class interval that contains the median. *June 2007*

22 The table shows some information about the weights, in grams, of 60 eggs.

Weight (w grams)	Frequency
$0 < w \leqslant 30$	0
$30 < w \leqslant 50$	14
$50 < w \leqslant 60$	16
$60 < w \leqslant 70$	21
$70 < w \leqslant 100$	9

Calculate an estimate for the mean weight of an egg. *March 2011*

21 PROCESSING, REPRESENTING AND INTERPRETING DATA

21.1 You can construct pie charts

Key Points

- A pie chart is a circle that is divided into sectors and shows how the total is split up between the different categories.
- In a pie chart the area of the whole circle represents the total number of items.
- The area of each sector represents the number of items in that category.
- The angles at the centre of a pie chart must add up to 360°.
- The angle for a particular sector is found by either:
  - working out the angle for one unit and then multiplying it by the frequency, or
  - using the formula: sector angle $= \dfrac{\text{frequency} \times 360°}{\text{total frequency}}$

Example 1

The table shows the favourite colours of a sample of 30 students.

Colour	Blue	Red	Green	Black
Frequency	10	15	3	2

Draw a pie chart to represent this information.

First calculate the angles.
There are two ways of doing this.

Method 1

$360 \div 30 = 12$

$12°$ represents 1 student.

Blue	$10 \times 12° = 120°$
Red	$15 \times 12 = 180°$
Green	$3 \times 12 = 36°$
Black	$2 \times 12 = 24°$

Method 2

Blue	$\frac{10}{30} \times 360° = 120°$
Red	$\frac{15}{30} \times 360° = 180°$
Green	$\frac{3}{30} \times 360° = 36°$
Black	$\frac{2}{30} \times 360° = 24°$

Now use this information to construct your pie chart.

> **ResultsPlus**
> **Exam Tip**
>
> Make sure the angles in a pie chart add up to 360°.

There are 360° in a full circle.
There are 30 students.

10 students will need $10 \times 12° = 120°$.

The angle for each of the other colours is found by multiplying its frequency by 12°.

10 out of 30 students chose blue so $\frac{10}{30}$ of the whole circle is needed to represent blue. $\frac{10}{30}$ of 360° = 120°.

The angles for the other colours can be found in the same way.

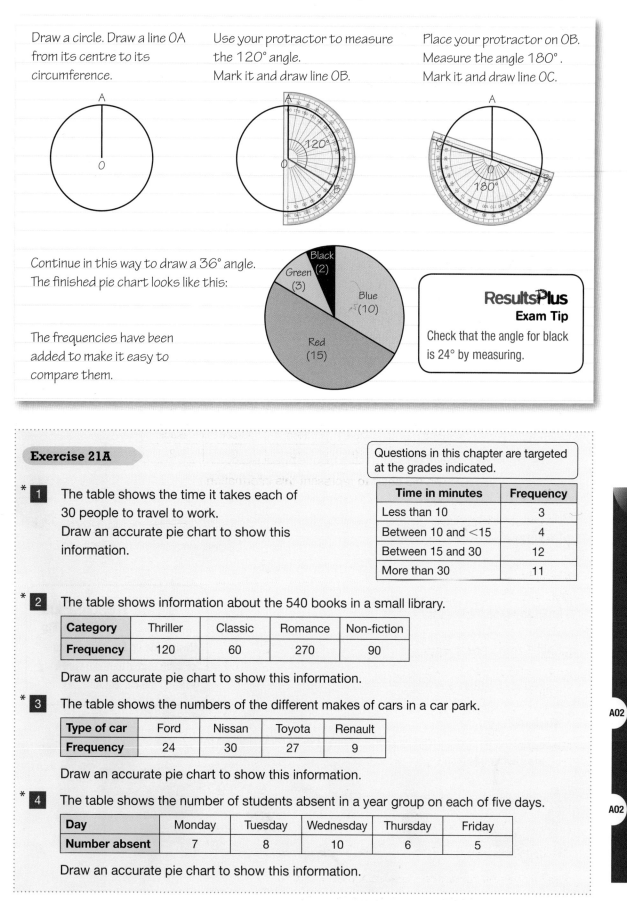

Draw a circle. Draw a line OA from its centre to its circumference.

Use your protractor to measure the 120° angle. Mark it and draw line OB.

Place your protractor on OB. Measure the angle 180°. Mark it and draw line OC.

Continue in this way to draw a 36° angle. The finished pie chart looks like this:

The frequencies have been added to make it easy to compare them.

Black (2)
Green (3)
Blue (10)
Red (15)

ResultsPlus
Exam Tip

Check that the angle for black is 24° by measuring.

Exercise 21A

Questions in this chapter are targeted at the grades indicated.

* **1** The table shows the time it takes each of 30 people to travel to work.
Draw an accurate pie chart to show this information.

Time in minutes	Frequency
Less than 10	3
Between 10 and <15	4
Between 15 and 30	12
More than 30	11

* **2** The table shows information about the 540 books in a small library.

Category	Thriller	Classic	Romance	Non-fiction
Frequency	120	60	270	90

Draw an accurate pie chart to show this information.

* **3** The table shows the numbers of the different makes of cars in a car park.

Type of car	Ford	Nissan	Toyota	Renault
Frequency	24	30	27	9

Draw an accurate pie chart to show this information.

* **4** The table shows the number of students absent in a year group on each of five days.

Day	Monday	Tuesday	Wednesday	Thursday	Friday
Number absent	7	8	10	6	5

Draw an accurate pie chart to show this information.

D

A02

A02

21.2 You can interpret pie charts

Key Points

- To read frequencies from a pie chart use the formula:

$$\text{frequency} = \frac{\text{sector angle} \times \text{total frequency}}{360°}$$

- The frequency represented by corresponding sectors of two pie charts might have the same sector angle but the frequency they represent depends on the total frequency.

Example 2

The pie chart shows the numbers of each type of pet seen in a vet's surgery one morning. There were 20 pets altogether.

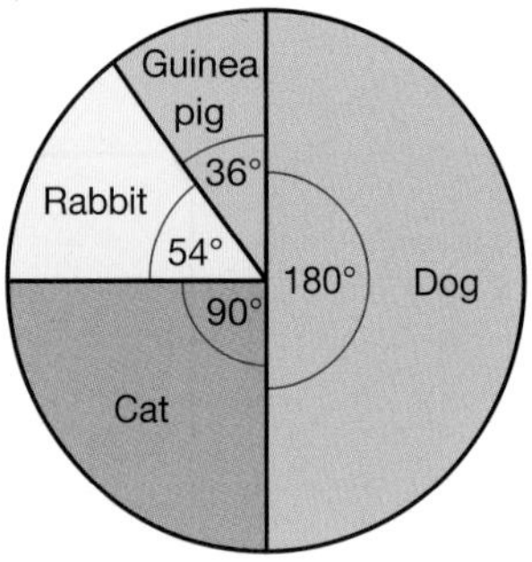

    a Which type of pet was most common?
    b Work out the number of each type of pet.

ResultsPlus
Exam Tip

In an exam 'work out' means calculate, do not just measure the angle.

---

a Dog is the most common pet.   This has the largest sector.

b Method 1

$$\text{Dog frequency} = \frac{\text{sector angle} \times \text{total frequency}}{360°}$$

$\dfrac{\text{sector angle}}{360°}$ is the fraction of the total frequency taken up by each sector.

$$= \frac{180° \times 20}{360°} = 10$$

$$\text{Cat frequency} = \frac{90° \times 20}{360°} = 5$$

$$\text{Rabbit frequency} = \frac{54° \times 20}{360°} = 3$$

$$\text{Guinea pig frequency} = \frac{36° \times 20}{360°} = 2$$

ResultsPlus
Exam Tip

Always add up the frequencies for each sector to make sure they give you the correct total.

Method 2

If 20 pets are represented by 360°, then 1 pet is represented by $\frac{360}{20} = 18°$.
Divide each angle by 18°.

$$\text{Dog frequency} = \frac{180°}{18°} = 10 \qquad \text{Cat frequency} = \frac{90°}{18°} = 5$$

$$\text{Rabbit frequency} = \frac{54°}{18°} = 3 \qquad \text{Guinea pig frequency} = \frac{36°}{18°} = 2$$

Exercise 21B

1   The pie chart shows the holiday destinations of 90 girls.
    a Which destination is the most popular?
    b How many degrees represent one person on the pie chart?
    c How many girls said Great Britain was their holiday
       destination?
    d What angle represents Greece on the pie chart?
    e How many girls said Greece was their holiday
       destination?

Holiday destinations

2   The pie chart shows information about how Letitia spends
    her time in one 24-hour day.
    Copy and complete the table. You will need to measure
    the angles in the pie chart.

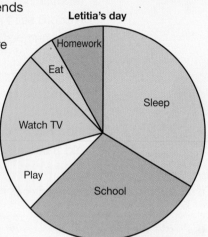

Letitia's day

Activity	Angle (degrees)	Number of hours
Sleep		
School		
Play		
Watch TV		
Eat		
Homework		

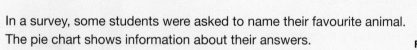

3   In a survey, some adults were asked to name their favourite
    ice cream flavour. The results are shown in the pie chart.
    30 adults said that mint was their favourite ice cream flavour.
    a How many degrees represent one person in the pie chart?
    b How many adults took part in the survey?
    A corner shop wishes to stock 2 varieties of ice cream.
    c Suggest, with reasons, what they should stock.

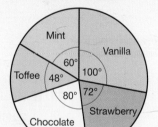

Favourite ice cream

4   In a survey, some students were asked to name their favourite animal.
    The pie chart shows information about their answers.
    a Write down the fraction of the students who answered horse.
       Write your fraction in its simplest form.
    12 students answered horse.
    b Work out the number of students that took part in the survey.

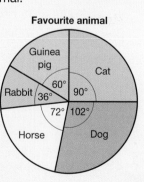

Favourite animal

21.3 You can construct and interpret dual and composite bar charts

Key Points

◉ Comparative or dual bar charts can be drawn to compare data. In a comparative bar chart:
  ◉ two (or more) bars are drawn side by side for each category
  ◉ the bars can be horizontal or vertical
  ◉ the heights of the bars can be compared category by category.
◉ A composite bar chart shows the size of individual categories split into their separate parts.

Example 3

The dual bar chart shows the number of houses sold by two agents in four months.

a In which month did A and B sell the same number of houses?

b Which agent sold the most houses in June?

c How many houses did B sell in April?

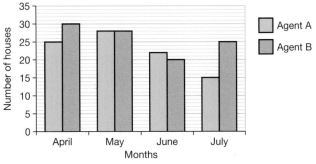

a A and B sold the same number of houses in May. ◄ — The bars are the same height for May.

b A sold more houses in June. ◄ — A's bar is higher than B's.

c B sold 30 houses in April. ◄ — Use the key to identify B's colour. Find the month April and read off B's sales from the left-hand scale.

Example 4

The composite bar chart shows the types of land use on three different farms.

a How many hectares of pasture are there on farm B?

b Which farm had the greatest amount of pasture land?

c How many hectares of land did farm B have altogether?

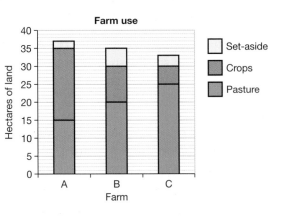

a 20 hectares ◄ — Identify the bar for farm B and use the colour key to find out which is pasture land. Read off from scale.

b Farm C ◄ — The highest bar for pasture was farm C (25 hectares).

c 35 hectares ◄ — Read off the total height of the bar for farm B.

236

Exercise 21C

1   The dual bar chart shows the temperature in a number of resorts in April and October.

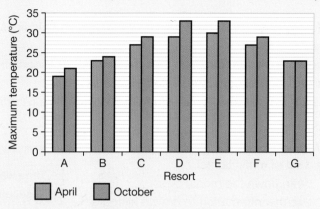

April   October

a   Write down the maximum temperature in April.

b   Write down the maximum temperature in October.

c   Write down the resort that had the same maximum temperature in both months.

d   Write down the resorts in which the maximum temperature in October was 29°C.

e   Write down the resort in which the maximum temperature in April was 19°C.

2   The composite bar charts show the make-up of 100 grams of each of two cereals: Wheatees and Fruitbix.

a   How many grams of carbohydrate are there in 100 g of Wheatees?

b   Estimate the number of grams of fat in 100 g of Fruitbix.

c   Write down the name of the cereal that has more fibre.

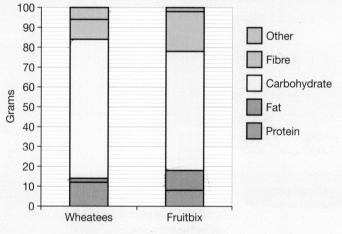

3   Market days in Ulvston are on Thursday and Saturday.

Mattie runs a market stall that sells jumpers on each of these days. The composite bar chart shows his sales in one week in November.

a   On which day were most jumpers sold overall?

b   On which day were most green jumpers sold?

c   How many red jumpers were sold on Saturday?

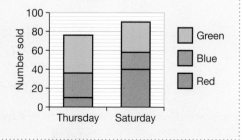

21.4 You can construct and interpret frequency polygons

Key Points

◉ When drawing a frequency polygon for discrete data, you draw straight lines to connect the tops of the lines on a vertical line chart.

◉ When drawing a frequency polygon for continuous data, mark the midpoints of the class intervals and join these with a straight line.

◉ Frequency polygons can be used to compare the frequency distributions of two (or more) sets of data.

Example 5

The frequency table gives information about the time waited, in seconds, at a set of traffic lights.

a Write down the modal class.

b Use the information to draw a histogram.

c Draw a frequency polygon to represent the information.

Time waited (t seconds)	Frequency
$90 \leqslant t < 95$	6
$95 \leqslant t < 100$	6
$100 \leqslant t < 105$	7
$105 \leqslant t < 110$	4
$110 \leqslant t < 115$	5
$115 \leqslant t < 120$	2

a The modal class is $100 \leqslant t < 105$.

b, c

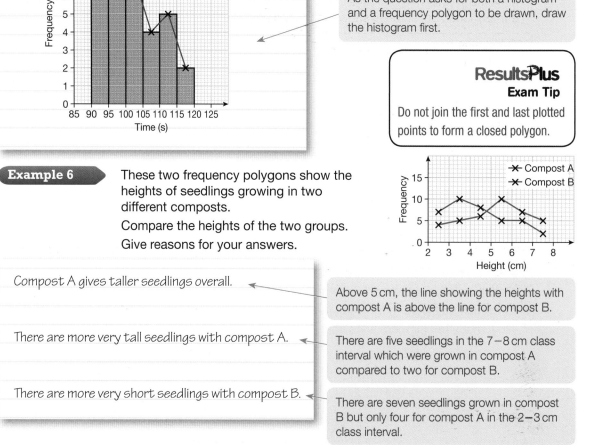

As the question asks for both a histogram and a frequency polygon to be drawn, draw the histogram first.

ResultsPlus
Exam Tip

Do not join the first and last plotted points to form a closed polygon.

Example 6

These two frequency polygons show the heights of seedlings growing in two different composts.

Compare the heights of the two groups.

Give reasons for your answers.

Compost A gives taller seedlings overall. ← Above 5 cm, the line showing the heights with compost A is above the line for compost B.

There are more very tall seedlings with compost A. ← There are five seedlings in the 7–8 cm class interval which were grown in compost A compared to two for compost B.

There are more very short seedlings with compost B. ← There are seven seedlings grown in compost B but only four for compost A in the 2–3 cm class interval.

Exercise 21D

1   A seed producer wants to know the numbers of peas in pods of a new variety of peas.
    He records the number of peas in 60 pods. The table shows this information.

Number of peas	3	4	5	6	7	8
Frequency	2	4	7	10	22	15

Draw a frequency polygon for these data.

2   The noise levels at 40 locations near an airport were measured in decibels.
    The data collected are shown in the grouped frequency table.

Noise level (d decibels)	$60 \leqslant d < 70$	$70 \leqslant d < 80$	$80 \leqslant d < 90$	$90 \leqslant d < 100$
Frequency	15	16	7	2

a   Write down the modal class.

b   Use the information in the table to draw a histogram.

c   Use your answer to part **b** to draw a frequency polygon.

3   In a fishing competition the lengths, in centimetres, of all the trout caught were measured.
    The information collected is shown in the table.

Trout length (l cm)	Frequency
$24 \leqslant l < 25$	4
$25 \leqslant l < 26$	14
$26 \leqslant l < 27$	6
$27 \leqslant l < 28$	10
$28 \leqslant l < 29$	6

Draw a frequency polygon for these data.

4   The two frequency polygons show the amount of time it took a group of boys and a group
    of girls to do a crossword puzzle.
    Who were better at doing the puzzle, boys or girls?
    Give a reason for your answer.

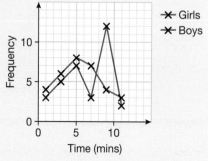

C

21.5 You can construct and interpret histograms with unequal class intervals

Key Points

⦿ In histograms, when there are unequal class intervals, you adjust the height of a bar by using a scale of frequency density rather than width, where:

$$\text{frequency density} = \frac{\text{frequency}}{\text{class width}}$$

or frequency = frequency density × class width.

⦿ The area of each bar gives its frequency.

Example 7

The table gives information about the times taken, in seconds, by a number of students to complete a puzzle.

Time taken (t seconds)	Frequency
$10 < t \leqslant 30$	10
$30 < t \leqslant 35$	5
$35 < t \leqslant 40$	10
$40 < t \leqslant 50$	30
$50 < t \leqslant 70$	30

Draw a histogram to show this data.

Time taken (t seconds)	Frequency	Class width	Frequency density $=\frac{\text{frequency}}{\text{class width}}$
$10 < t \leqslant 30$	10	20	$\frac{10}{20} = 0.5$
$30 < t \leqslant 35$	5	5	$\frac{5}{5} = 1.0$
$35 < t \leqslant 40$	10	5	$\frac{10}{5} = 2.0$
$40 < t \leqslant 50$	30	10	$\frac{30}{10} = 3.0$
$50 < t \leqslant 70$	30	20	$\frac{30}{20} = 1.5$

Work out the width of each class interval (the class width). Divide the frequency by the class width to find the frequency density which gives the height of each bar.

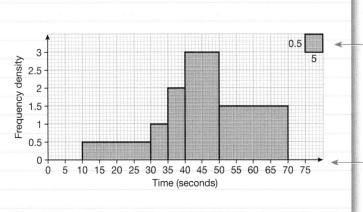

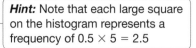

Hint: Note that each large square on the histogram represents a frequency of 0.5 × 5 = 2.5

On a grid label the horizontal axis 'Time (seconds)' and the vertical axis 'Frequency density'. Scale the horizontal axis from 0 to 75 and the vertical axis from 0 to 3. Draw the bars with no gaps between them. The first bar goes from 10 to 30 and has a height of 0.5.

Exercise 21E

1 The histogram gives information about the weight, in kg, of some rocks.

Weight (w kg)	Frequency
$0 < w \leqslant 20$	
$20 < w \leqslant 30$	80
$30 < w \leqslant 40$	
$40 < w \leqslant 50$	
$50 < w \leqslant 70$	

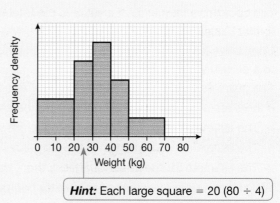

Copy and complete the frequency table.

Hint: Each large square = 20 (80 ÷ 4)

2 The table gives information about the lifetime of a certain make of torch battery.

Lifetime (l hours)	Frequency	Class width	Frequency density
$10 \leqslant l < 15$	4		
$15 \leqslant l < 20$	10		
$20 \leqslant l < 25$	20		
$25 \leqslant l < 30$	15		
$30 \leqslant l < 40$	6		

a Copy and complete the table.
b Draw a histogram for these data.

3 The table gives information about the distances a group of workers have to travel to work.

Distance (d kilometres)	Frequency
$0 < d \leqslant 5$	8
$5 < d \leqslant 10$	16
$10 < d \leqslant 20$	30
$20 < d \leqslant 30$	20
$30 < d \leqslant 40$	6

Draw a histogram for these data and find an estimate of the number of workers who travel between 15 and 25 minutes.

A02
A03

21.6 You can construct and interpret cumulative frequency diagrams

Key Points

◉ The cumulative frequency of a value is the total number of observations that are less than or equal to that value.

◉ Cumulative frequency diagrams (graphs) can be used to find estimates for the number of items up to a certain value.

◉ The quartiles divide the frequency into four equal parts.

◉ If there are n values then the quartiles can be estimated from the cumulative frequency graph.

  ◉ The estimate for the lower quartile is the $\frac{n}{4}$th value.

  ◉ The estimate for the median is the $\frac{n}{2}$th value.

  ◉ The estimate for the upper quartile is the $\frac{3n}{4}$th value.

◉ You can compare measures of spread for two cumulative frequency graphs.

Example 8

The grouped frequency table shows information about the time, in minutes, taken by 40 runners to complete a cross-country race.

a Draw up a cumulative frequency table.

b Draw a cumulative frequency graph.

Time (t minutes)	Frequency
$t \leqslant 60$	0
$60 < t \leqslant 65$	2
$65 < t \leqslant 70$	12
$70 < t \leqslant 75$	21
$75 < t \leqslant 80$	5

a

Time (t minutes)	Frequency	Cumulative frequency
$t \leqslant 60$	0	0
$60 < t \leqslant 65$	2	0 + 2 = 2
$65 < t \leqslant 70$	12	2 + 12 = 14
$70 < t \leqslant 75$	21	14 + 21 = 35
$75 < t \leqslant 80$	5	35 + 5 = 40

Each time add the frequency to the previous cumulative frequency. The previous frequency was 2 so add the frequency 12 to get the new cumulative frequency 14.

b

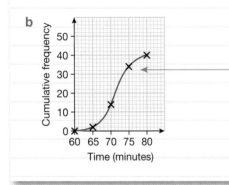

The cumulative frequency 35 for the interval $70 < t \leqslant 75$ is plotted at (75, 35). The plotted points may be joined by a curve or by straight lines.

Example 9

Forty students took a test.
The cumulative frequency graph
gives information about their marks.

a Use the graph to estimate the number
of students who had marks less than
or equal to 26.

b Use the graph to work out an estimate
for the number of students whose mark
was greater than 44.

c 26 students passed the test. Work out the pass mark for the test.

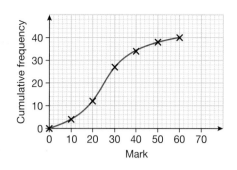

a There are 20 students with a mark less than 26.

b There are 36 students with a mark less than or
equal to 44, so there are 40 − 36 = 4 with a mark
greater than 44.

c If 26 pass there will be 40 − 26 = 14 that fail.
From the graph the pass mark was 22.

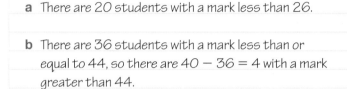

Example 10

The cumulative frequency graph shows
information about the times, in minutes,
taken by 40 runners who competed in a
cross-country race.

a Find estimates for the median and
quartiles.

b Find estimates for the range and
interquartile range.

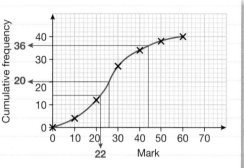

a
LQ = 69 min
median = 71.5 min
UQ = 73.5 min

LQ is the $\frac{40}{4}$ = 10th value.
Median is the $\frac{40}{2}$ = 20th value.
UQ is the $3 \times \frac{40}{4}$ = 30th value.

b Range = 80 − 60 = 20 min
IQR = 73.5 − 69 = 4.5 min

Range = highest − lowest values
IQR = UQ − LQ

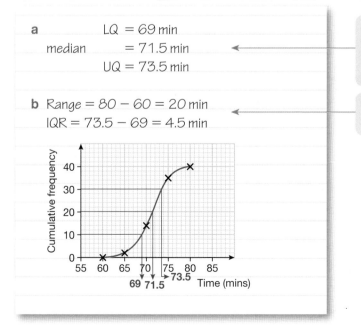

Exercise 21F

1   The table shows the ages of people using a bowling alley.

Age (x years)	Frequency	Cumulative frequency
$x \leqslant 10$	3	
$10 < x \leqslant 15$	7	
$15 < x \leqslant 20$	10	
$20 < x \leqslant 25$	15	
$25 < x \leqslant 30$	8	
$30 < x \leqslant 35$	5	
$35 < x \leqslant 40$	2	

a Copy and complete the table.
b Draw a cumulative frequency graph for these data.

2   The cumulative frequency graph shows the speeds of cars on a motorway.
a Use the cumulative frequency graph to find an estimate for the number of motorists
    i driving at 45 mph or less
    ii driving at between 40 mph and 70 mph.
b How many motorists' speeds were recorded altogether?
c The speed limit on a motorway is 70 mph. Estimate the percentage of cars with a speed greater than 70 mph.

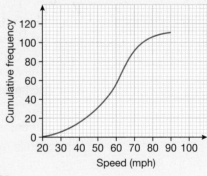

3   The cumulative frequency graph shows the scores a group of 100 apprentices got in an engineering examination.
a Find an estimate for the median.
b Find an estimate for LQ and UQ.
c Work out the interquartile range.
d Work out the range.

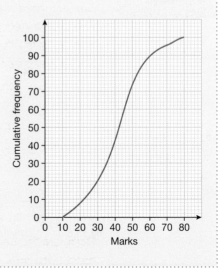

21.7 You can compare two or more sets of data

Key Points

- Comparison of data can be made using diagrams and charts, for example, dual bar charts, pie charts, back-to-back stem and leaf diagrams, frequency polygons and cumulative frequency graphs.
- Comparison of data can be made using measures of average and spread.

Example 11

The table shows information about the number of Year 7 pupils absent from Keith's school last week.

	Mon	Tues	Wed	Thurs	Fri
Boys	8	11	12	14	13
Girls	10	9	12	13	11

Keith wants to compare this information.
Draw a suitable diagram or chart.

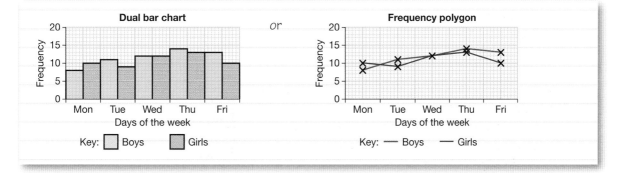

Note: pie charts could be used but the total number of absences for the boys (58) and the girls (55) would make calculations of angles difficult.

ResultsPlus
Exam Tip

Axes must be fully labelled.
A key must be included to distinguish the separate data.

Example 12

Zoe recorded the heart rates, in beats per minute, of each of 15 people.
Zoe then asked the 15 people to walk up some stairs.
She recorded their heart rates again.
She showed her results in a back-to-back stem and leaf diagram.

Before   **After**

```
              9  8 │  5 │
     7  6  6  4  1 │  6 │ 5  8  8  9
        9  8  6  3 │  2  7 │ 2  4  7  8
                4  1 │  8 │ 5  6  8
                     │  9 │ 1  3  7
                     │ 10 │ 2
```

Key for before
8 | 5 means 58
beats per minute

Key for after
6 | 5 means 65
beats per minute

Compare the heart rates of people before they walked up the stairs with their heart rates after they walked up the stairs.

		Before							**After**			

			9	8	5
	⑦	6 6 4 1	0	6	
		9 8 6 3	2	7	
			4	1	8	

6	5 8 8 9
7	2 4 7 ⑧
8	5 6 8
9	1 3 7
10	2

Median = 67 beats/minute

Median = 78 beats/minute

Median = 67 beats per minute
Mean   = sum of the heart rates ÷ 15
        = 1044 ÷ 15 = 69.6
Range = 84 − 58 = 26
Upper quartile = 78
Lower quartile = 61
Interquartile range = 78 − 61 = 17

Median = 78 beats per minute
Mean   = sum of the heart rates ÷ 15
        = 1213 ÷ 15 = 80.9
Range = 102 − 65 = 37
Upper quartile = 91
Lower quartile = 69
Interquartile range = 91 − 69 = 22

One measure of spread is required;
either the range or the interquartile range.

One measure of average is required;
either the median or the mean.

The median after is greater than the median before.
The mean after is greater than the mean before.
The range after is greater than the range before.
The interquartile range after is greater than the interquartile range before.

At least one of the comparisons
must be made to gain some credit.

The heart rates have risen as a result of walking up the stairs,
as shown by the increase in median (or mean) and are more
varied, as shown by the greater range (or interquartile range).

ResultsPlus
Exam Tip

Full credit is only given when
comparisons are made within the
context of the question.

Exercise 21G

D

1 The stem and leaf diagram shows information about the number of minutes a sample of
20 people waited to receive treatment at the Bakefield General Hospital.

0	8 9
1	2 4 7 7
2	3 5 6 6 8 9
3	0 1 6 7 7 8
4	0 2

Here are the number of minutes another sample of 20 people had to wait for treatment at Tudor Royal Hospital.

20	21	13	10	5
6	19	31	28	14
17	10	9	12	13
4	11	22	30	15

Compare the waiting times at Bakefield General Hospital to the waiting times at Tudor Royal Hospital.

2   Some students did a French test and a German test.
Here are their results.

French test results	44	28	39	50	14
	20	32	34	20	45

German test results	50	25	38	36	31
	22	54	45	51	48

Compare the French test results with the German test results.

3   Here are the number of points scored by two rugby teams so far this season.

Hawk Bulls	27	20	12	28	35	28	37	

Shaw Tigers	29	31	35	15	18	25	35	27	40

Compare fully the points scored by these two teams.

4   The two pie charts show information about the membership of two golf clubs.

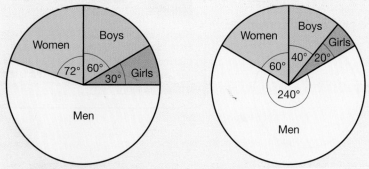

The Picton Golf Club has a total of 960 members.
The Chad Golf Club has a total of 120 members.
Compare fully the membership of the two golf clubs.

Exam review

Self-assessment checklist

I can:

Exam practice

1 Colin carried out a survey. He asked some students in Year 10 which type of film they liked best.
   He used the results to draw this pie chart.

   a What fraction of the students said "Comedy"?

   20 students said "Horror".

   b Work out the total number of students Colin asked.

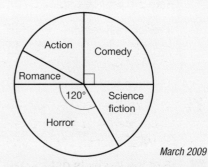

March 2009

2 Julie recorded the colour of each of 40 cars.
   Information about her results is shown in the table.

Car colour	Frequency
Blue	10
Red	4
Silver	18
Black	6
Green	2

   Copy and complete the pie chart accurately to show this information.

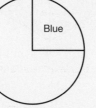

ResultsPlus
Achieving Full Marks

C candidates
D candidates

To get full marks on this question, draw an extra column to work out the size of each sector, check that the sum of all the angles is 360°, and label all of the sectors. This last one is often missed.

Nov 2009

3 The table gives information about the drinks sold in a café one day.

Drink	Frequency	Size of angle
Hot chocolate	20	80°
Soup	15	
Coffee	25	
Tea	30	

   Copy and complete the pie chart to show this information.

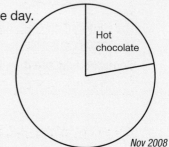

Nov 2008

248

4 The pie chart below shows government spending for 2008/9

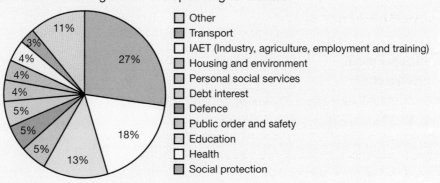

☐ Other
☐ Transport
☐ IAET (Industry, agriculture, employment and training)
☐ Housing and environment
☐ Personal social services
☐ Debt interest
■ Defence
☐ Public order and safety
☐ Education
☐ Health
■ Social protection

The government spent £21 billion on transport.

a How much did it spend on health?

b How much did it spend on public order and safety?

c What is the total amount of money that the government spent?

5 The pie chart gives information about the mathematics exam grades of some students.

a What fraction of the students got grade D?

8 of the students got grade C.

b i How many of the students got grade F?

ii How many students took the exam?

This accurate pie chart gives information about the English exam grades for a different set of students.

Sean says "More students got a grade D in English than in mathematics."

c Sean could be **wrong**.
Explain why.

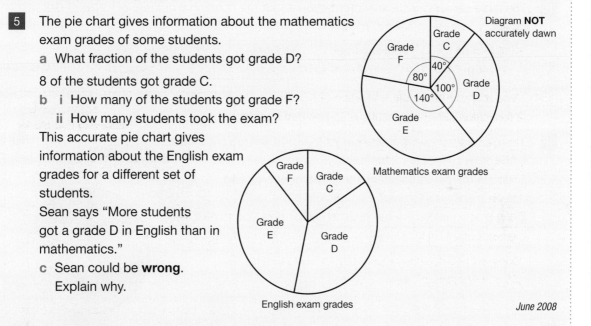

Diagram **NOT** accurately dawn

Mathematics exam grades

English exam grades

June 2008

6 The table shows some information about the weights (*w* grams) of 60 apples.

Weight (*w* grams)	Frequency
$100 \leqslant w < 110$	5
$110 \leqslant w < 120$	9
$120 \leqslant w < 130$	14
$130 \leqslant w < 140$	24
$140 \leqslant w < 150$	8

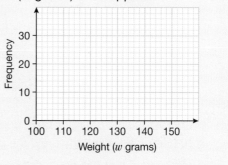

On a copy of the grid, draw a frequency polygon to show this information. *March 2009*

7 60 students take a science test.

The test is marked out of 50.

This table shows information about the students' marks.

Science mark	0–10	11–20	21–30	31–40	41–50
Frequency	4	13	17	19	7

On a copy of the grid, draw a frequency polygon
to show this information.

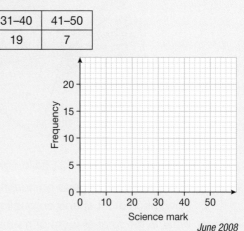

June 2008

8 The table below gives some information about the nutritional content of 120 g of baked
beans.

Protein	Carbohydrate	Fibre	Other
6 g	16 g	5 g	

Copy and complete the table.

Draw a chart for these data.

9 The pie chart shows the sources of the UK's energy production
in the early part of the 21st century.

Estimate the percentages of each type of energy and
use your answers to draw a composite bar chart.

Draw a new composite bar chart showing how you think it will
have changed by 2050, stating reasons for your answers.

Methods of UK Energy Production

* 10

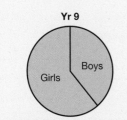

Pie chart showing proportion
of boys and girls in Year 9

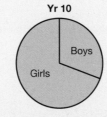

Pie chart showing proportion
of boys and girls in Year 10

To draw the pie chart for boys and girls in Years 9 and
10 combined, Kimberly drew the pie chart on the right:

James said that this could not be correct.

Explain who is right.

Pie chart showing proportion of boys
and girls in Year 9 and Year 10

11 The cumulative frequency graph shows some information about the ages of 100 people.

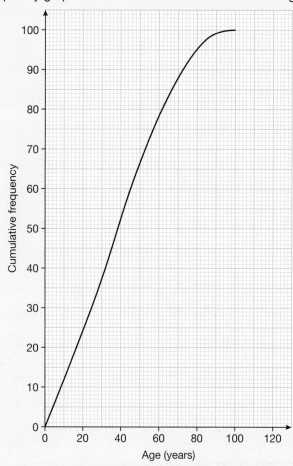

a Use the graph to find an estimate for the number of these people less than 70 years of age.

b Use the graph to find an estimate for the median age.

c Use the graph to find an estimate for the interquartile range of the ages.

> **Hint:** Interquartile range
> = Upper quartile − Lower quartile.

Nov 2008

* 12 Lucy did a survey about the amounts of money spent by 120 men during their summer holidays. The cumulative frequency table gives some information about the amounts of money spent by the 120 men.

A survey of the amounts of money spent by 200 women during their summer holidays gave a median of £205. Compare the amounts of money spent by the women with the amounts of money spent by the men.

Amount (£A) spent	Cumulative frequency
0 < A ≤ 100	13
0 < A ≤ 150	25
0 < A ≤ 200	42
0 < A ≤ 250	64
0 < A ≤ 300	93
0 < A ≤ 350	110
0 < A ≤ 400	120

May 2009

B
A03

13 The frequency polygons show information about the IQs of a group of boys and a group of girls.

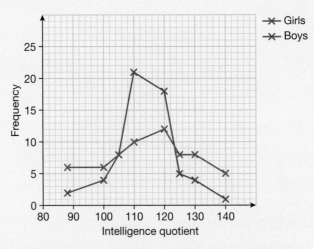

a Write down an estimate for the number of girls with an IQ of 110.
b Write down an estimate for the number of boys with an IQ of 110.
c Use the frequency polygon to compare the overall IQs of the boys and the girls.

A

14 The table gives some information about the lengths of time some boys took to run a race.
Draw a histogram for the information in the table.

Time (t minutes)	Frequency
$40 \leqslant t < 50$	16
$50 \leqslant t < 55$	18
$55 \leqslant t < 65$	32
$65 \leqslant t < 80$	30
$80 \leqslant t < 100$	24

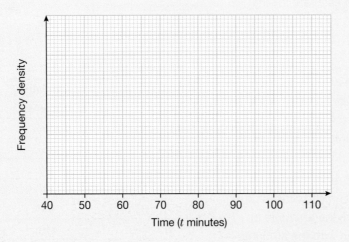

Hint: Decide the frequency that each large square will represent.

March 2009

15 The speeds of 100 cars on a motorway were recorded.
The grouped frequency table shows some information about the speeds of these cars.

Speed (s mph)	Frequency
$40 < s \leq 50$	4
$50 < s \leq 60$	19
$60 < s \leq 70$	34
$70 < s \leq 80$	27
$80 < s \leq 90$	14
$90 < s \leq 100$	2

a On a copy of the grid, draw an appropriate graph for your table.

b Find an estimate for the median speed.

c Find an estimate for the interquartile range.

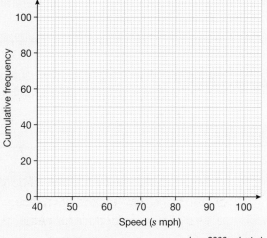

June 2008, adapted

16 The incomplete histogram and table give some information about the distances some teachers travel to school.

a Use the information in the histogram to complete the frequency table.

Distance (d km)	Frequency
$0 < d \leq 5$	15
$5 < d \leq 10$	20
$10 < d \leq 20$	
$20 < d \leq 40$	
$40 < d \leq 60$	10

Hint: Decide the frequency that each large square will represent.

b Use the information in the table to complete the histogram.

Nov 2008

22 LINE DIAGRAMS AND SCATTER GRAPHS

22.1 You can draw and use line graphs and scatter graphs

> **Key Points**

- Over time observations can be plotted on a line graph.
- If you measure 10 people's heights, you are making a single observation of each member in a sample size of 10. However, if you measure their weights as well as their heights then you are making 10 pairs of observations.
- A scatter graph shows whether there is any relationship between two variables.

> **Example 1**

The line graph shows the rate at which water flows in a river measured on the same day for each month of a year.

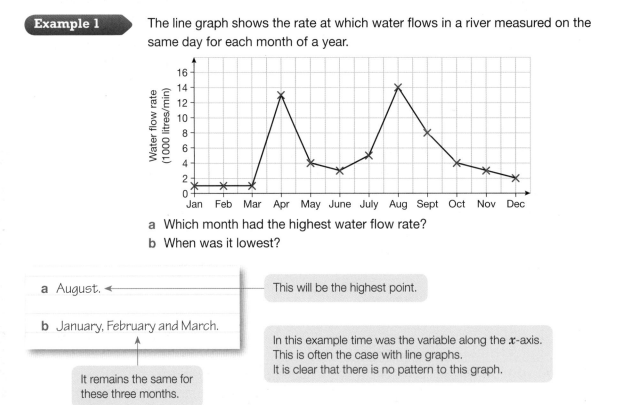

a Which month had the highest water flow rate?

b When was it lowest?

a August. ←   This will be the highest point.

b January, February and March.

It remains the same for these three months.

In this example time was the variable along the x-axis.
This is often the case with line graphs.
It is clear that there is no pattern to this graph.

> **Example 2**

The table below shows, for a range of cars, the engine size, in litres, and the average distance (miles) they can travel on 1 gallon of petrol.

Engine size (l)	1.4	1.6	1.8	2.0	2.5
Miles per gallon	42.8	42.2	40.3	39.8	30.4

a Draw a scatter graph for these data.

b Comment on the relationship between engine size and the average miles per gallon.

a

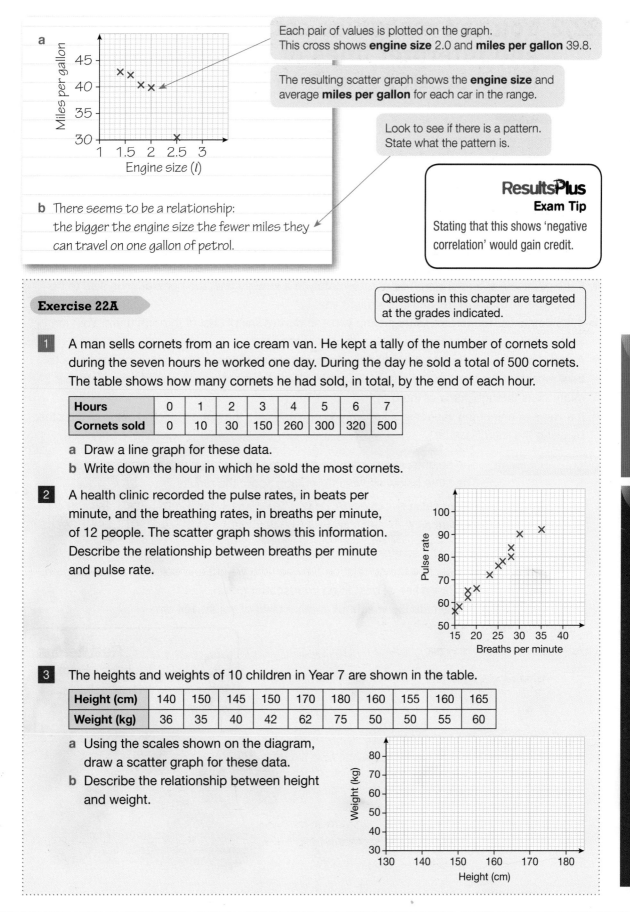

Each pair of values is plotted on the graph.
This cross shows **engine size** 2.0 and **miles per gallon** 39.8.

The resulting scatter graph shows the **engine size** and
average **miles per gallon** for each car in the range.

Look to see if there is a pattern.
State what the pattern is.

b There seems to be a relationship:
the bigger the engine size the fewer miles they
can travel on one gallon of petrol.

Results Plus
Exam Tip

Stating that this shows 'negative
correlation' would gain credit.

Exercise 22A

Questions in this chapter are targeted
at the grades indicated.

1 A man sells cornets from an ice cream van. He kept a tally of the number of cornets sold
during the seven hours he worked one day. During the day he sold a total of 500 cornets.
The table shows how many cornets he had sold, in total, by the end of each hour.

Hours	0	1	2	3	4	5	6	7
Cornets sold	0	10	30	150	260	300	320	500

a Draw a line graph for these data.
b Write down the hour in which he sold the most cornets.

2 A health clinic recorded the pulse rates, in beats per
minute, and the breathing rates, in breaths per minute,
of 12 people. The scatter graph shows this information.
Describe the relationship between breaths per minute
and pulse rate.

3 The heights and weights of 10 children in Year 7 are shown in the table.

Height (cm)	140	150	145	150	170	180	160	155	160	165
Weight (kg)	36	35	40	42	62	75	50	50	55	60

a Using the scales shown on the diagram,
draw a scatter graph for these data.
b Describe the relationship between height
and weight.

E

D

255

22.2 You can recognise correlation, construct and interpret lines of best fit by eye, and use a scatter graph to make predictions

Key Points

● On a scatter graph, there is a relationship between two variables if they vary together. If this is the case, we say the two variables are correlated. A relationship between pairs of variables is called a correlation.

Positive correlation

As one value increases the other one increases.

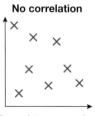

Negative correlation

As one value increases the other decreases.

No correlation

The points are random and widely spaced.

● If the points on a scatter graph lie approximately in a straight line, the correlation is said to be linear. The word 'linear' means in a straight line.

● If the points are roughly in a straight line you can draw a line of best fit through them. You can work out the gradient of the line of best fit (see section 8.2).

● A line of best fit is a straight line that passes as near as possible to the various points so as to best represent the trend of the graph. It does not have to pass through any of the points, but it might pass through some of them.

● If a value of one of the variables is known you can estimate the corresponding value of the other by using the line of best fit.

Example 3

The heights, in cm, and the weights, in kg, of 10 children are recorded. The table below shows information about the results.

Height (cm)	145	148	147	151	152	155	157	158	160	164
Weight (kg)	38	40	42	43	45	49	49	50	51	53

a Draw a scatter graph of these data.
b Describe the correlation between the weight and height of these children.
c Draw a line of best fit on your scatter graph.
d Estimate the weight of another child of height 154 cm.

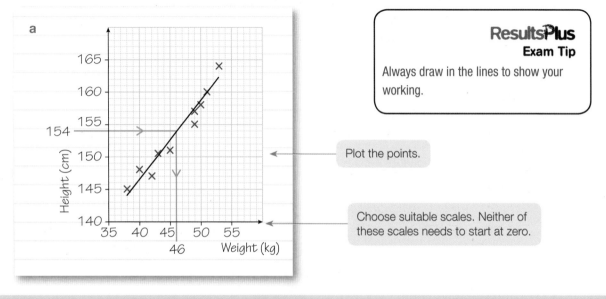

ResultsPlus
Exam Tip

Always draw in the lines to show your working.

Plot the points.

Choose suitable scales. Neither of these scales needs to start at zero.

b They are positively correlated.

c See scatter graph.

> Look to see what happens to the other variable when one variable increases. Draw a line so it best represents the trend, and has the points equally spaced either side.

d Weight = 46 kg

> Draw a horizontal line from 154 cm to the line of best fit. read the value of 46 cm from the weight axis by drawing a vertical line from the line of best fit.

Exercise 22B

1 An NHS Trust has seven hospitals. Some data on the average number of operations and the number of operating theatres for each hospital are shown in the table.

Number of operating theatres	2	4	5	5	6	7	8
Average number of operations per week	60	80	90	85	100	130	150

a Copy the diagram and complete the scatter graph for these data.

b Describe the correlation.

c Draw a line of best fit on your diagram.

d Describe the relationship between the number of operating theatres and the average number of operations per week.

e Estimate the number of operations carried out in a hospital with three operating theatres.

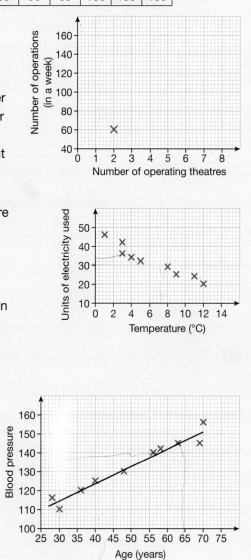

2 The scatter graph shows the midday temperature and the number of units of electricity used by a house on each of 10 days.

a Describe the correlation.

b Find an estimate for:

   i the number of units of electricity used when the midday temperature was 7°C

   ii the midday temperature when 35 units of electricity were used.

3 The scatter graph shows the ages and blood pressures of a group of 10 men.

a Estimate the blood pressure of a man aged 65.

b Predict the age of a man whose blood pressure is 135.

c Describe the relationship between age and blood pressure.

Exam review

Self-assessment checklist

I can:

◉ draw and use a line graph to find values [p.254]
◉ draw and use a scatter graph to see if there is any relationship between pairs of variables [p.254]
◉ recognise correlation, distinguishing between positive, negative and zero correlation [p.256]
◉ construct and interpret a line of best fit [p.256]
◉ use a scatter graph to make predictions. [p.256]

Exam practice

1 The table gives information about the number of people who were unemployed in a seaside town over the course of a year.

Month	Jan	Feb	Mar	Apr	May	Jun	Jul	Aug	Sep	Oct	Nov	Dec
No. of unemployed	110	98	56	50	48	34	40	30	45	–	85	105

a Plot a line graph for these data.

b Estimate the number of unemployed people in October.

c For which month of the year was the number of unemployed lowest? Give a reason for this.

2 Some students revised for a mathematics exam.
They used an internet revision site.
The scatter graph shows the amount of time seven students spent on the internet revision site and the marks the students got in the mathematics exam.
Here is the information for three more students.

Hours on the site	7	10	16
Mark	50	56	78

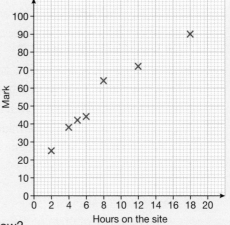

a Plot this information on a copy of the scatter graph.

b What type of correlation does this scatter graph show?

c Draw a line of best fit on your scatter graph.

Nov 2008

3 The scatter graph shows some information about 10 students.
It shows the arm length and the height of each student.

a What type of correlation does this scatter graph show?

b Draw a line of best fit on a copy of the scatter graph.

Another student has an arm length of 75 cm.

c Use your line of best fit to estimate the height of this student.

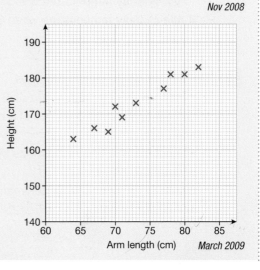

March 2009

4 The scatter graph shows some information about the age, in years, of apprentices and the time, in minutes, it takes them to learn a certain skill.

A line of best fit is drawn on the graph.

a Work out an estimate for the gradient of the line of best fit.

b Use the line of best fit to estimate how long it would take a 16.5 year old to learn the skill.

c Describe the correlation.

d What conclusions can you draw about the time it takes apprentices to learn skills?

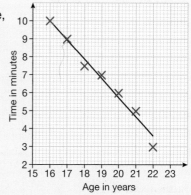

5 The scatter graph shows information for some weather stations.

It shows the height of each weather station above sea level (m) and the mean July midday temperature (°C) for that weather station.

The table shows this information for two more weather stations.

Height of weather station above sea level	1000	500
Mean July midday temperature (°C)	20	22

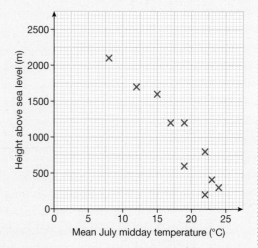

a Plot this information on the scatter graph.

b What type of correlation does this scatter graph show?

c Draw a line of best fit on a copy of the scatter graph.

A weather station is 1800 metres above sea level.

d Estimate the mean July midday temperature for this weather station.

At another weather station the mean July midday temperature is 18°C.

e Estimate the height above sea level of this weather station. *June 2008*

6 The scatter graph shows some information about 10 cars.

It shows the time, in seconds, it takes each car to go from 0 mph to 60 mph.

For each car, it also shows the maximum speed, in mph.

a What type of correlation does this scatter graph show?

The time a car takes to go from 0 mph to 60 mph is 11 seconds.

b Estimate the maximum speed for this car.

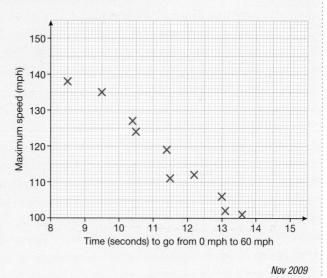

Nov 2009

C

7 Jake recorded the weight, in kg, and the height, in cm, of each of ten children.

The scatter graph shows information about his results.

a Describe the relationship between the weight and the height of these children.

b Draw a line of best fit on a copy of the scatter graph.

c Use your line of best fit to estimate the height of a child whose weight is 47 kg.

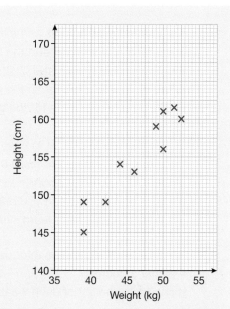

June 2008

8 A garage sells motorcycles.

The scatter graph shows information about the price and age of the motorcycles.

a What type of correlation does the scatter graph show?

b Draw a line of best fit on a copy of the scatter graph.

Mae buys a motorcycle from this garage for £1500.

c Use your line of best fit to estimate the age of the motorcycle.

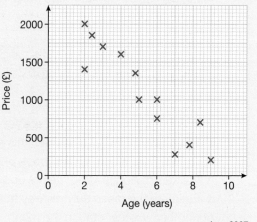

June 2007

A03

9 The table gives the age and price of 10 second-hand Minis.

a Estimate the approximate price of a new Mini.

b Which Mini is different to the others? Suggest reasons why it is priced like it is.

Age (years)	Price
5	£5400
2	£7000
4	£5600
6	£3400
7	£5200
3	£6800
8	£1700
1	£10 500
8	£2000
6	£3200

10 Mr Wither sells umbrellas.

The scatter graph shows some information about the number of umbrellas he sold and the rainfall, in cm, each month last year.

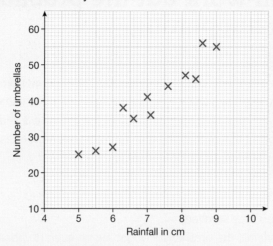

In January of this year, the rainfall was 6.1 cm.

During January, Mr Wither sold 32 umbrellas.

a Copy this scatter graph and show this information on it.

b What type of correlation does this scatter graph show?

In February of this year, Mr Wither sold 40 umbrellas.

c Estimate the rainfall for February.

Hint: You may wish to draw a line of best fit.

June 2010

11 A beach cafe sells ice creams.

Each day the manager records the number of hours of sunshine and the number of ice creams sold.

The scatter graph shows this information.

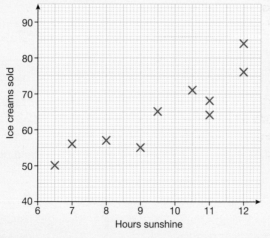

On another day there were 11.5 hours of sunshine and 73 ice creams sold.

a Show this information on a copy of the scatter graph.

b Describe the relationship between the number of hours of sunshine and the number of ice creams sold.

One day had 10 hours of sunshine.

c Estimate how many ice creams were sold.

March 2011

23 PROBABILITY

23.1 You can work out the probability of events happening

Key Points

- The probability that an event will happen is a number in the range from 0 (impossible) to 1 (certain).
- Outcomes are mutually exclusive when they cannot happen at the same time. Rolling a 3 and rolling a 4 on a dice are mutually exclusive outcomes – you cannot roll a 3 and a 4 at the same time.
- For equally likely outcomes the probability that an event will happen is

$$\text{probability} = \frac{\text{number of successful outcomes}}{\text{total number of possible outcomes}}$$

- Two-way tables can be used to find probabilities.

Example 1   A fair dice is rolled.
Work out the probability of getting an even number.

$P(\text{even}) = \dfrac{\text{number of successful outcomes}}{\text{total number of possible outcomes}}$

$= \dfrac{3}{6}$

There are three successful outcomes: 2, 4 and 6.

There are six possible outcomes: 1, 2, 3, 4, 5 or 6.

$= \dfrac{1}{2}$

Simplify the fraction. Divide top and bottom by 3.

So $\dfrac{3 \div 3}{6 \div 3} = \dfrac{1}{2}$

ResultsPlus
Exam Tip

A fair dice is one that is not biased. Each number has an equal chance of being thrown. So the outcomes are equally likely.

Example 2   Carmen asks 20 people where they went for their summer holidays.
This two-way table gives her results.

	France	Italy	Spain	Total
Boys	4	5	2	11
Girls	1	2	6	9
Total	5	7	8	20

Carmen picks one of the 20 students at random.
Write down the probability that this student:

a will be a girl   **b** went to Italy   **c** will be a girl who went to France.

a From the table above, it can be seen that
9 students are girls.
So, $P(\text{girl}) = \dfrac{9}{20}$

Use $P = \dfrac{\text{number of successful outcomes}}{\text{total number of possible outcomes}}$

b The table shows that 7 students went to Italy.
So, $P(\text{Italy}) = \dfrac{7}{20}$
The table shows that just 1 girl went to France.

c $P(\text{girl, France}) = \dfrac{1}{20}$

Exercise 23A

Questions in this chapter are targeted at the grades indicated.

1 A letter is chosen at random from the word STATISTICS. Write down the probability that it will be:
 a A   b S   c I   d S or T   e G.

2 A fair dice is rolled. Work out the probability of getting:
 a a 5   b a 1 or a 2   c an odd number
 d a number less than 5   e a number greater than 6   f a prime number.

3 There are 120 raffle tickets in a hat. Of these, 67 are yellow and the rest are green.
 A raffle ticket is taken at random from the hat. Work out the probability that it will be:
 a yellow   b green.

4 A box of sweets contains 3 mints, 7 toffees and 5 lemon drops.
 A sweet is taken at random from the box. Write down the probability that it will be:
 a a mint   b a toffee   c a lemon drop
 d a mint or a toffee   e not a toffee   f not a lemon drop or a toffee.

5 The table gives information about how some students travel to school.
 One of the students is picked at random.
 Work out the probability that this student is:

	Walk	Bus	Cycle	Total
Boys	4	5	3	12
Girls	7	4	2	13
Total	11	9	5	25

 a a girl
 b a girl who walks to school
 c a boy who cycles to school
 d a student who comes by bus.

6 Some students each had one drink and one snack in the school canteen.
 The table gives some information about what the students had to eat and drink.

	Orange	Lemonade	Milk	Total
Sandwiches	5			13
Biscuits	4		5	
Crisps			1	16
Total	17	18	7	

 a Copy and complete the table.
 b One of the students is picked at random.
  Use your table to write down the probability that this student had:
   i lemonade   ii crisps
  iii orange and biscuits   iv lemonade and biscuits.
 c John says that the probability of picking someone who had milk and biscuits is the same as picking someone who had orange and sandwiches. Is he right? Give a reason for your answer.

7 A card is taken at random from an ordinary pack of cards.
 Work out the probability of getting:
 a a 3 of hearts or a 5 of spades   b a heart or a spade
 c a king of clubs or a queen of any suit   d a diamond or the ace of hearts
 e a picture card (jack, queen or king) or a red 10.

F

E

D

C

23.2 You can work out the probability of an event not happening

Key Points

- The sum of the probabilities of all the mutually exclusive outcomes of an event is 1.
- If the probability of an event happening is P then the probability of it not happening is therefore 1 − P.

Example 3 The probability that it will rain tomorrow is 0.2.
Work out the probability that it will not rain tomorrow.

P(not rain) = 1 − P(rain)
$\qquad$ = 1 − 0.2
$\qquad$ = 0.8

> If the probability that it will rain tomorrow is 0.2, then the probability it will not rain is 1 − 0.2.

Example 4 The diagram shows a 4-sided spinner that is biased.
The spinner is spun.
This table gives the probability that it will land on B, C or D.

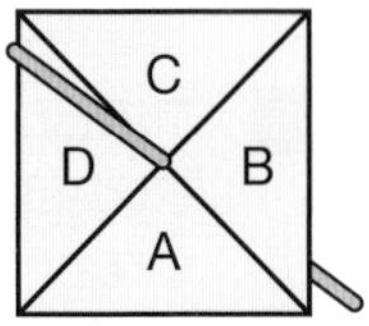

	A	B	C	D
Probability		0.13	0.45	0.25

Work out the probability that the spinner will land on A.

P(A) + 0.13 + 0.45 + 0.25 = 1

> It is certain that the spinner will land on A or B or C or D. So the probabilities add up to 1.

P(A) + 0.83 = 1

> Add the decimals: 0.13 + 0.45 + 0.25 = 0.83

P(A) = 1 − 0.83
$\qquad$ = 0.17

> Take 0.83 from both sides of the equation.

Exercise 23B

1 The probability that my bike will get a puncture on the way to school today is 0.15.
Work out the probability that my bike will not get a puncture on the way to school today.

2 The probability that my lottery ticket will win a prize is $\frac{3}{53}$.
Work out the probability that my lottery ticket will not win a prize.

3 A weather forecaster says that there is a 70% chance of getting rain tomorrow.
What is the probability that it will not rain tomorrow?

4 The probability that Kimberley's train will be late is 0.32. Kimberley says that the probability that her train will not be late is 0.78.
She is wrong. Explain why.

D

5   Heather's bus can either be early, on time or late.
    This table gives the probability that her bus will
    be early and the probability that her bus will be late.

    Hint: The probabilities must always add up to 1.

	early	on time	late
Probability	0.1		0.6

    Work out the probability that Heather's bus will be on time.

6   A biased dice is rolled.
    This table gives the probability that it will land on each of the numbers 1, 2, 3, 4 and 5.

	1	2	3	4	5	6
Probability	0.2	0.1	0.3	0.2	0.1	

    Work out the probability that the dice will land on 6.

7   Imran has some coloured cards. Each card is either red or yellow or blue or green. One of
    these cards is taken at random. This table gives the probability that the card will be red or
    blue or green.

Colour	red	yellow	blue	green
Probability	0.36		0.19	0.28

    Work out the probability that the card will:

    a   be yellow

    b   not be blue

    c   be a red card or a green card.

8   A bag contains a number of balls. Each ball is either red or blue or yellow or green.
    A ball is taken at random from the bag.

    The probability that the ball will be red is 0.25.
    The probability that the ball will be blue is 0.3.
    The probability that the ball will be yellow is 0.2.
    Work out the probability that the ball will be green.

9   When Weymouth Wanderers play football they can win, lose or draw the game.
    The probability that they will win the game is $\frac{3}{5}$.
    The probability that they will lose the game is $\frac{3}{10}$.
    Work out the probability that they will draw the game.

    Hint: Either convert fractions to decimals or change $\frac{3}{5}$ to tenths.

10 Here is a four-sided spinner.
    The spinner is not fair.
    The table shows the probability that the spinner will land on
    1 or 2 or 3 or 4.

    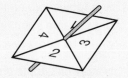

Number	1	2	3	4
Probability	0.25	x	0.15	x

    The spinner is spun once.
    Work out the probability that the spinner will land on

    a   2   b   1 or 4.

23.3 You can record all possible outcomes of an event in a sample space diagram

Key Point

⊙ A sample space diagram can be used to find a theoretical probability.

Example 5

An ordinary dice is rolled and a 4-sided spinner is spun.
  a Draw a sample space diagram to show all the possible outcomes.
  b Work out the probability of getting a total score of 7.

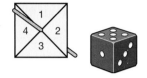

a

Spinner	4	(1, 4)	(2, 4)	(3, 4)	(4, 4)	(5, 4)	(6, 4)
	3	(1, 3)	(2, 3)	(3, 3)	(4, 3)	(5, 3)	(6, 3)
	2	(1, 2)	(2, 2)	(3, 2)	(4, 2)	(5, 2)	(6, 2)
	1	(1, 1)	(2, 1)	(3, 1)	(4, 1)	(5, 1)	(6, 1)
		1	2	3	4	5	6

Dice

A sample space diagram shows all the possible outcomes, e.g. (6, 4) is the outcome of rolling a 6 on the dice and spinning a 4 on the spinner.

Identify all the possible ways of getting a total score of 7: (3, 4), (4, 3), (5, 2) and (6, 1).

b $P(7) = \dfrac{\text{number of successful outcomes}}{\text{total number of possible outcomes}}$

$= \dfrac{4}{24}$

$= \dfrac{1}{6}$

This is the theoretical probability. The probability you expect to get for a fair dice and a fair spinner.

There are four outcomes which give a total score of 7.

There are a total of 24 possible outcomes.

Exercise 23C

1　A coin is spun, and an ordinary dice is rolled. Show all the possible outcomes.

2　An ordinary dice is rolled and a 4-sided spinner is spun.
Use the sample space diagram in Example 5 to work out the probability of getting:
  a a total score of 4
  b the same number on the dice and the spinner
  c a total score less than 6.

3　Mandy has some sheets and pillowcases in a drawer. The colours of the sheets are either white or yellow or blue or green. The colours of pillowcases are either white or green or orange. Mandy takes at random a sheet and a pillowcase from the drawer.
  a Draw a sample space diagram to show all the possible combinations of colours for the sheets and pillowcases.
  b Work out the probability that Mandy takes a sheet and a pillowcase of:
    i the same colour　　ii different colours.

4 The ace, king, queen and jack of clubs and the ace, king, queen and jack of diamonds are put into two piles. The sample space diagram shows all the possible outcomes when a card is taken from each pile.

	J	AJ	KJ	QJ	JJ
	Q	AQ	KQ	QQ	JQ
Clubs	K	AK	KK	QK	JK
	A	AA	KA	QA	JA
		A	K	Q	J

Diamonds

Work out the probability that:

a both cards will be aces   b the cards will be a pair

c only one of the cards will be a jack   d at least one card will be a king

e one card will be a diamond   f neither card will be a queen

g both cards will be diamonds.

5 Two 3-sided spinners are spun.

a Draw a sample space diagram to show all the possible outcomes.
One possible outcome is (2, 3).

b Bronwen spins spinner 1 two times.
Work out the probability that it lands on 1 and then on 3.

c Claire spins spinner 2 two times.
The total score is the sum of the numbers it lands on.
The probability that the total score will be 4 is $\frac{1}{3}$. Explain why.

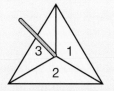

Spinner 1

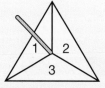

Spinner 2

6 Simon is going to spin a 3-sided spinner and a 4-sided spinner. The spinners are fair.
What is the most likely total score.
Give a reason for your answer.

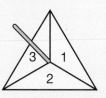

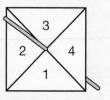

7 An ordinary dice is rolled and a fair coin is spun.

a Copy and complete the following sample space diagram to show all the possible outcomes.

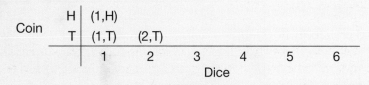

	H	(1,H)					
Coin	T	(1,T)	(2,T)				
		1	2	3	4	5	6

Dice

b Work out the probability of getting:

i a 1 on the dice and a head on the coin

ii a number greater than 3 on the dice

iii a number less than 3 on the dice and a tail.

23.4 You can use relative frequency to estimate probability and predict results

Key Points

⊙ Estimated probability = $\dfrac{\text{number of successful trials}}{\text{total number of trials}}$

⊙ The estimated or experimental probability may be different from the theoretical probability.

⊙ Generally, the more trials you undertake the nearer your estimate will be to the actual probability.

⊙ Probabilities can be used to predict results. Use the formula:

Predicted number of outcomes = probability × number of trials

Example 6   Samina spins a fair coin 50 times.
She gets 21 heads.
Write down the estimated and theoretical probability of getting a head.

Estimated probability = $\dfrac{\text{number of successful trials}}{\text{total number of trials}} = \dfrac{21}{50}$

Theoretical probability = $\dfrac{1}{2}$

Example 7   A fair 4-sided spinner is spun 100 times.
Find an estimate for the number of times it will land on a 3.

The theoretical probability that the spinner will land on a 3 is $\dfrac{1}{4}$.

So, when the spinner is spun 100 times we expect it to land on a 3.

$\dfrac{1}{4} \times 100 = 25$ times.

Use P(3) = ...
Here there is one outcome which is successful (i.e. '3'), and the total number of possible outcomes = 4 (i.e. 1, 2, 3 or 4).

Predicted number of outcomes = probability × number of trials
$\dfrac{1}{4} \times 100 = 100 \div 4 = 25$

Exercise 23D

1 Roll a dice 60 times and record your results in a frequency table like this.

a Use the results in your table to work out the estimated probability of getting:

  i a 6

  ii an odd number

  iii a number bigger than 4.

Number	Tally	Frequency
1		
2		
3		
4		
5		
6		
	Total	**60**

b Write down the theoretical probability of getting:

  i a 6   ii an odd number   iii a number bigger than 4.

c Do you think your dice is fair? Give a reason for your answer.

2   a Write down the theoretical probability of getting a head when you spin an ordinary coin.
     b Now spin a coin 50 times and record your results in a frequency table.
     c Use your results to write down the estimated probability of getting a head.
        Comment on your answer.

3   An ordinary coin is spun 100 times. How many times do you expect it to land on a head?

4   Piers spins an ordinary 5-sided spinner (numbered 1 to 5) 150 times.
     How many times can he expect it to land on 4?

5   Harry is going to roll an ordinary dice 90 times. Work out an estimate for the number of
     times it will land on:
     a 6   b an even number   c 1 or 2.

6   The table gives information about the probability
     that Tom will win, draw or lose a game of Go.
     Tom is going to play 40 games of Go.
     Find an estimate for the number of games he will:
     a win   b lose.

	Win	Draw	Lose
Probability	0.4	0.25	0.35

7   A bag contains 3 red balls and 5 blue balls.
     A ball is taken at random from the bag and its colour is recorded. The ball is now put back
     into the bag and another ball is taken at random from the bag. This is repeated 60 times.
     Find an estimate for the total number of times:
     a a red ball is taken from the bag   b a blue ball is taken from the bag.

8   The probability that an insurance company will get a claim for an accident in the home is
     0.72. If the insurance company gets 340 claims during the next month, find an estimate
     for the number of these claims that will not be for an accident in the home.

9   The probability that a seed will grow into a flower is 0.85.
     Loren plants 800 seeds.
     Work out an estimate for the number of seeds that will grow into flowers.

*10 The diagram shows part of Holly's design for a game. In her game
     a player pays x pence to spin a star. When the star stops spinning
     the player wins the amount shown by the arrow.
     Holly wants to gain an average of 5p each time the game is played.
     Show how this can be done by adding six more numbers to the star
     and finding a suitable value for x.

11   Laura has a 4-sided dice. The sides of the dice are numbered 1, 2, 3 and 4.
     The table shows the probabilities that the dice will land on 1 or land on 2 or land on 3.

Number	1	2	3	4
Probability	0.25	0.1	0.35	

     Laura rolls the dice 200 times. Estimate the number of times that the dice will land on 4.

23.5 You can complete and use a probability tree diagram

Key Point

- A probability tree diagram shows all possible outcomes of an experiment.

Example 8

Box A contains 3 red balls and 4 blue balls.
Box B contains 2 red balls and 3 blue balls.
One ball is taken at random from each box.
- **a** Draw a tree diagram to show all the outcomes.
- **b** Work out the probability that the balls will have the same colour.

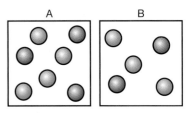

a Work out the probability of getting each event and show these on the tree diagram. For example, the probability of getting a ball from box A = $\dfrac{\text{number of successful outcomes}}{\text{total number of possible outcomes}} = \dfrac{3}{7}$.

Box A	Box B		Outcome	Probability
		$\frac{2}{5}$ red	red, red	$\frac{3}{7} \times \frac{2}{5} = \frac{6}{35}$
$\frac{3}{7}$ red				
		$\frac{3}{5}$ blue	red, blue	$\frac{3}{7} \times \frac{3}{5} = \frac{9}{35}$
		$\frac{2}{5}$ red	blue, red	$\frac{4}{7} \times \frac{2}{5} = \frac{8}{35}$
$\frac{4}{7}$ blue				
		$\frac{3}{5}$ blue	blue, blue	$\frac{4}{7} \times \frac{3}{5} = \frac{12}{35}$

This branch represents taking a red ball from box A followed by a red ball from box B.

To find the probability of taking a red ball from box A **and** taking a red ball from box B, we **multiply** the probabilities.
So P(red and red) = P(red) × P(red) = $\frac{3}{7} \times \frac{2}{5} = \frac{6}{35}$

b P(same colour) = P(both red or both blue)
= P(red, red) + P(blue, blue)

To find the probability of taking two red balls **or** two blue balls, we **add** the probabilities.

= $\frac{6}{35} + \frac{12}{35}$

From the tree diagram, P(red, red) = $\frac{6}{35}$ and P(blue, blue) = $\frac{12}{35}$

= $\frac{18}{35}$

Add the fractions.

Example 9

Daniel plays a game of chess and a game of draughts.
The probability that Daniel will win the game of chess is 0.7.
The probability that Daniel will win the game of draughts is 0.6.
Complete the probability tree diagram.

Chess   Draughts

0.7 win
  0.6 win
  0.4 not win

0.3 not win
  0.6 win
  0.4 not win

Daniel either wins or does not win the game of draughts, so the sum of the probabilities must be 1. Therefore P(not win) = 1 − 0.6 = 0.4

Success at the two games is independent.

Daniel either wins the game or does not win the game of chess, so the sum of the probabilities must be 1. Therefore P(not win) = 1 − 0.7 = 0.3

Exercise 23E

1   Bag A contains 2 blue counters and 3 white counters.
    Bag B contains 3 blue counters and 4 white counters.
    A counter is taken at random from each bag.
    a   Copy and complete the tree diagram to show all the
        possible outcomes.
    b   Work out the probability that the counters will both be:
        i   white
        ii blue
        iii the same colour.

    Remember: When *multiplying* fractions,
    multiply the numerators and multiply
    the denominators. See chapter 2.

2   There are 10 pencils in a pencil case.
    3 of the pencils are HB pencils.
    A pencil is taken at random from the pencil case and
    then returned.
    A second pencil is now
    taken at random from the
    pencil case and then returned.

    Remember: When *adding*
    fractions, the denominators
    must be the same.

    a   Copy and complete the tree diagram to show all the
        possible outcomes.
    b   Work out the probability that only one of the pencils will be an HB pencil.

3   Ryan and Ibrahim each have a bag of sweets. In Ryan's
    bag there are 3 orange sweets and 5 red sweets.
    In Ibrahim's bag there are 2 orange sweets and 3 red sweets.
    The boys each take a sweet at random from their own bag.
    a   Copy and complete the tree diagram to show all the
        possible outcomes.
    b   Use your tree diagram to work out the probability that
        the sweets will:
        i   both be orange
        ii each have a different colour.

4   On her way home from work Taylor must drive through
    two sets of traffic lights.
    The probability that she will be stopped at the first set
    of traffic lights is 0.4.
    The probability that she will be stopped at the second
    set of traffic lights is 0.7.
    a   Work out the probability that she will not be stopped at:
        i   the first set of traffic lights
        ii the second set of traffic lights.
    b   Copy and complete the tree diagram to show all the possible outcomes.
    c   Work out the probability that she will be stopped by:
        i   both sets of traffic lights
        ii only one set of traffic lights.

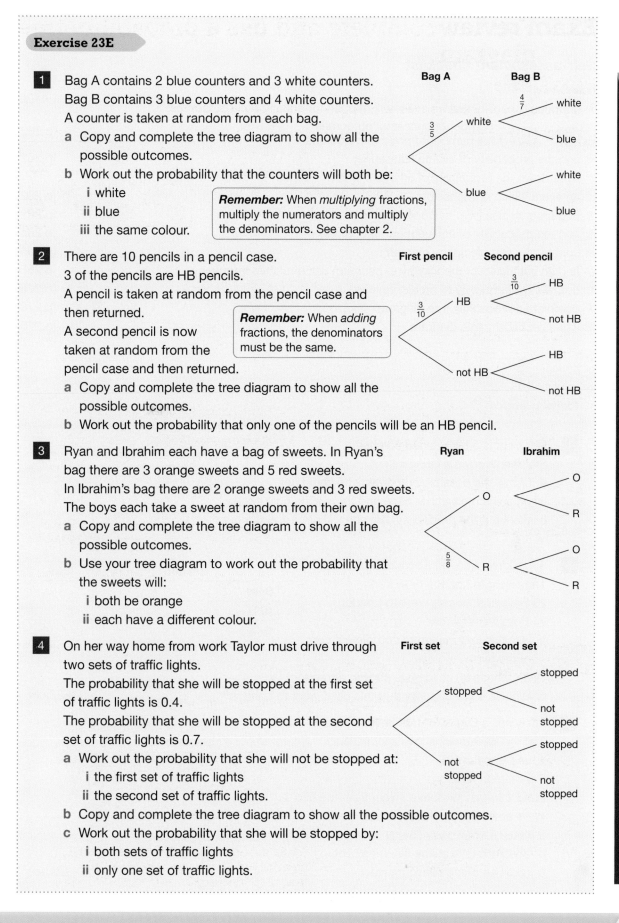

Exam review

Self-assessment checklist

I can:

- find the probability that an event will happen for equally likely outcomes:

  $$\text{probability} = \frac{\text{number of succesful outcomes}}{\text{total number of positive outcomes}}$$ [p.262]

- find the probability of events happening [p.262]
- write down the probability of an event which is certain to happen and the probability of an event which is impossible [p.262]
- find probabilities from a two-way table [p.262]
- find the probability of an event not happening [p.264]
- construct a sample space diagram [p.266]
- find an estimated probability by experiment using relative frequency [p.268]
- use relative frequency to predict results [p.268]
- complete a probability tree diagram [p.270]
- use a probability tree diagram. [p.270]

Exam practice

1 Ishah spins a fair 5-sided spinner.
She then throws a fair coin.
a List all the possible outcomes she could get.
Ishah spins the spinner once and throws the coin once.
b Work out the probability that she will get a 1 and a head.

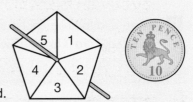

March 2009 adapted

2 80 children went on a school trip.
They went to London or to York.
23 boys and 19 girls went to London.
14 boys went to York.
a Use this information to complete a copy of the two-way table.
One of these 80 children is chosen at random.
b What is the probability that this child went to London?

	London	York	Total
Boys			
Girls			
Total			

March 2009

3 Emily has a bag of 20 fruit flavour sweets.
7 of the sweets are strawberry flavour,
11 are lime flavour,
2 are lemon flavour.
Emily takes at random a sweet from the bag.
Write down the probability that Emily

Hint: For more on ratio, see section 5.2.

a takes a strawberry flavour sweet
b does **not** take a lime flavour sweet
c takes an orange flavour sweet.

June 2006

4 A bag contains only red, green and blue counters.
The table shows the probability that a counter chosen at random from the bag will be red or will be green.

Colour	Red	Green	Blue
Probability	0.5	0.3	

Mary takes a counter at random from the bag.

a Work out the probability that Mary takes a blue counter.

The bag contains 50 counters.

b Work out how many green counters there are in the bag.   *March 2009*

5 Here is a 5-sided spinner.
The sides of the spinner are labelled 1, 2, 3, 4 and 5.
The spinner is biased.
The probability that the spinner will land on each of the numbers 1, 2, 3 and 4 is given in the table.

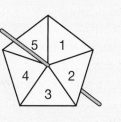

Number	1	2	3	4	5
Probability	0.15	0.05	0.2	0.25	x

Work out the value of x.   *Nov 2008*

6 Here is a 4-sided spinner.
The sides of the spinner are labelled Red, Blue, Green and Yellow.
The spinner is biased.
The table shows the probability that the spinner will land on each of the colours Red, Yellow and Green.

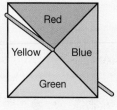

Colour	Red	Blue	Green	Yellow
Probability	0.2		0.3	0.1

Work out the probability the spinner will land on Blue.   *May 2008*

7 Here are the ages, in years, of 15 teachers.

    35 52 42 27 36 23 31 41 50 34 44 28 45 45 53

One of these teachers is picked at random.
Work out the probability that the teacher is more than 40 years old.   *May 2008 adapted*

8 A jar of sweets contains toffees, truffles and creams in the ratio 3 : 7 : 8.
A sweet is chosen at random. Write down the probability that it is a truffle.

9 Louise spins a four-sided spinner and a
five-sided spinner.
The four-sided spinner is labelled 2, 4, 6, 8.
The five-sided spinner is labelled 1, 3, 5, 7, 9.
Louise adds the score on the four-sided spinner to the score on the five-sided spinner.
She records the possible total scores in a table.

a Copy and complete the table of possible total scores.

b Write down all the ways in which Louise can get a total score of 11.
The first way is (2, 9).

Both spinners are fair.

c Find the probability that Louise's total score is less than 6.   *Nov 2010*

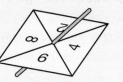 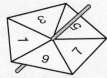

4-sided spinner

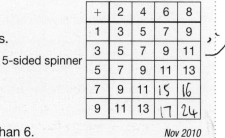

5-sided spinner

+	2	4	6	8
1	3	5	7	9
3	5	7	9	11
5	7	9	11	13
7	9	11	15	16
9	11	13	17	24

10 Laura has a four-sided spinner.
The spinner is biased.
The table shows each of the probabilities that the spinner will land on 1 or land on 3.
The probability that the spinner will land on 2 is equal to the probability that it will land on 4.

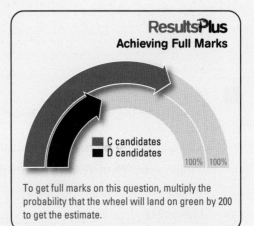

Number	1	2	3	4
Probability	0.25		0.35	

Laura is going to spin the spinner once.
a Work out the probability that the spinner will **not** land on 1.
b Work out the probability that the spinner will land on 2.

Nov 2010

11 This coloured wheel spins round.
The sectors are coloured yellow, red, green and blue.

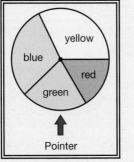

Diagram **NOT** accurately drawn

Pointer

ResultsPlus
Achieving Full Marks

■ C candidates
■ D candidates

100% 100%

To get full marks on this question, multiply the probability that the wheel will land on green by 200 to get the estimate.

Harry spins the wheel.
When the wheel stops spinning. Harry writes down the colour shown by the pointer.

The probability that the wheel will stop at yellow or red or green is given in the table.

Colour	yellow	red	green	blue
Probability	0.35	0.1	0.3	

a Work out the probability that the wheel will stop at blue.
b Work out the probability that the wheel will stop at either yellow or red.

Hannah is going to spin the wheel 200 times.
c Work out an estimate for the number of times the wheel will stop at green.

June 2009

12 Two spinners are each numbered 1 to 4.
When they are both spun, the score is found by adding the two numbers.
E.g. a 1 and a 4 scores 5.
Three friends are playing with these spinners and devise a set of rules.

If Alice gets a score of 6, 7 or 8 she wins.
If Robbie scores 4 or 5 he wins.
If Megan scores 1, 2 or 3 she wins.
Who should win the most games?

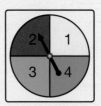

13 Mike rolls an ordinary dice and spins a fair 4-sided spinner.
By drawing a sample space diagram or otherwise,
work out the probability that the total score will be:
a 7
b less than 5
c a prime number.

14 A card is taken at random from an ordinary pack of cards.
It is then replaced. This is done 390 times.
How many times would you expect to see:
a a heart   b the ace of spades   c a jack?

15 Martin and Luke are students in the same
maths class.
The probability that Martin will bring a
calculator to a lesson is 0.8
The probability that Luke will bring a
calculator to a lesson is 0.6
a Copy and complete the probability
   tree diagram.
b Work out the probability that both Martin
   and Luke will not bring a calculator to a lesson.

March 2011

16 Nicola is going to travel from Swindon to
London by train.
The probability that the train will be late leaving
Swindon is $\frac{1}{5}$.
If the train is late leaving Swindon, the probability
that it will arrive late in London is $\frac{7}{10}$.
If the train is **not** late leaving Swindon, the
probability that it will arrive late in London is $\frac{1}{10}$.
a Copy and complete the probability tree diagram.
b Work out the probability that Nicola will arrive late in London.

Nov 2008

17 There are 10 socks in a drawer.
7 of the socks are brown.
3 of the socks are grey.
Bevan takes at random two socks from the drawer
at the same time.
a Copy and complete the probability tree diagram.
b Work out the probability that Bevan takes two
   socks of the same colour.

Nov 2010

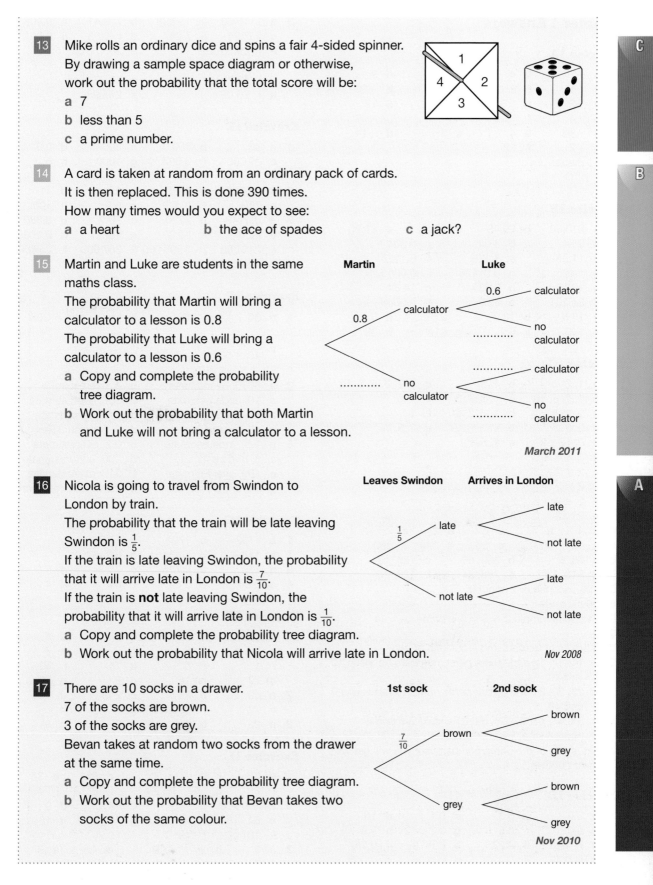

C

B

A

275

Chapter 1 Answers

Exercise 1A

1 a −7   b 4   c 10   d 9
   e −1   f 2   g −2   h −10
2 a −3   b −3   c 4   d 12
   e −4   f −12
3 a −90   b 4   c 5   d −14
   e −2   f 12
4 11 metres
5 −12°C

Exercise 1B

1 a £13.50   b £5.48   c £5.20   d £1.20
2 a 30.4   b 3.04   c 0.304
   d 11.25   e 1.125   f 0.1125
   g 1.125   h 0.01125 i 0.001 125
3 a 16.12   b 0.633   c 14.84
   d 34.221   e 5.027   f 0.0046
4 a 15.5   b 13.2   c 21   d 3.5
   e 1.07   f 6.2   g 41.4   h 32

Exercise 1C

1 a 1, 2   b 1, 5   c 1, 2, 3, 4, 6, 12
   d 1, 2, 5, 10   e 1, 2, 4, 8   f 1, 5
   g 1, 2, 4   h 1, 2, 3, 6   i 1
2 a 2, 3, 5   b 5   c 2, 3, 7
   d 3, 13   e 3, 5, 7
3 a $3 \times 3 \times 5$
   b $2 \times 2 \times 3 \times 3$
   c $2 \times 2 \times 7$
   d $2 \times 2 \times 2 \times 2 \times 5$
   e $2 \times 2 \times 2 \times 3 \times 3$
4 a 4   b 3   c 6   d 2   e 7
5 a 12   b 12   c 60   d 144   e 850
6 a 36, 6   b 360, 60   c 168, 12
   d 910, 13   e 288, 24   f 120, 20
7 120 seconds or 2 minutes
8 20 seconds
9 Yes, for example $2 + 3 = 5$ is prime.
10 4
11 3 boxes of burgers and 4 packets of buns
12 a 11, 13, 17 and 19 are prime numbers between 10 and 20.
    b 23, 29, 31 and 37 are prime numbers between 20 and 40.
    c 37, 41, 43, 47, 53, 59, 61 and 67 are prime numbers between 34 and 68.
13 No. If one of the prime numbers is 2 you will get an even number.

Exercise 1D

1 a 3.6   b 5.3   c 0.1   d 10.7
   e 8.0   f 0.5   g 0.1   h 9.9
2 a i 4.23   ii 4.226   b i 9.79   ii 9.787
   c i 0.42   ii 0.416   d i 0.06   ii 0.058
   e i 10.52 ii 10.517 f i 7.50   ii 7.503
   g i 21.73 ii 21.730 h i 9.09   ii 9.089

3 a i 15.60   ii 15.598   b i 0.41   ii 0.408
   c i 7.25   ii 7.247   d i 6.05   ii 6.051
   e i 29.16 cm   ii 29.158 cm
   f i 0.05 kg   ii 0.055 kg
   g i 13.38 km   ii 13.379 km
   h i £6.00   ii £5.998

Exercise 1E

1 a 40   b 700   c 300   d 0.3
   e 20 000   f 0.007   g 1000   h 5
   i 10   j 20
2 a 0.062   b 0.16   c 96   d 41
   e 730   f 0.079   g 5.7   h 590
3 a 0.0148   b 2220   c 76.2   d 0.380
   e 8.38   f 36.0   g 187   h 0.0666
   i 219 000   j 3 990 000 k 307 000   l 25 600
4 83.3 seconds

Exercise 1F

1 a $60 \times \dfrac{60}{30} = 120$ b $\dfrac{200 \times 300}{200} = 300$
   c $\dfrac{500}{10 \times 50} = 1$
2 $30 \times 5 = £150$
3 a 8000, overestimate   b 4, overestimate
   c 10, underestimate   d 300, overestimate
4 a 50, overestimate   b 4, underestimate
   c 40, overestimate   d 8, overestimate
5 a 1.5, underestimate   b 0.2, overestimate
   c 5, underestimate   d 200, underestimate
   e 400, overestimate   f 210, overestimate
   g 30, underestimate   h 4000, underestimate

Exercise 1G

1 a 1792   b 1792   c 17.92
2 a 146.4   b 1.464   c 0.1464
3 a 726   b 0.726   c 7.26   d 5.5
4 a 0.64   b 0.64   c 64   d 4.75

Exercise 1H

1 a 25   b 13   c 6   d 4
   e −5   f 8   g 6   h 2
   i 1   j 5   k 14   l 52
   m 32   n 15   o 8   p 70
2 a 49   b 25   c 243   d 123
   e 72   f 69   g 7   h −7
3 a 25   b 4   c 8   d 31

Exercise 1I

1 a 6^{12} b 4^5 c 7^6 d 5^6 e 3^{10}
   f 3^4 g 5^9 h 2^6 i 6^5 j 4^2
2 a 100 000   b 125   c 64   d 9
   e 64   f 9   g 16   h 16
   i 10 000   j 49
3 a 5   b 3   c 5   d 4   e 9
   f 3   g 5   h 2   i 4   j 3

Exercise 1J

1 a 7×10^5 b 6×10^2 c 2×10^3
   d 9×10^8 e 8×10^4 f 4.3×10^4
   g 5.61×10^5 h 5.6×10^1 i 3.47×10^1
   j 6×10^1

2 a 600 000   b 10 000   c 800 000
   d 300 000 000   e 70   f 39 600
   g 68 000 000   h 8020   i 57   j 9.23

3 7×10^9

Exercise 1K

1 a 5×10^{-3} b 4×10^{-2} c 7×10^{-6}
   d 9×10^{-1} e 8×10^{-4} f 4.7×10^{-3}
   g 9.87×10^{-1} h 8.034×10^{-4}
   i 1.5×10^{-4} j 6.01×10^{-1}

2 a 0.000 06   b 0.08   c 0.000 000 5
   d 0.3   e 0.000 000 01
   f 0.000 084 3   g 0.0201   h 0.000 000 42
   i 0.078 54   j 0.000 94

3 a 4.57×10^5 b 2.3×10^{-3} c 3×10^{-4}
   d 2.356×10^6 e 7.82×10^{-1}

4 a 0.000 412   b 3000   c 20 650 000
   d 0.000 004   e 327 000 000

5 6.25×10^{-2} mm

Exercise 1L

1 a 4.5×10^4 b 9.8×10^{-1}
   c 3.4×10^1 d 1.86×10^{12}

2 a 9×10^2 b 4.5×10^4
   c 3.708×10^{-13} d 6×10^{-10}

3 a In standard form   b 8.9×10^8
   c 1.32×10^{-4} d 5.6×10^8
   e 6×10^{-4} f In standard form
   g 4.005×10^{-12} h 9.08×10^{18}

4 6 290 000, 6.3×10^6, 63.4×10^5, 0.637×10^7

5 a 5.38×10^4 b 6.20×10^{14} c 5.38×10^{16}
   d 6.20×10^6

Exam practice

1 a 9°C   b 25°C
2 a −4   b 2   c −15   d 10   e −2
3 a −21   b 20   c −8   d 5   e −7
4 a −4°C   b 7°C   c Leeds
5 2 multiplied by another prime number will give an even number.
6 a 11.7   b 1.44   c 0.12
   d 40.96   e 5.1   f 20.35
7 £64.75
8 a −1°C   b 14°C
   c No, because halfway is −2°C.
9 146.2 km
10 She buys 13 bottles and has 16p left.
11 a 57   b 0.103   c 600
12 a 23.5   b 1.8   c 0.3   d 150.0
13 a 7.26   b 73.04   c 0.042   d 0.721
14 a 8300   b 20 100   c 0.5   d 20.9
15 40 × 8 = £320   16 6 ÷ 20 = £0.30 or 30p
17 £42.96   18 31

19 £268.65
20 No. Yusuf's total costs are £1610, his total revenue is only £1600.
21 5 times (every 12 seconds)
22 a −4   b 4   c −2   d 4   e −2
23 a (800 × 5000)/3000 = 1333
   b (4 × 5)/10 = 2
   c (2 × 8)/(4 × 2) = 2
24 a 1632   b 16.32   c 3.4
25 a 15 456   b 0.15456   c 3220
26 It costs £548 to buy from Comp Parts, but only £525 to buy from Z Parts. So, buy from Z Parts.
27 24
28 a 2 × 2 × 3 × 3 × 3   b 12
29 a i 2 × 2 × 3 × 5   ii 2 × 2 × 2 × 2 × 3
   b 12   c 480
30 3 packs of doughnuts, 4 packs of cakes
31 5^3
32 a 32   b 4   c 212   d 52
33 2 × 2 × 2 × 3 × 3
34 a £21   b 32
35 a She buys 3 packs of bread rolls and 5 packs of sausages.
   b 120
36 9, 15
37 It costs £408.75 to stay in June and £470.75 to stay in November. It is cheaper to stay in June.
38 a 75, underestimate   b 150, underestimate
   c 3.6, overestimate   d 6000, overestimate
39 $\dfrac{4000}{200 \times 5} = 4$
40 a 2 × 2 × 2 × 7   b 14
41 a i 7.9×10^3 ii 3.5×10^{-4} b 5×10^7
42 9.3×10^8
43 a False, e.g. 3 + 5 = 8   b False, e.g. 5 − 3 = 2
   c False, e.g. 2 × 3 = 6

Chapter 2 Answers

Exercise 2A

1 a $\frac{3}{18}$ b $\frac{6}{14}$ c $\frac{18}{48}$ d $\frac{12}{21}$ e $\frac{30}{36}$ f $\frac{6}{9}$
  g $\frac{24}{54}$ h $\frac{40}{56}$ i $\frac{90}{100}$ j $\frac{84}{144}$ k $\frac{49}{56}$ l $\frac{18}{81}$

2 a $\frac{8}{20}, \frac{5}{20}, \frac{1}{4}$ b $\frac{10}{20}, \frac{16}{20}, \frac{2}{4}$ c $\frac{8}{12}, \frac{9}{12}, \frac{2}{3}$ d $\frac{6}{10}, \frac{7}{10}, \frac{3}{5}$

3 a $\frac{1}{2}, \frac{2}{3}, \frac{3}{4}$ b $\frac{7}{15}, \frac{4}{5}, \frac{5}{6}$ c $\frac{1}{2}, \frac{3}{4}, \frac{4}{5}$ d $\frac{5}{14}, \frac{3}{7}, \frac{1}{2}, \frac{4}{7}$

Exercise 2B

1 a $2\frac{1}{2}$ b $1\frac{3}{4}$ c $1\frac{2}{7}$ d $1\frac{3}{8}$ e $1\frac{1}{8}$ f $3\frac{1}{5}$
  g $2\frac{3}{10}$ h $4\frac{4}{5}$ i $2\frac{2}{7}$ j $2\frac{2}{5}$ k $6\frac{2}{3}$ l $1\frac{7}{9}$
  m $9\frac{3}{4}$ n $5\frac{2}{5}$ o $2\frac{8}{9}$ p $1\frac{7}{10}$

2 a $\frac{3}{2}$ b $\frac{11}{2}$ c $\frac{11}{4}$ d $\frac{5}{3}$ e $\frac{13}{4}$ f $\frac{22}{5}$
  g $\frac{37}{10}$ h $\frac{26}{5}$ i $\frac{31}{4}$ j $\frac{9}{4}$ k $\frac{19}{10}$ l $\frac{28}{3}$
  m $\frac{17}{6}$ n $\frac{43}{8}$ o $\frac{29}{8}$ p $\frac{109}{100}$

Answers

Exercise 2C

1 a $\frac{3}{4}$ b $\frac{5}{8}$ c $\frac{11}{8} = 1\frac{3}{8}$ d $\frac{5}{6}$
   e $\frac{7}{6} = 1\frac{1}{6}$ f $\frac{7}{10}$ g $\frac{4}{3} = 1\frac{1}{3}$ h $\frac{11}{10} = 1\frac{1}{10}$

2 a $\frac{11}{8} = 1\frac{3}{8}$ b $\frac{17}{20}$ c $\frac{31}{36}$ d $\frac{71}{40} = 1\frac{31}{40}$
   e $\frac{17}{30}$ f $\frac{13}{12} = 1\frac{1}{12}$ g $\frac{23}{24}$ h $\frac{19}{18} = 1\frac{1}{18}$

3 a $\frac{5}{6}$ b $\frac{17}{30}$ c $\frac{33}{40}$ d $\frac{31}{36}$
   e $\frac{53}{42} = 1\frac{11}{42}$ f $\frac{83}{70} = 1\frac{13}{70}$ g $\frac{41}{30} = 1\frac{11}{30}$ h $\frac{31}{35}$

4 a $\frac{29}{8} = 3\frac{5}{8}$ b $\frac{53}{8} = 6\frac{5}{8}$ c $\frac{65}{16} = 4\frac{1}{16}$ d $\frac{35}{8} = 4\frac{3}{8}$
   e $\frac{67}{16} = 4\frac{3}{16}$ f $\frac{89}{30} = 2\frac{29}{30}$ g $\frac{145}{42} = 3\frac{19}{42}$ h $\frac{167}{42} = 3\frac{41}{42}$

5 $7\frac{1}{2}$ miles

Exercise 2D

1 a $\frac{1}{4}$ b $\frac{1}{8}$ c $\frac{1}{8}$ d $\frac{5}{8}$
   e $\frac{1}{2}$ f $\frac{1}{4}$ g $\frac{1}{2}$ h $\frac{1}{5}$

2 a $\frac{1}{6}$ b $\frac{7}{24}$ c $\frac{1}{30}$ d $\frac{13}{30}$
   e $\frac{2}{15}$ f $\frac{3}{20}$ g $\frac{11}{30}$ h $\frac{3}{20}$

3 $\frac{9}{16}$

4 a $\frac{19}{8} = 2\frac{3}{8}$ b $\frac{5}{4} = 1\frac{1}{4}$ c $\frac{11}{5} = 2\frac{1}{5}$ d $\frac{27}{10} = 2\frac{7}{10}$
   e $\frac{9}{10}$ f $\frac{3}{4}$ g $\frac{14}{5} = 2\frac{4}{5}$ h $\frac{77}{24} = 3\frac{5}{24}$

Exercise 2E

1 a $\frac{3}{8}$ b $\frac{3}{32}$ c $\frac{8}{25}$ d $\frac{9}{32}$
   e $\frac{5}{36}$ f $\frac{21}{40}$ g $\frac{9}{50}$ h $\frac{4}{9}$

2 a $\frac{2}{5}$ b $\frac{3}{5}$ c $\frac{1}{2}$ d $\frac{6}{25}$
   e $\frac{5}{8}$ f $\frac{1}{8}$ g $\frac{4}{15}$ h $\frac{4}{7}$

3 a $\frac{7}{2} = 3\frac{1}{2}$ b $\frac{10}{3} = 3\frac{1}{3}$ c $\frac{24}{5} = 4\frac{4}{5}$ d 6
   e 14 f 6 g 4 h 10

4 a 4 b 5 c 7 d 9
   e 7 f 21 g 44 h 181

5 a $\frac{8}{9}$ b $\frac{14}{15}$ c $\frac{3}{8}$ d $\frac{15}{4} = 3\frac{3}{4}$
   e $\frac{13}{8} = 1\frac{5}{8}$ f $\frac{17}{6} = 2\frac{5}{6}$ g $\frac{10}{9} = 1\frac{1}{9}$ h $\frac{7}{4} = 1\frac{3}{4}$

6 a $82\frac{1}{2}$ hours

Exercise 2F

1 a $\frac{4}{3} = 1\frac{1}{3}$ b $\frac{3}{4}$ c $\frac{3}{2} = 1\frac{1}{2}$ d $\frac{5}{7}$
   e $\frac{10}{3} = 3\frac{1}{3}$ f $\frac{15}{8} = 1\frac{7}{8}$ g $\frac{10}{9} = 1\frac{1}{9}$ h $\frac{7}{8}$

2 a 16 b 16 c 10 d $\frac{64}{7} = 9\frac{1}{7}$
   e 5 f $\frac{12}{7} = 1\frac{5}{7}$ g 15 h 24

3 a 5 b $\frac{26}{20}$ c $\frac{5}{3} = 1\frac{2}{3}$ d $\frac{39}{76}$
   e $\frac{1}{2}$ f 2 g $\frac{17}{27}$ h $\frac{21}{40}$

4 a $\frac{3}{32}$ b $\frac{5}{12}$ c $\frac{1}{10}$ d $\frac{4}{25}$
   e $\frac{1}{3}$ f $\frac{13}{24}$ g $\frac{17}{60}$ h $\frac{1}{6}$

Exercise 2G

1 a 5 b 42 c 96 d 45
   e £14 f £84 g £5.60 h £6

2 a 105 b 15
3 28
4 a $\frac{5}{6}$ b $\frac{1}{6}$
5 880 m³ 6 £5.60 7 £78
8 525 9 $4\frac{1}{12}$ hours 10 $\frac{1}{2}$
11 $\frac{7}{8}$ km 12 192 13 £8.40

Exam practice

1 a $\frac{2}{3}$ b $\frac{4}{5}$ c $\frac{3}{4}$ d $\frac{4}{9}$
2 $\frac{4}{5}$ 3 $\frac{1}{3}$, $\frac{3}{10}$, $\frac{29}{100}$, $\frac{4}{15}$
4 a $\frac{2}{15}$ b $\frac{1}{9}$ c $\frac{3}{4}$
5 a $\frac{2}{3}$ b $\frac{5}{9}$ c $\frac{39}{40}$ d $1\frac{1}{36}$ e $\frac{4}{9}$
6 $3\frac{2}{15}$ m
7 $\frac{9}{20}$ 8 $\frac{7}{12}$
9 a $8\frac{1}{2}$ b $1\frac{5}{16}$ c $\frac{98}{125}$
10 $3\frac{1}{3}$
11 a $1\frac{5}{16}$ b $1\frac{3}{4}$ c $2\frac{7}{8}$ d $2\frac{11}{15}$
12 $480 - (320 + 120) = 40$ studied Spanish. $\frac{1}{10}$ of 480 is 48. As $40 < 48$ less than $\frac{1}{10}$ studied Spanish.
13 22 14 Yes, it is $6\frac{2}{16}$ cm long
15 15 glasses

Chapter 3 Answers

Exercise 3A

1 £8.90 2 £56.70 3 14
4 17 days 12 hours
5 a 6.25 b 2209 c 216
   d 32 e 14 641
6 a 299 b 12.71 c 11.221 d 1.2
7 a 25 b 1.6 c 4.7 d 9
8 a 12.2 b 8.94 c 3.11 d 7.52
9 a 12 b 7.7 c 0.2 d 3
10 a $\frac{1}{10}$ b $\frac{1}{4}$ c $\frac{1}{8}$
11 a 0.4 b 0.02 c 0.0625 d 5
   e 8

Exercise 3B

1 a 62.41 b 7.2361 c 79.507 d 2.744
2 a 313 b 1372 c 1199 d 1120
3 a 5.6 b 16 c 4 d 1.5
4 a 4 b 5.2 c 4.5 d 5.2
5 a 1.02415(...) b 5.27441(...) c 0.62222(...)
   d 2.85209(...) e 1.55266(...) f 0.0625
6 a 2.577030498 b 0.8695303339
7 800
8 Jim got it right. Inewara got the 2×4.4 wrong; Gemma got the $\sqrt{10.56} \div (2 \times 4.4)$ wrong and Bill got it all wrong.
9 $4.8 \times (6.4^2 + 6.4) \times 4.8^2 = 5237.63712$; So yes.

Exam practice

1 £3.80   2   80
3 a 8.41   b 1728   c 7.2   d 2.5
4 a 13.7   b 2.2   c 16.8   d 7.4
5 $\frac{5}{6}$ and $\frac{1}{7}$
6 −4.96
7 a 40.1956   b 6.5   c 28.812
8 a 4.05975(...)   b 0.10053(...)   c 1.24531(...)
9 a 2.752380952   b 3
10 2.26541555(...)
11 Recommended daily calorie intakes:
Sophie 655 + (9.6 × 68) + (1.8 × 165) − (4.7 × 32)
= 1454.4
Chelsea 655 + (9.6 × 55) + (1.8 × 175) − (4.7 × 47)
= 1277.1
Kenny 66 + (13.7 × 98) + (5 × 191) − (6.8 × 27)
= 2180
Hassan 66 + (13.7 × 117) + (5 × 182) − (6.8 × 38)
= 2320.5
Hassan has the greatest daily calorie requirement.
Chelsea has the smallest daily calorie requirement.
12 a $1\frac{3}{5}$ b 0.4   c 4
13 11.94117(...)
14 Large costs 380 ÷ 200 = 1.9p per gram
Regular costs 350 ÷ 175 = 2p per gram
So Rob is correct. The regular tub is better value for money.
15 a 0.7966101695   b $\frac{2}{3}$ $\frac{4}{5}$ 0.82 85% $\frac{7}{8}$

Chapter 4 Answers

Exercise 4A

1 a £12   b 40 kg   c 8 m   d 57p
   e £6   f 14 km   g 3 kg   h £14
2 No, he has saved £3540
3 £5400   4 £72   5 £42   6 £16 280

Exercise 4B

1 a £4.80   b 38.7 kg   c £199.80   d 32 km
2 115   3 £48   4 £7.50   5 £14.70
6 £5.60 profit

Exercise 4C

1 £96.57   2 £27 295   3 £611.60
4 £57.60   5 £3726   6 £7200
7 £1.47
8 a £59.50   b £153   c £11.90
9 £108
10 a £255   b £34   c £1020
11 77.9 kg

Exercise 4D

1 £1102.50   2 £815.81   3 £250 880   4 £8670
5 a 1.1136   b £66 816
6 No. It is the same as an increase of 68%.
7 8 years

Exercise 4E

1 45%
2 a 50%   b 25%   c 40%   d 20%
   e 25%   f 25%   g 60%   h 12.5%
3 90%   4 45%
5 a 20%   b 60%   c 11.25%   d 8.75%

Exercise 4F

1 a +50%   b +60%   c −12%   d −8%
2 15%   3 40%
4 Shop C – as percentage increases are
A 5.19%, B 4.77%, C 5.50%

Exam practice

1 a $\frac{3}{5}$ b 45%
2 30%
3 a 0.92   b $\frac{3}{100}$ c 20 g
4 a £240   b 5 kg   c 10.5 kg   d £10.50
5 a 20 g   b 60 g
6 23% $\frac{1}{3}$ 0.38 $\frac{3}{5}$ 70% 0.8
7 22.5 g
8 a £249   b £357   c £6600
9 60 480
10 Emma, Majda got 67.5%
11 Sheds For U $\frac{75}{100}$ × 320 = £240
Garden World $17\frac{1}{2}$% of £210 = £36.75
                210 + 36.75 = £246.75
Ed's Sheds $\frac{2}{3}$ × 345 = £230
Jack should buy his shed at Ed's Sheds.
12 £423   13 £17   14 £17.04
15 a 55%   b 60%   c 56.25%
16 After 1 year = 1 × 1.1 = 1.1
After 2 years = 1 × 1.05 = 1.155 = 15.5%
Ziggy is not correct. Rachael had a 15.5% pay rise over the two years.
17 £405   18 £4867.20   19 £8400

Chapter 5 Answers

Exercise 5A

1 4 : 3
2 5 : 9 : 6
3 a 1 : 3   b 2 : 5   c 1 : 4   d 3 : 10
4 a 3 : 1   b 1 : 3
5 a $\frac{1}{10}$ b $\frac{7}{10}$
6 1 : 2
7 a 1 : 2.5   b 1 : 2.4   c 1 : 0.3   d 1 : 1.25
8 1 : 14.5
9 7 adults
10 a $\frac{4}{9}$ b 4 : 5   c 1 : 1.25

Exercise 5B

1 a 4   b 6   c 20
2 a 200 m*l*   b 750 m*l*
3 1.25 litres   4 400 cm   5 720 cm   6 6 km
7 15   8 £6   9 40 *l*

Exercise 5C

1 £1.20 **2** £74.90
3 200 g flour, 100 g margarine, 150 g cheese
4 **a** 525 g **b** 75 g **c** 75 g
5 216 euros
6 **a** $426 **b** £250
7 £40 **8** $58.50
9 **a** 4 days **b** 5 days
10 2 hours **11** 8

Exam practice

1 5 : 2
2 45 apples **3** 10 British cars
4 **a** 50 cm **b** 16 m
5 110 green counters
6 900 g of sugar, 18 g of butter, 720 g of condensed milk, 135 m*l* of milk
7 **a** €280 **b** £8
8 5:03 pm **9** Paris
10 **a** £775 **b** £2
11 45 litres **12** 192 cm **13** £80

Chapter 6 Answers

Exercise 6A

1 $7h + 2$ **2** $6m + 1$ **3** $-3p - 4q$
4 $-5e - 1$ **5** $-2g - 3h$ **6** $2p^2 - 5r^3$
7 $-3k$ **8** $-m^3 - 8n$ **9** $-2a - 5b$
10 $-ab$ **11** $-2m - 2$ **12** $-3p - 6$
13 $-e - f$ **14** $-2g^2 - 2$ **15** $-4p + 2r + 2$
16 $-2j + 3k$ **17** $-8n - 5$ **18** $3a - 8b$
19 $-3p - 7j$ **20** -8 **21** $-4x + 1$
22 0 **23** $-3g^3$ **24** $-8mn + 2m^2$

Exercise 6B

1 $20h^2$ **2** $25s^2$ **3** $12t^3$ **4** $12rt$ **5** $35xy$
6 $18mn$ **7** $30abc$ **8** $4g^2$ **9** $49h^2$ **10** $8x^3$
11 $25n^2$ **12** $30fgh$ **13** $24jk$ **14** $36hi$ **15** $4a^2b$
16 $4p$ **17** p **18** 4 **19** $4n$ **20** $2t$
21 15 **22** $6k$ **23** $2a$ **24** $2x$ **25** 3
26 $5x$ **27** 8 **28** $2p$ **29** 2 **30** $4c$

Exercise 6C

1 $5a - 20$ **2** $6n + 12$ **3** $20 - 5h$
4 $21 - 3w$ **5** $6a - 15$ **6** $12n + 42$
7 $20 - 15h$ **8** $21 - 12w$ **9** $a^2 + 4a$
10 $2y^2 - 2y$ **11** $5g + g^2$ **12** $4h - 5h^2$
13 $10p^2 + 15p$ **14** $15x^2 - 5xy$ **15** $5x + 14$
16 $20x + 17$ **17** $23x + 14$
18 $28x + 12$ or $12 - 8x$ **19** $9 - 21x$
20 $15 - 23x$ **21** $12x - 22y$ **22** $22y - 2x$
23 $x^2 + 8x - 10$ **24** $2y^2 + y + 8$

Exercise 6D

1 **a** $2(x + 3)$ **b** $2(3y + 1)$ **c** $5(3b - 1)$
  d $x(3 + 5y)$ **e** $4(3x + 2y)$ **f** $4(3x - 4)$

2 **a** $x(3x + 4)$ **b** $y(5y - 3)$ **c** $b(5b - 2)$
  d $c(7 - 3c)$ **e** $m(6m - 1)$ **f** $x(4y + 3)$
3 **a** $4x(2x + 1)$ **b** $3p(2p + 1)$ **c** $3x(2x 2 1)$
  d $3b(b - 3)$ **e** $3a(4 + a)$ **f** $5c(3 - 2c)$
4 **a** $ax(x 1 1)$ **b** $pr(r - 1)$ **c** $ab(b - 1)$
  d $q(r^2 + q)$ **e** $ax(a + x)$ **f** $3a^2(2a - 3)$
5 **a** $6ab(2a + 3b)$ **b** $2xy(2x - y)$
  c $4ab(a + 2b + 3)$ **d** $2xy(2x + 3y - 1)$
  e $3ax(4x + 2a - 1)$ **f** $abc(a + b + c)$
6 **a** $5(x + 4)$ **b** $2(6y - 5)$ **c** $x(3x + 5)$
  d $y(4 - 3y)$ **e** $2a(4 + 3a)$ **f** $4b(3b - 2)$
  g $cy(y + 1)$ **h** $3dx(x - 2)$ **i** $3cd(3c + 5d)$
7 **a** $a(x + y)$ **b** 39 000

Exercise 6E

1 15 **2** 3 **3** 15 **4** 18
5 8 **6** 19 **7** 7 **8** 10
9 27 **10** 10 **11** 0 **12** 3
13 36 **14** 40 **15** -8 **16** -5
17 35 **18** 2 **19** 76 **20** 4
21 102 **22** 20 **23** -36 **24** -20
25 **a** 8 **b** 5 **c** 30 **d** 9 **e** 40
  f 18 **g** 9 **h** 26 **i** 64

Exercise 6F

1 18 **2** -2 **3** -36 **4** 2
5 -18 **6** -30 **7** 54 **8** 30
9 -6 **10** -15 **11** -20 **12** 25
13 6 **14** 97 **15** 14 **16** 65
17 16 **18** 1 **19** 1 **20** 49
21 9 **22** 432 **23** -375 **24** -48
25 32 **26** -11 **27** -27
28 Meg. $2 \times 4^2 = 2 \times 16 = 32$

Exercise 6G

1 **a** x^{10} **b** y^{11} **c** x^{14}
2 **a** a^8 **b** b^6 **c** d^{11}
3 **a** p^3 **b** q^{10} **c** t^4
4 **a** j^6 **b** k **c** n^2
5 **a** x^9 **b** y^9 **c** z^{10}
6 **a** $6x^5$ **b** $15y^{29}$ **c** $24z^{10}$
7 **a** $3p^5$ **b** $5q^2$ **c** $2r^3$
8 **a** d^{12} **b** e^{10} **c** f^9 **d** g^{63}
9 **a** g^{24} **b** h^4 **c** 1 **d** 1
10 **a** $2187d^{14}$ **b** $64e^3$ **c** 1
11 **a** 1 **b** b^4 **c** c^{10}
12 **a** $8d^{10}$ **b** $2e^4$ **c** $16f^4$
13 **a** x **b** y^6 **c** z^8
14 **a** $7d^3$ **b** $2e^5$ **c** $3f^7$
15 **a** $9g^{10}$ **b** $16h^8$ **c** $100i^{24}$
16 Davish. $(2x^4)^3 = 2^3 x^{4 \times 3} = 8x^{12}$
17 **a** $5a^2b^4$ **b** $5pq^3$ **c** $4c^2d^4$ **d** $3x^5$
  e $10m^2n$
18 **a** $16x^{12}y^8$ **b** $49e^{10}f^6$ **c** $125p^{15}q^3$ **d** $\dfrac{8x^9}{27y^6}$
19 **a** $\dfrac{1}{a}$ **b** $\dfrac{1}{b^2}$ **c** $\dfrac{1}{c^2}$ **d** $\dfrac{1}{d^3}$
20 **a** $\dfrac{1}{e^6}$ **b** $\dfrac{1}{f^8}$ **c** x^2 **d** y

Exercise 6H

1
 a $x^2 + 7x + 12$ **b** $x^2 + 3x + 2$
 c $x^2 - 3x - 10$ **d** $y^2 + y - 6$
 e $y^2 - y - 2$ **f** $x^2 - 5x + 6$
 g $a^2 - 9a + 20$ **h** $x^2 + 4x + 4$
 i $k^2 - 14k + 49$

2
 a $2x^2 + 3x + 1$ **b** $3x^2 - 2x - 1$
 c $3y^2 - 8y - 3$ **d** $2p^2 + 7p + 3$
 e $6s^2 + 19s + 10$ **f** $4x^2 + 4x - 15$
 g $6a^2 - 7a + 2$ **h** $9x^2 + 12x + 4$
 i $4k^2 - 4k + 1$

3
 a $x^2 + 3xy + 2y^2$ **b** $x^2 + xy - 2y^2$
 c $x^2 - 3xy + 2y^2$ **d** $6s^2 - 7st + 2t^2$
 e $4a^2 + 12ab + 9b^2$ **f** $4a^2 - 12ab + 9b^2$

Exercise 6I

1
 a $(x + 3)(x + 5)$ **b** $(x + 1)(x + 7)$
 c $(x + 4)(x + 5)$ **d** $(x - 5)(x - 1)$
 e $(x - 8)(x - 1)$ **f** $(x - 1)^2$
 g $(x - 3)(x + 6)$ **h** $(x - 6)(x + 3)$
 i $(x - 4)(x + 7)$ **j** $(x - 4)(x + 3)$
 k $(x - 4)(x + 6)$ **l** $(x - 2)(x + 2)$
 m $(x - 9)(x + 9)$ **n** $(y + 8)(y - 8)$
 o $(a + 1)(a - 1)$ **p** $(a + 4)(a + 3)$
 q $(b + 5)(b - 4)$ **r** $(c + 5)(c + 3)$
 s $(d - 2)(d - 1)$ **t** $(e + 6)(e - 2)$
 u $(f + 3)(f - 7)$ **v** $(t + 6)(t - 5)$
 w $(y + 6)(y - 7)$ **x** $(p + 1)^2$
 y $(r + 3)(r - 3)$ **z** $(s - 5)(s - 8)$

Exam practice

1 **a** $3c$ **b** $2x + 6y$
2 $8a + 4x$
3 **a** $10x - 20y$ **b** 210
4 **a** $3a$ **b** $3e + 2f$ **c** $5a$
 d $4xy$ **e** $2a + 7b + 8$
5 **a** $3bc$ **b** $2x + 5y$ **c** m^3 **d** $6np$
6 $x(x + 4)$
7 $12a - 28$
8 **a** $5(x + 3y)$ **b** $3(5p - 3q)$ **c** $c(d + e)$
9 **a** $5(p - 4)$ **b** $x = 5.5$
10 **a** 5 **b** -23
11 **a** 87 **b** 22 **c** 7.5 **d** 8
12 20
13 **a** 80 **b** 29.5
14 **a** -5 **b** 73
15 **a** x^9 **b** x^3 **c** x^{15} **d** x
 e x^5 **f** x^{12} **g** 1 **h** x^6
 i x^{11} **j** x^9 **k** x^3 **l** x^{11}
16 **a** $4x^8$ **b** $15x^8$ **c** $21x^5$ **d** $4x^4$
 e $8x^5$ **f** $9x$ **g** x^{10} **h** x^9
17 **a** a^7 **b** $15x^3y^4$
18 **a** $9ab - 6a^2 - 4b^2$ **b** $11pq + 18p^2$
 c $13c^2 + 12cd$ **d** $a^2 + 2ab + b^2$
 e $5ab + ac - bc$ **f** $-4ab - 4ac - 9bc$
19 **a** $x(x - 7)$ **b** $t(t + a)$ **c** $x(bx - 1)$
 d $p(3p + y)$ **e** $a(q^2 - t)$
20 **a** $x(x - 5)$ **b** $10\,500$

21 7 **22** $5x - 2$
23 **a** $5(m + 2)$ **b** $y(y - 3)$
24 $x^2 + 4x + 3$
25 **a** $13x + 3$ **b i** $5(x + 2)$ **ii** $x(x - 7)$
26 **a i** e^{11} **ii** e^8 **b** $5x + 2y$
27 $x^2 - x - 12$
28 **a** $a^2 + 4a + 4$ **b** $c^2 - 6c + 9$
 c $d^2 + 2d + 1$ **d** $x^2 + 2xy + y$
29 **a** $x^2 + 15x + 50$ **b** $y^2 + 18y + 81$
 c $x^2 - 2x - 8$ **d** $x^2 - x - 6$
 e $t^2 - 7t + 6$ **f** $2x^2 + 11x + 12$
 g $6p^2 + p - 1$ **h** $4c^2 - d^2$
 i $16y^2 - 8y + 1$
30 **a** $(t + 5)(t + 6)$ **b** $(x + 7)^2$
 c $(p + 5)(p - 3)$ **d** $(y - 6)^2$
 e $(x - 4)(x - 1)$ **f** $(s - 8)(s + 8)$
31 **a** $3x + 6$ **b** $6xy(2x^2 - 3y)$
 c $2x^2 + 5x - 12$ **d** $10x^7y^5$
32 $8x^2 + 6xy - 20y^2$
33 **a** $4wy(5w + 6y^2)$ **b** $(m + 8)(m - 5)$
34 **a** a^{20} **b** $9b^8$ **c** $27e^{15}f^3$
35 Three consecutive even numbers are $2n$, $2n + 2$, $2n + 4$.
 Their sum $= 2n + 2n + 2 + 2n + 4 = 6n + 6$, which is always a multiple of 6.
36 $\dfrac{6x^2y}{4y^3} = \dfrac{3x^2}{2y^2}$. Squared numbers cannot be negative.
37 **a** $(x - 20)(x + 20)$ **b** $(3t - 2)(3t + 2)$
 c $(10 - y)(10 + y)$ **d** $(5 - 2p)(5 + 2p)$
38 **a** 41 **b** 1.99 **c** 16

Chapter 7 Answers

Exercise 7A

1 **a** 13, 16; add 3 **b** 23, 28; add 5
 c 12, 10; subtract 2 **d** 17, 10; subtract 7
 e 16, 32; multiply by 2 **f** 250, 1250; multiply by 5
 g 4, 2; divide by 2 **h** 50, 10; divide by 5

2 **a** 17, 20; add 3 **b** 31, 37; add 6
 c 15, 12; subtract 3 **d** 37, 31; subtract 6
 e 32, 64; multiply by 2 **f** 324, 972; multiply by 3
 g 4, 2; divide by 2 **h** 30, 10; divide by 3

3 question 1
 a 28 **b** 48 **c** 2 **d** -18
 question 2
 a 29 **b** 55 **c** 0 **d** 7

4 question 1
 e 128 **f** 156 250 **g** 0.5 **h** 0.08
 question 2
 e 256 **f** 8748 **g** 0.5 **h** $1.\dot{1}$ or $1\frac{1}{9}$

5

Day	M	Tu	W	Th	F
Money left at end of day (£)	17	14	11	8	5

£5

6 17 weeks

7 **a**

Month	1	2	3	4	5
Number of rabbits	2	4	8	16	32

 b 1024 rabbits

8 a

Years	0	10	20	30	40
Number of atoms	2560	1280	640	320	160

b 2.5 atoms

9 a 5, 9, 13

b

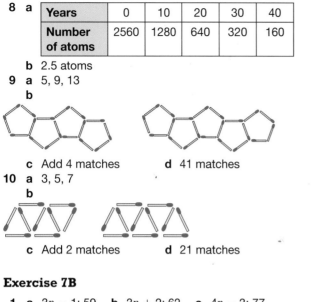

c Add 4 matches **d** 41 matches

10 a 3, 5, 7

b

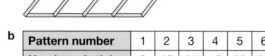

c Add 2 matches **d** 21 matches

Exercise 7B

1 a $3n - 1$; 59 **b** $3n + 2$; 62 **c** $4n - 3$; 77
 d $5n - 3$; 97 **e** $5n + 3$; 103 **f** $45 - 5n$; -55
 g $38 - 3n$; -22 **h** $22 - 2n$; -18

2 a

b

Pattern number	1	2	3	4	5	6
Number of sticks	6	10	14	18	22	26

c $4n + 2$ **d** 82 sticks

3 a The sequence is of all the odd numbers, so 21 is a member of the number pattern because it is an odd number. 34 is not in the pattern as it is not an odd number.
 b The nth term is $3n - 1$. If 50 is in the pattern, $50 = 3n - 1$, giving $n = 17$, so 50 is in the pattern. None of the terms are a multiple of 3. 66 is a multiple of 3, so 66 is not in the pattern.
 c The nth term is $3n + 2$. If 50 is in the pattern, $50 = 3n + 2$, giving $n = 16$, so 50 is in the pattern. The nth term is $3n + 2$. If 62 is in the pattern, $62 = 3n + 2$, giving $n = 20$, so 62 is in the pattern.
 d The sequence contains all the numbers ending in 2 or 7, so 97 is in the pattern. All the numbers end in 2 or 7, so 120 is not in the pattern.
 e The sequence contains all the numbers below 45 ending in 0 or 5, so 85 is not in the pattern, as it is higher than 40. All the numbers end in 0 or 5, so 4 is not in the pattern.
 f All the terms are odd, so 46 is not in the pattern. The nth term is $4n - 1$. If 79 is in the pattern, $79 = 4n - 1$, giving $n = 20$, so 79 is in the pattern.

4 No. The 49th and 50th terms are 199 and 203.

5 a £172 **b** $11n$

Exam practice

1 a

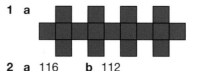

b 41 squares

2 a 116 **b** 112
 c No. 9 is an odd number and all the terms in the sequence are even.

3 No. When $n = 9$, $n^2 + 4 = 85$, which is not a prime number.

4 a 8, 13 **b** 55

5 Dylan could be right if you are doubling the previous term. Evie could be right if the difference between the terms was increasing by one.

6 a Pattern 4 is even so 5 white rectangles are added to the existing 4 white and 6 black to get 9 white and 6 black rectangles.
 b 25 **c** 5151

7 The nth term is $3n + 2$. If 140 is in the sequence, $140 = 3n + 2$, giving $n = 46$, so 140 is in the sequence.

8 $x = 4.5$

9 a 31 **b** $4n - 1$

10 2, 5, 10

11 a

b 37
 c No. Because he will need 61 sticks for pattern number 20, or, 70 sticks will be needed for pattern number 23.

Chapter 8 Answers

Exercise 8A

1 a i

x	-3	-2	-1	0	1	2	3
$y = x - 1$	-4	-3	-2	-1	0	1	2

ii

x	-3	-2	-1	0	1	2	3
$y = 2x - 4$	-10	-8	-6	-4	-2	0	2

iii

x	-3	-2	-1	0	1	2	3
$y = 3x + 1$	-8	-5	-2	1	4	7	10

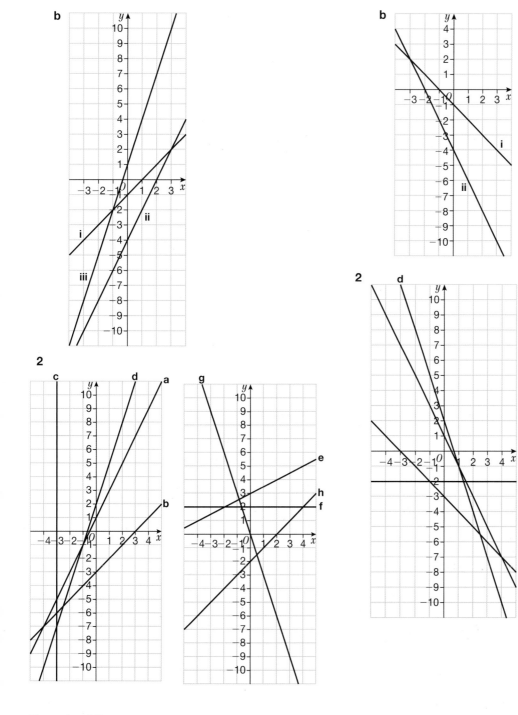

Exercise 8B

1 a i

x	-3	-2	-1	0	1	2	3
$y = -x - 1$	2	1	0	-1	-2	-3	-4

ii

x	-3	-2	-1	0	1	2	3
$y = -2x + 4$	2	0	-2	-4	-6	-8	-10

3

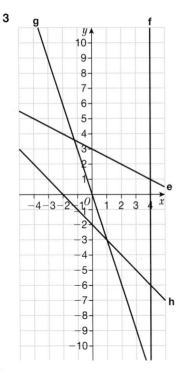

3

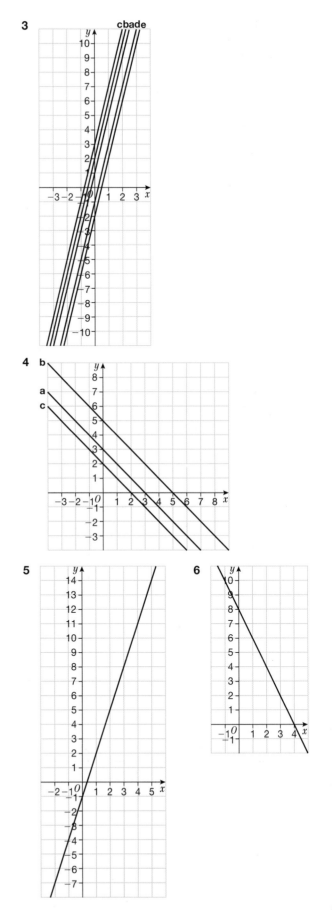

Exercise 8C

1

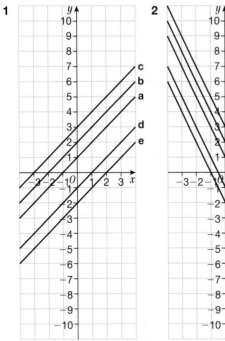

2

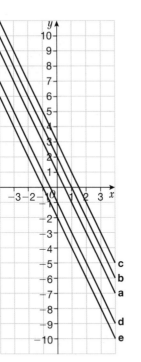

Exercise 8D

1 a $y = x + 3$ b $y = 2x + 1$ c $x + y = 4$
   d $y = -\frac{4}{3}x + 1$
2 a $y = -1$ b $y = 3x + 2$ c $y = -\frac{1}{2}x + 1$
   d $x = 3$ e $y = -2x - 1$

Exercise 8E

1 a (1, 2)   b (3.5, −0.5)   c (−1.5, 3)
   d (−2.5, −0.5) e (−4, 0.5)   f (−0.5, −2)
   g (2.5, −0.5)   h (0.5, 2.5)   i (−2, 3)
   j (4.5, −0.5)
2 a (1.5, 0.5)   b (4, 1)
   c (1.5, 1)   d (3.5, 2.5)
3 a (4, 4)   b (−2, 2.5)   c (−3, 4.5)
   d (2, −2.5)

Exercise 8F

1 a

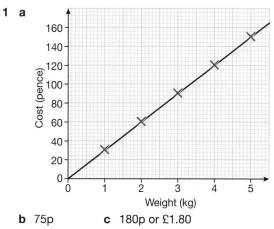

   b 75p   c 180p or £1.80

2 a

Usage time in minutes	Cost in pounds
0	15
5	15.5
10	16
15	16.5
20	17
25	17.5
30	18
35	18.5
40	19
45	19.5
50	20

b

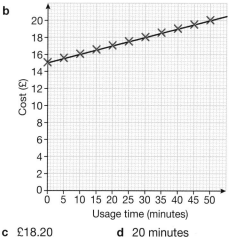

   c £18.20   d 20 minutes
3 a Tariff 1 B   Tariff 2 A   Tariff 3 C
   b Tariff 2 would be cheapest because the cost of £24 is the lowest of the three tariffs.
4 a Upper line A, Lower line B
   b £7.50   c 40 km
   d Taxi firm B. The cost was £5. Taxi firm C cost £6 while taxi firm A cost £6.25.

Exercise 8G

1 a 10 minutes   b 300 m   c 15 minutes
   d 15 minutes
   e 30 m per minute = 1.8 km per hour
   f 20 m per minute = 1.2 km per hour
2 A→B: The depth of the water goes up 10 cm to 30 cm in 5 minutes.
   B→C: The depth stays at 30 cm for 5 minutes.
   C→D: Imran gets into the bath and the depth increases to 60 cm.
   D→E: The depth stays constant at 60 cm for 15 minutes.
   E→F: Imran takes the plug out and the depth decreases from 60 cm to zero in 5 minutes.
3 a

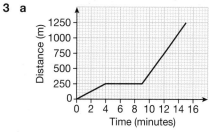

   b 167 m per minute = 10 km per hour
4 a 12 km   b 24 km   c 36 km/h
   d

Answers

Exercise 8H

1 a i

x	-3	-2	-1	0	1	2	3
$y = x^2 + 2$	11	6	3	2	3	6	11

ii

x	-3	-2	-1	0	1	2	3
$y = -x^2 + 1$	-8	-3	0	1	0	-3	-8

b

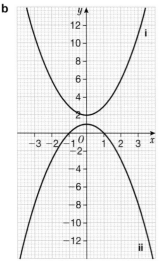

2 a i

x	-3	-2	-1	0	1	2	3
$y = 2x^2 - 1$	17	7	1	-1	1	7	17

ii

x	-3	-2	-1	0	1	2	3
$y = -2x^2 - 1$	-19	-9	-3	-1	-3	-9	-19

b

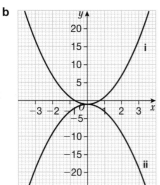

3

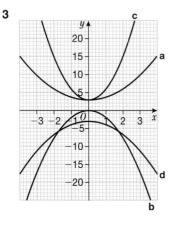

Exercise 8I

1 a

x	-3	-2	-1	0	1	2	3
x^2	$+9$	$+4$	$+1$	0	$+1$	$+4$	$+9$
$2x$	-6	-4	-2	0	$+2$	$+4$	$+6$
$+1$	$+1$	$+1$	$+1$	$+1$	$+1$	$+1$	$+1$
$y = x^2 + 2x + 1$	4	1	0	1	4	9	16

b

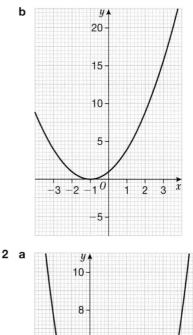

2 a

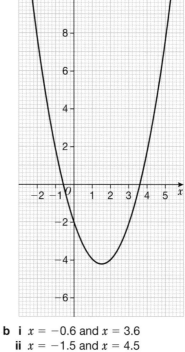

b i $x = -0.6$ and $x = 3.6$
ii $x = -1.5$ and $x = 4.5$

3 a

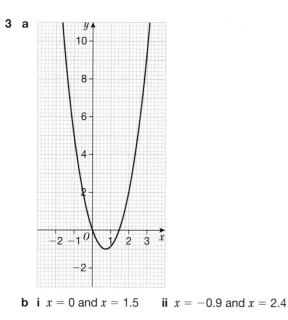

b i $x = 0$ and $x = 1.5$ **ii** $x = -0.9$ and $x = 2.4$

Exam practice

1 a 11 gallons **b** 27.5 litres **c** £57.50
d £5.18

2

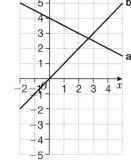

c $x = 2.67$

3

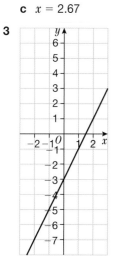

4

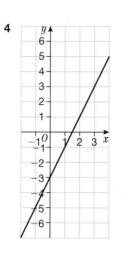

5 (6.5, 7)

6 a

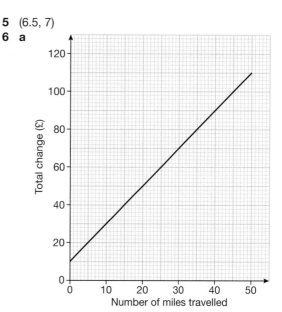

b Up to 20 miles

7 a

x	−2	−1	0	1	2
y	−5	−1	3	7	11

b

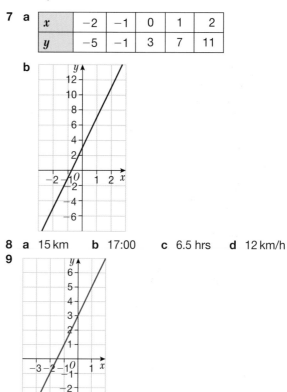

8 a 15 km **b** 17:00 **c** 6.5 hrs **d** 12 km/h

9

10 a

x	−2	−1	0	1	2	3
y	−2	0	2	4	6	8

b

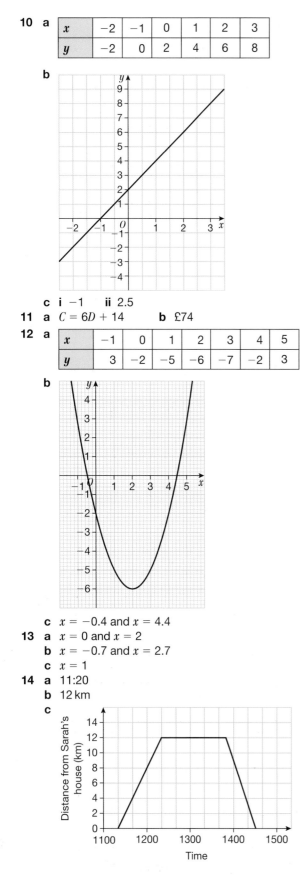

c i −1 **ii** 2.5

11 a $C = 6D + 14$ **b** £74

12 a

x	−1	0	1	2	3	4	5
y	3	−2	−5	−6	−7	−2	3

b

c $x = -0.4$ and $x = 4.4$

13 a $x = 0$ and $x = 2$

b $x = -0.7$ and $x = 2.7$

c $x = 1$

14 a 11:20

b 12 km

c

15 a £5

b Jill's taxi is more expensive for journeys up to 10 miles. A journey of 10 miles costs £15 in both taxis. Jill's is cheaper thereafter.

16 (Students' completed graphs). For mileages greater than 5 use Aleph Taxis. Otherwise use Kari Cabs.

17 (1, 5)

18 a 20°C **b** 25 seconds **c** 50°C

19 a

x	−2	−1	0	1	2	3
y	−15	−8	−7	−6	1	20

b

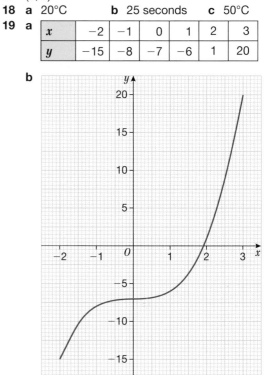

Chapter 9 Answers

Exercise 9A

1 $s = 3$	**2** $d = 3$	**3** $h = 4$
4 $k = 9$	**5** $p = 1\frac{2}{5}$	**6** $f = 3\frac{1}{4}$
7 $g = -2\frac{2}{7}$	**8** $f = 4\frac{1}{4}$	**9** $s = -5\frac{2}{3}$
10 $j = 3\frac{2}{3}$	**11** $r = 3\frac{1}{2}$	**12** $t = -3\frac{2}{5}$
13 $e = -\frac{1}{3}$	**14** $f = -1\frac{1}{4}$	**15** $h = -1$
16 $z = 4$	**17** $x = 25$	**18** $p = 4$
19 $c = -18$	**20** $a = 48$	**21** $e = -24$

Exercise 9B

1 $a = 19$	**2** $b = 0$	**3** $c = 24$
4 $d = 10$	**5** $e = 6$	**6** $f = 16$
7 $g = 6$	**8** $h = 21$	**9** $m = 7$
10 $p = \frac{1}{3}$	**11** $q = 0$	**12** $v = \frac{4}{5}$
13 $x = -6$	**14** $y = 1\frac{2}{3}$	**15** $c = -1$
16 $b = 4\frac{1}{2}$	**17** $d = 7$	**18** $n = 15$
19 $t = -4$	**20** $c = \frac{2}{3}$	

Exercise 9C

1 $a = -4$	**2** $c = 5$	**3** $p = 6$
4 $b = 1$	**5** $q = 3$	**6** $x = 3$
7 $d = 5$	**8** $y = 3$	**9** $n = 7$
10 $k = 0$	**11** $u = 2\frac{1}{2}$	**12** $r = 2\frac{2}{5}$
13 $v = 4\frac{2}{3}$	**14** $t = \frac{4}{5}$	**15** $m = 2\frac{1}{2}$
16 $g = \frac{5}{6}$	**17** $b = \frac{1}{2}$	**18** $h = 1\frac{1}{3}$
19 $e = 4\frac{1}{2}$	**20** $f = \frac{2}{3}$	**21** $x = \frac{3}{5}$
22 $x = 9$	**23** $x = -6$	**24** $= -\frac{1}{2}$
25 $x = -15$	**26** $x = \frac{1}{4}$	**27** $x = -2$
28 $x = 4\frac{1}{10}$	**29** $y = 2$	**30** $x = -1\frac{1}{2}$

Exercise 9D

1 $x = 2$	**2** $x = 4$	**3** $x = 13$
4 $x = 2$	**5** $x = 1$	**6** $x = 3$
7 $x = 1$	**8** $x = 1$	**9** $x = 8$
10 $x = 2$	**11** $x = 1$	**12** $x = 4$
13 $x = -3$	**14** $x = 0$	**15** $x = 2\frac{1}{2}$
16 $x = \frac{3}{5}$	**17** $x = -1$	**18** $x = 1\frac{2}{3}$
19 $x = -2$	**20** $x = -\frac{2}{3}$	

Exercise 9E

1 $a = 40°$, largest angle is $80°$ **2** $130°, 80°, 150°$
3 8 cm, 9 cm, 7 cm   **4** 11
5 $y = 7$ **6** 52 years
7 $x = 6, y = 4$

Exercise 9F

1 $x = 1.8$ **2** $x = 4.4$ **3** $x = 7.9$ **4** $x = 2.81$

Exercise 9G

1
a $4 < 6$	**b** $5 > 2$ **c** $12 > 8$
d $6 = 6$	**e** $15 > 8$ **f** $3 < 24$
g $10 > 3$	**h** $0 < 0.1$ **i** $6 > 0.7$
j $4.5 = 4.5$	**k** $0.2 < 0.5$ **l** $4.8 > 4.79$

2
a True	**b** False, $2 < 6$
c False, $6 = 6$	**d** False, $6 < 8$
e False, $6 > 5$	**f** False, $8 < 14$
g False, $7 > 6.99$	**h** False, $6 < 6.01$
i False $7 > 0$	**j** False, $4 = 4$
k False, $6 > 4$	**l** True

3
a 5	**b** 4, 5, 6, 7
c 0, 1, 2, 3	**d** 4, 5
e 2, 3, 4	**f** 3, 4, 5
g 4, 5, 6	**h** $-2, -1, 0, 1, 2, 3$
i 0, 1, 2, 3, 4	**j** $-1, 0, 1, 2, 3, 4, 5, 6$
k $-3, -2, -1, 0, 1, 2$	**l** $-4, -3, -2, -1, 0, 1, 2$
m 1, 2, 3, 4	**n** 0, 1, 2, 3, 4
o $-5, -4, -3, -2, -1$	**p** $-3, -2, -1, 0, 1, 2, 3$

Exercise 9H

1
a number line 0 to 10: open circle at 6, line extending right
b number line 0 to 10: open circle at 5, line extending right
c number line 0 to 10: line extending left to open circle at 4
d number line 0 to 10: open circle at 8, line extending right
e number line 0 to 10: line extending left to open circle at 6
f number line 0 to 10: open circle at 9, line extending right

2
a number line 0 to 10: open circle at 3 to open circle at 7
b number line 0 to 10: open circle at 5 to open circle at 8
c number line 0 to 10: closed circle at 4 to open circle at 8
d number line 0 to 10: open circle at 6 to closed circle at 8
e number line 0 to 10: closed circle at 4 to closed circle at 6
f number line 0 to 10: open circle at 3 to closed circle at 8
g number line 0 to 10: closed circle at 3 to open circle at 5
h number line 0 to 10: open circle at 4 to open circle at 7

3
a number line -5 to 5: closed circle at -5 to open circle at 5
b number line -5 to 5: open circle at -2 to open circle at 5
c number line -5 to 5: open circle at -2 to closed circle at 3
d number line -5 to 5: closed circle at -4 to closed circle at -1
e number line -5 to 5: open circle at 1 to open circle at 4
f number line -5 to 5: open circle at -2 to closed circle at 2
g number line -5 to 5: closed circle at -3 to open circle at 1
h number line -5 to 5: closed circle at 0 to closed circle at 3

Answers

4 a $2 < x \leqslant 6$ **b** $7 \leqslant x \leqslant 8$ **c** $1 < x < 6$
 d $3 \leqslant x < 7$ **e** $-3 < x \leqslant 1$ **f** $-1 \leqslant x \leqslant 3$
 g $-4 < x < 1$ **h** $-3 \leqslant x < 4$

Exercise 9I

1 $x < 4$ **2** $x \geqslant 6$ **3** $x \leqslant 6$
4 $x > 6$ **5** $x < 9$ **6** $x > 4$
7 $x \geqslant 0$ **8** $x \leqslant 5$ **9** $x \geqslant 3$
10 $x < 2$ **11** $x > 3$ **12** $x \geqslant 1$
13 $x > 2\frac{3}{4}$

14 $x \leqslant \frac{1}{2}$

15 $x \geqslant -2$

16 $x > 1\frac{1}{4}$

17 $x < -1\frac{1}{2}$

18 $x \leqslant \frac{3}{4}$

19 2, 3, 4   **20** $-3, -2, -1, 0, 1$
21 $-2, -1, 0, 1$ **22** 0, 1, 2, 3
23 $-3, -2, -1, 0$ **24** 1, 2
25 $-1, 0, 1, 2, 3$ **26** $-2, -1, 0, 1, 2$
27 $-3, -2, -1$ **28** $x > -3$
29 $x > -8$ **30** $x \geqslant 2\frac{3}{4}$
31 $x \leqslant -\frac{2}{3}$ **32** $x > \frac{7}{8}$
33 $x > 1$ **34** $x \leqslant -1$
35 $x > 0$ **36** $x < 3$
37 $x \geqslant 6$ **38** $x \leqslant 3$
39 $x \geqslant 2$
40 $x > -4\frac{2}{3}$, smallest integer satisfying inequality is -4
41 $x \leqslant -\frac{3}{5}$, largest integer satisfying inequality is -1
42 $x = 43$
43 $3\frac{1}{5}\,\text{cm} < x < 5\frac{1}{5}\,\text{cm}$
44 a The sum of the two shorter sides is always larger than the longest side on a triangle.
 b 3

`Exercise 9J

1 $x = 4, y = 1$ **2** $x = 5, y = 3$
3 $x = 1, y = -2$ **4** $x = 2, y = 1$
5 $x = 1, y = 4$ **6** $x = 1, y = 2$
7 $x = -1, y = -1$ **8** $x = -2, y = -1$
9 $x = 0.5, y = 2$ **10** $x = 1, y = -2$
11 Pen costs £0.45, pencil costs £0.15

Exam practice

1 a $d = 12$ **b** $x = 3$ **c** $b = 4$
2 a $r = 3$ **b** $x = 5$ **c** $c = 5$
 d $b = \frac{1}{2}$ **e** $d = 1\frac{2}{3}$ **f** $y = \frac{4}{5}$
 g $t = 2\frac{1}{3}$ **h** $w = 2\frac{1}{2}$
3 a $x = 2$ **b** $y = \frac{1}{2}$
4 a $x = 7$ **b** $y = 1\frac{1}{2}$
5 $5\frac{1}{2}$
6 a $a = 3$ **b** $b = 7$ **c** $c = 5$
 d $d = 7$ **e** $e = 6$ **f** $f = 3\frac{3}{7}$
 g $m = 1$ **h** $t = 3\frac{1}{4}$ **i** $a = 3$
7 48 cm
8 a $4x + 10$ **b** $x = 6$
9 a $x = 3.76$ **b** $x = 2.41$
10 $x = 1.7$
11 a 55.927 125
 b $x = 3.65$ gives an answer that is too small.
   $x^3 + 2x$ gets bigger as x gets bigger, so the solution must be greater than 3.65.
   Yousef is correct.
12 a $5x + 60 = 360$ **b** $x = 60$
13 Uzma £18, Hajra £38, Mabintou £76
14 A 2.5 cm, B 7.5 cm, C 30 cm
15 A £8, B £12, C £4
16 a If Emil has x CDs, $4x + 12 = 32$.   **b** 18 CDs
17 a $x = 3.6$ **b** 7.6 cm

18 a

 b

 c

 d

 e

 f

19 a $x \leqslant -1$ **b** $x > 3$ **c** $0 \leqslant x < 2$
 d $-3 < x < 3$ **e** $-2 < x \leqslant 0$ **f** $-1 \leqslant x \leqslant 3$
20 a $-3, -2, -1, 0$ **b** 1, 2, 3
 c $-2, -1, 0, 1, 2, 3, 4$ **d** $-3, -2$
21 a $x > 10$ **b** $x \leqslant 5$ **c** $x < 4\frac{1}{2}$
 d $x \leqslant -2$ **e** $x \geqslant -1\frac{1}{2}$ **f** $x < 0$
 g $x > -\frac{1}{2}$ **h** $x < 6\frac{1}{2}$ **i** $x \geqslant -2$

22 a $x = \frac{3}{5}$ **b** $-2, -1, 0, 1, 2, 3$

23 a A is x B is $x + 4$ C is $2(x + 4)$
     $L = x + x + 4 + 2(x + 4)$
     $L = 2x + 4 + 2x + 8$
     $L = 4x + 12$
   b $4x + 12 < 50$ **c** $0 < x < 9.5$

24 $0 < x < 4$

25 a

```
    o━━━━━━━━━━━━●
 ┼──┼──┼──┼──┼──┼──┼──┼──┼──┼
 -4 -3 -2 -1  0  1  2  3  4  5
```

   b $-2 < x \leqslant 3$ **c** $t > 4$

26 $70°$

27 a $x = 12.5$ **b** $-1, 0, 1, 2$ **c** $y \geqslant 2$

28 a $-2, -1, 0, 1, 2$ **b** $x < 15$

29 a $x = 2, y = 2$ **b** $x = 0, y = 2$
   c $x = -4, y = 3$

30 $x = \frac{1}{2}, y = -3$

Chapter 10 Answers

Exercise 10A

1 a 21   **b** 63   **c** 22.2   **d** 37.8
2 a 50   **b** 212   **c** -22 **d** 32
3 a 40   **b** 140   **c** 240   **d** 199.206
4 a 20   **b** 20   **c** 20   **d** 59

Exercise 10B

1 $P = 6l$
   a 18   **b** 42   **c** 174   **d** 51.6
2 a $P = 70n$ **b i** £2.80   **ii** £4.20   **iii** £8.40
3 $A = 6s^2$
   a 24 cm²   **b** 121.5 cm²
4 $s = \sqrt{A}$
   a 2 cm   **b** 1.2 cm
5 a $P = 11x - 1$ **b** 32 cm

Exercise 10C

1 a i 6   **ii** 14   **b i** 7   **ii** 20
2 a 6   **b** 12   **c** $-6\frac{1}{2}$ **d** -3
3 a i 3   **ii** 14   **b i** 3   **ii** $5\frac{1}{2}$
4 a 2   **b** $-6\frac{1}{2}$ **c** 20   **d** $-\frac{1}{4}$
5 a i 5   **ii** 7   **b** 6   **c** 4
6 a 15   **b** -72 **c** 45   **d** -58.24

Exercise 10D

1 $w = \dfrac{A}{l}$ **2** $d = \dfrac{C}{\pi}$

3 $h = \dfrac{V}{lw}$ **4** $x = \dfrac{y + 3}{4}$

5 $m = \dfrac{y - c}{x}$ **6** $u = v + gt$

7 $b = 2\dfrac{A}{h}$ **8** $V = \dfrac{D}{T}$

9 $V = \dfrac{kT}{P}$ **10** $b = \dfrac{2A}{h} - a$

11 $x = 3(y + 2)$ **12** $x = \dfrac{1}{2}y + 1$

Exam practice

1 a 17.6   **b** 20
2 a 15   **b** 28
3 a $P = 2(l + w)$ **b i** 26   **ii** 20.2
4 9 trees
5 20
6 a 80   **b** 29.5
7 a 25°C   **b** 32°F   **c** Fahrenheit, 37.8°
8 a $8x + 11$ **b** 3.5 cm
9 $T = 7x + 5y$
10 a $P = 4x + 8$ **b** 15.5 cm
11 a $x = \frac{1}{2}(P - y)$ **b** $D = TV$ **c** $x = 5 - 2y$
12 a $x = \dfrac{S}{180} + 2$ **b** 10
13 a $T = 4p + 20b$ **b** $C = 2p + 9b$

Chapter 11 Answers

Exercise 11A

1 $a = 62°$, angles on a straight line $= 180°$
   $b = 169°$, angles around a point $= 360°$
   $c = 38°$, vertically opposite angles
   $d = 142°$, angles on a straight line $= 180°$
   $e = 142°$, vertically opposite angles
   $f = 127°$, angles on a straight line $= 180°$
   $g = 53°$, vertically opposite angles
   $h = 127°$, vertically opposite angles
   $l = 64°$, angles around a point $= 360°$, $2l = 128°$
   $m = 60°$, angles on a straight line $= 180°$, $3m = 180°$
2 80°
3 53°
4 28°. Vertically opposite angles and angles in a triangle.
5 a 70°   **b** 60°   **c** 90°
6 a 55°
   b angle DEF = 25°, angle FDE = 130°
   c 60°

Exercise 11B

1 a 110°   **b** 50°   **c** 90°
2 51°, angles on a straight line, angles around a point, angles in a quadrilateral.
3 115°

Exercise 11C

1 a $a = 25°$ corresponding
   b $b = 110°$ alternate
   c $a = 111°$ corresponding
     $b = 111°$ vertically opposite/alternate
2 a $a = 125°$ $b = 55°$ $c = 125°$ $d = 55°$
   b $e = 108°$ $f = 72°$ $g = 72°$ $h = 108°$

Exercise 11D

1 a No   **b** Yes, 1 line
2 a   **b**

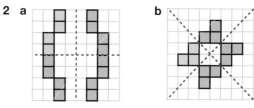

Exercise 11E

1 **a** Yes, order 2 **b** No
   c Yes, order 4 **d** Yes, order 2

2

3

Exercise 11F

1 $a = 102°$ $b = 55°$ $c = 93°$ $d = 85°$
   $e = 95°$ $f = 138°$ $g = 42°$
2 **a** 72° **b** 120° **c** 18°
3 **a** 108° **b** 60° **c** 162°
4 30 sides 5 36°, 10 sides
6 **a** 24 **b** 3960°
7 192°
8 7.5°, angle ABC from polygon interior angles; angles at base of isosceles triangle equal.

Exercise 11G

1 **a** 080° **b** 111° **c** 291°
2 Students' drawings
3 **a** 293° **b** 075° **c** 203°
4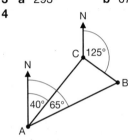

5 235° 6 348° 7 123° 8 295° 9 177°

Exercise 11H

1 11 km
2 **a** 1.4 km **b** 17.4 cm
3

4 N
   120°
   2 km
   (2 cm)

5 **a**
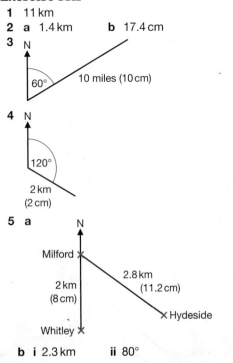

   b i 2.3 km **ii** 80°

6 Students' accurate drawings 7 19.9 km, 344°
8 108 yards, 017° 9 024°, 124 km

Exam practice

1 **a** 140° **b** Sum of angles at a point is 360°
2 **a** 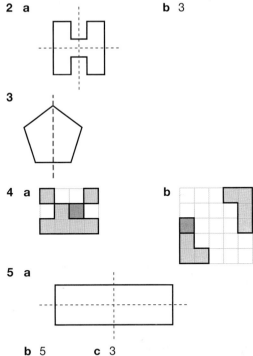 **b** 3

3

4 **a** **b**

5 **a**

   b 5 **c** 3
6 **a** 130°
   b Sum of angles on a straight line is 180°.
7 **a** 40°
   b Sum of angles on a straight line is 180°, and angles at base of isosceles triangle are equal.
8 **a** Vertically opposite angles are equal.
   b Sum of angles on a straight line is 180°, so $y = 30°$.
9 **a** 75°
   b Sum of angles on a straight line is 180°, and sum of angles in a triangle is 180°.
10 **a** 65°
    b Sum of angles in a quadrilateral is 360°.
11 **a i** 25° **ii** 130°
    b 65°
12 122°
13 **a** 078°
    b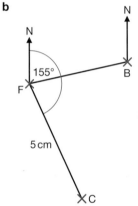

14 a 30°   **b** 48°

15 2.25 cm

16 a 120°

   b Each angle in an equilateral triangle is 60°, and sum of angles on a straight line is 180°.

17 1.46 m

18 150°

19 68°

20

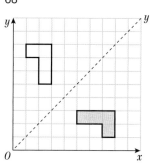

21 a 112°

   b Corresponding angles are equal, and sum of angles on a straight line is 180°.

22 x is 130° because angles on a straight line add up to 180°.

   y is 50° because it is a corresponding angle to angle PBC.

23 a i 63°

   ii Angles in a triangle add up to 180°. Angles ABC and ACB are the two equal angles of the isosceles triangle.

   b 117°

24 a 330°

   b

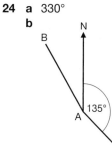

25 a Bearings should be measured clockwise. It is 320°.

   b 140°

26 72°

27 a 130°   **b** 325 km

   c

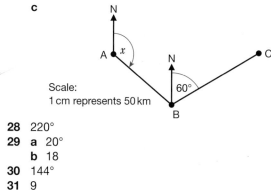

    Scale:
   1 cm represents 50 km

28 220°

29 a 20°

   b 18

30 144°

31 9

Chapter 12 Answers

Exercise 12A

1 500   **2** 90 litres   **3** 25

4 a 24 km   **b** 22 pounds   **c** 7 pints

   d 15 cm   **e** 30 miles   **f** 5 kg

5 4 gallons   **6** 3 bottles   **7** 640 km

8 93.75 miles   **9** 50 days   **10** 4

11 £83.16   **12** 4 kg (A)

Exercise 12B

1 80 miles   **2** 4 hours

3 30 mph   **4** 8 mph

5 $1\frac{1}{2}$ hours   **6** 4 hours

7 1400 miles   **8** 160 miles

9 2 mph   **10** 50 mph

11 32 km/h   **12** 80 km/h

13 400 km/h   **14** 87.5 miles

15 3 hours 12 min   **16** 7 hours 48 min

17 50 km/h

18 a 34 m   **b** 306 km/h

19 Van, 45 mph = 72 km/h so 45 mph > 60 km/h or, 60 km/h = 37.5 mph so 45 mph > 60 km/h.

20 Jean, Jean cycles at 15 km/h and Rob only cycles at $\left(\frac{32\ km}{2.5\ hrs}=\right)$ 12.8 km/h.

Exercise 12C

1 12.5 cm   **2** 44.5 g   **3** 3.5 litres

4 a 9.65 cm   **b** 9.75 cm

5 a 1.585 m   **b** 1.595 m

6 The pencil could be as long as 105 mm, which is longer than the shortest possible length of the pencil case, 101.5 mm.

7 The cupboard could as narrow as 81.5 cm, and the gap as wide as 81.75 cm.

8 a 84.5, 83.5   **b** 84.05, 83.95

   c 84.005, 83.995

9 a 0.95, 0.85   **b** 0.905, 0.895

   c 0.095, 0.085

10 a 118.5 cm   **b** 117.5 cm

11 a 6450 g   **b** 6350 g

12 a 48.05 l **b** 47.95 l

13 a 1.005 m   **b** 0.995 m

Exam practice

1 432 mph

2 Great Britain. 70 mph $\times \frac{8}{5}$ = 112 k/h, so 70 mph < 120 k/h

3 James is correct. 285 $\times$ 1000 $\div$ 60² ≈ 80.

4 Kamala. $\frac{42}{2}$ = 21 km/h > $\frac{30}{1.5}$ = 20 km/h

5 600 mph   **6** 16.5 m

7 a 48 mph   **b i** 22.5 litres   **ii** 23.5 litres

8 a 62.5 cm   **b** 63.5 cm

9 a 126.5 g   **b** 127.5 g

10 a 100.5 m   **b** 10.515 seconds

11 28.8 m

12 Lower bound for length is 199.5 cm, so rod may fit into slot of length 199.8 cm.

Chapter 13 Answers

Exercise 13A

1 **a** 26 cm **b** 15 cm **c** 13.7 cm
2 40 cm
3 34 cm
4 7.2 cm
5 No. The edging will cost £3.80 × 36 = £136.80

Exercise 13B

1 19.76 m²
2 **a** 6 cm² **b** 15 cm² **c** 21.6 cm²
3 4500 cm² **4** 24 000 cm²
5 **a** 14 cm² **b** 40 cm²
6 4 cm

Exercise 13C

1 150 **2** £103.80
3 **a** 2 **b** 220 g
4 **a** 88 cm² **b** 22.5 m² **c** 108 m²
5 **a** 150 cm² **b** 36 cm² **c** 55.5 mm²

Exam practice

1 **a** 60 cm **b** 200 cm²
2 60 m **3** 7.8 m by 2.9 m **4** 28 cm²
5 **a** 11.25 cm² **b** 18 cm
6 264 paving stones **7** 3 tins needed for 63.5 m²
8 6x + 4 **9** 45 cm²
10 45 cm² **11** 56 cm²
12 £31 425 **13** 3 boxes
14 1750 kg **15** 36 cm²

Chapter 14 Answers

Exercise 14A

1 **a** 39.6 m **b** 59.7 cm **c** 26.4 cm
   d 78.5 mm **e** 184.7 cm
2 **a** 21.7 cm **b** 31.7 mm **c** 16.7 cm
   d 30.5 cm **e** 15.7 m
3 11.3 m
4 100.5 cm
5 **a** 4.49 m **b** 0.94 m **c** 4.78
6 **a** 14.5 m **b** 6.4 cm **c** 18.5 cm
   d 11.8 mm **e** 31.8 cm
7 **a** 4.8 cm **b** 11.4 mm **c** 10.2 cm
   d 14.8 cm **e** 7.9 m
8 59.8 cm **9** 71.7 cm

Exercise 14B

1 **a** 81.7 m² **b** 28.3 cm² **c** 238 cm²
   d 726 mm² **e** 278 cm²
2 **a** 707 cm² **b** 468 mm² **c** 43.0 cm²
   d 119 cm² **e** 50.3 m²
3 154.6 m² **4** 58.1 cm²
5 **a** 380 cm² **b** 81 cm² **c** 299 cm²
6 411 cm² **7** 70.7 cm² **8** 13 cm

Exercise 14C

1 **a** **i** 46.3 cm **ii** 127 cm²
   b **i** 25.7 m **ii** 39.3 m²
   c **i** 30.8 cm **ii** 56.5 cm²
   d **i** 14.3 cm **ii** 12.6 cm²
   e **i** 22.1 cm **ii** 30.2 cm²
   f **i** 57.8 m **ii** 103 m²
2 **a** 3.21 m² **b** £89.96
3 **a** 28.5 cm² **b** 35.7 cm
4 193 cm²

Exam practice

1 78.5 cm² **2** 30.9 cm²
3 **a** 2 cm **b** 175.9 cm²
4 157 cm² **5** 2.04 m **6** 20.57 cm
7 **a** 7854 cm² **b** 125.7 cm
8 £134.40

Chapter 15 Answers

Exercise 15A

Diagrams in the following section are not drawn to scale. Please check that you have drawn the lines in your own constructions accurately according to the instructions in the question.

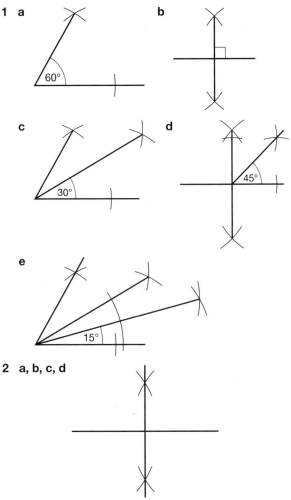

1 **a**

   b

   c

   d

   e

2 **a, b, c, d**

3 a, b, c, d

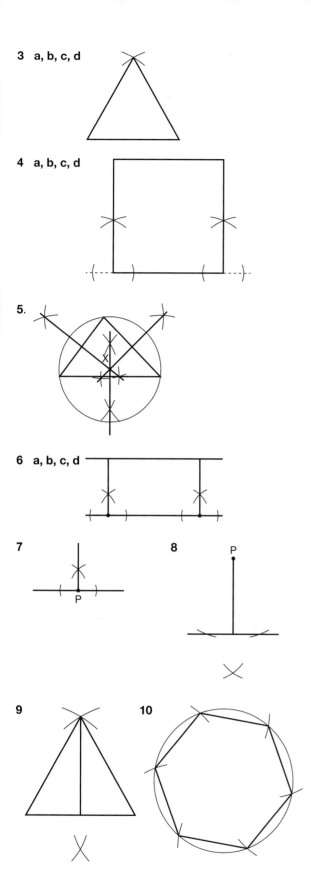

4 a, b, c, d

5.

6 a, b, c, d

7

8

9

10

11

12

Exercise 15B

Diagrams in the following section are not drawn to scale. Please check that you have drawn the lines in your own constructions accurately according to the instructions in the question.

1

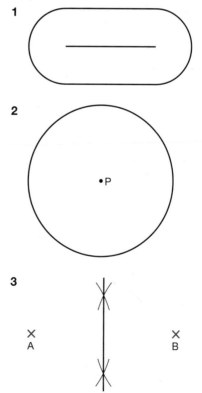

2

3

Answers

4

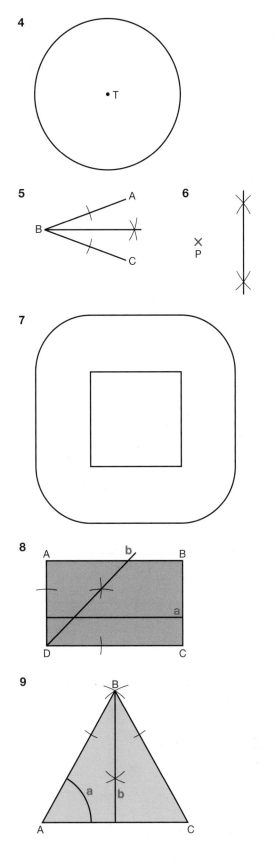

5

6

7

8

9

10

11

12

Exercise 15C

1

2

3

4

5

6

7

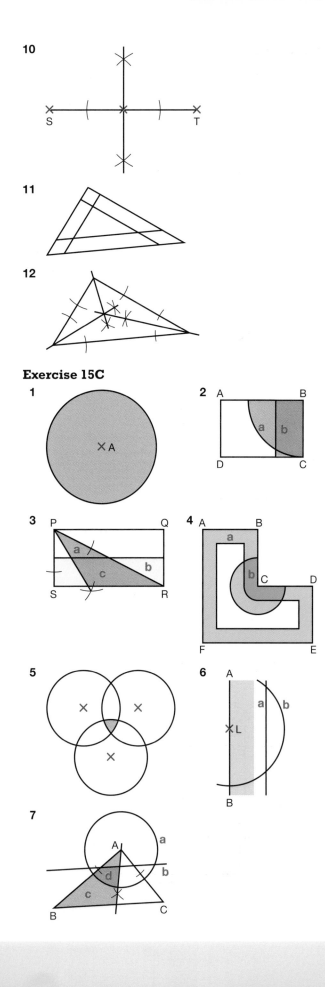

Exam practice

1

2

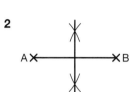

3

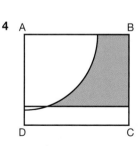

4

5

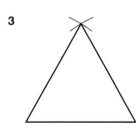

6

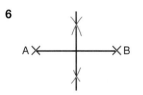

7

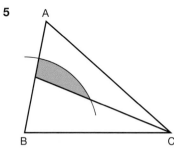

8

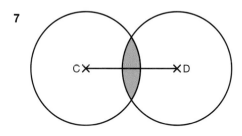

9

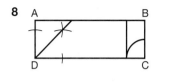
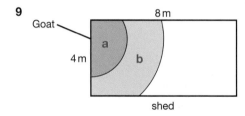

10   **11**

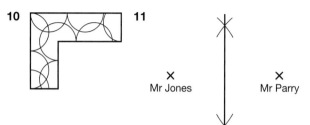

Chapter 16 Answers

Exercise 16A

1

2 a   Plan   Front elevation   Side elevation

b   Plan   Front elevation   Side elevation

c   Plan   Front elevation   Side elevation

d   Plan
Front elevation   Side elevation

e   Plan
Front elevation   Side elevation

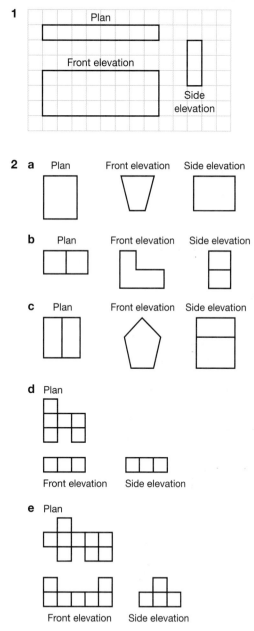

f

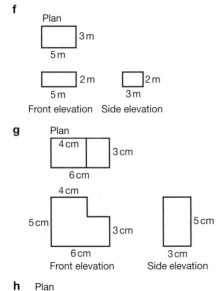

Plan

3 m
5 m

2 m
5 m
Front elevation

2 m
3 m
Side elevation

g

Plan
4 cm
3 cm
6 cm

4 cm
5 cm
3 cm
6 cm
Front elevation

5 cm
3 cm
Side elevation

h

Plan
4 cm

5 cm
8 cm
Front elevation

5 cm
8 cm
Side elevation

3 a

b

4 a

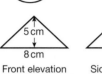

b

c

Exercise 16B

1 a 3 cm³   **b** 96 cm³
2 a 224 m³   **b** 612 mm³
3 5 cm   **4** 125
5 a 486 cm³   **b** 378 cm³   **c** 204 cm³
6 a 78 cm³   **b** 0.498 75 m³
7 a 225 cm³   **b** 10 500 cm³
8 9 cm

Exercise 16C

1 122 cm²   **2** 144 cm
3 a 10 950 cm²   **b** 11 700 cm²   **c** 3524 cm²
    d 3 m²   **e** 684 cm²   **f** 1392 cm²
4 £94   **5** 2 cm   **6** 96 cm²

Exercise 16D

1 a 565 cm³   **b** 188 cm³   **c** 198 cm³
2 a 94.25 cm²   **b** 226.19 cm²
3 251.33 cm²
4 1600 π m³
5 3.56 m³ = 3560 litres   **6** 9425 minutes

Exercise 16E

1 a 30 000 cm²   **b** 45 000 cm²   **c** 3 cm²
    d 0.34 cm²
2 a 6 000 000 m²   **b** 400 000 m²   **c** 2 m²
    d 0.345 m²
3 a 4 000 000 cm³   **b** 4.5 cm³   **c** 0.4 cm³
    d 3000 cm³
4 a 0.4 litres   **b** 5.6 litres
    c 1 000 000 m*l*   **d** 0.0035 litres
5 200 tiles
6 a 144 cm³   **b** 144 000 mm³
7 11.7 m²   **8** 42 000 cm³
9 100 doses   **10** 675 000 litres

Exercise 16F

1 250 g/cm³   **2** 0.777 cm³   **3** 1.96 g/cm³
4 The aluminium block has the greater mass by 155 kg.

Exam practice

1 a 12   **b** 200 cm³
2 5 cm
3 126 cm²   **4** 85 cm³
5 a   **b**

6 a   **b**

7 a   **b**

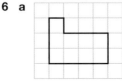

8 120 boxes
9

10 Yes. Each brick has a volume of 125 cm³, box has a
    volume of 4500 cm³, and 4500 ÷ 125 = 36
11 a 5 cm
    b i 19   **ii** 8

12 a

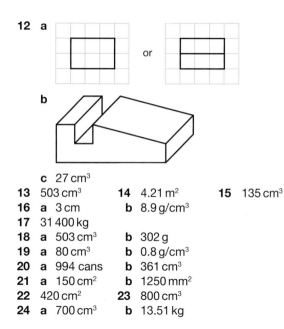

c 27 cm³

| **13** 503 cm³ | **14** 4.21 m² | **15** 135 cm³ |

16 a 3 cm   **b** 8.9 g/cm³

17 31 400 kg

18 a 503 cm³   **b** 302 g

19 a 80 cm³   **b** 0.8 g/cm³

20 a 994 cans   **b** 361 cm³

21 a 150 cm²   **b** 1250 mm²

22 420 cm²   **23** 800 cm³

24 a 700 cm³   **b** 13.51 kg

Chapter 17 Answers

Exercise 17A

1 a

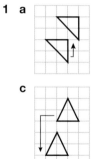

b

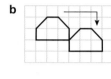

c

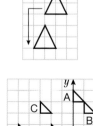

2

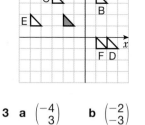

3 a $\begin{pmatrix} -4 \\ 3 \end{pmatrix}$ **b** $\begin{pmatrix} -2 \\ -3 \end{pmatrix}$ **c** $\begin{pmatrix} 3 \\ 2 \end{pmatrix}$

4 a $\begin{pmatrix} 6 \\ -1 \end{pmatrix}$ **b** $\begin{pmatrix} 1 \\ 4 \end{pmatrix}$ **c** $\begin{pmatrix} -7 \\ -3 \end{pmatrix}$

   d $\begin{pmatrix} 7 \\ 3 \end{pmatrix}$ **e** $\begin{pmatrix} -6 \\ 1 \end{pmatrix}$ **f** $\begin{pmatrix} 5 \\ -4 \end{pmatrix}$

Exercise 17B

1 a

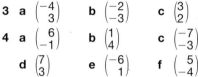

2 a

 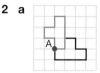 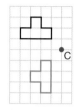

b

  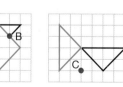

c

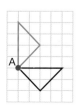

3

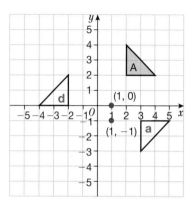

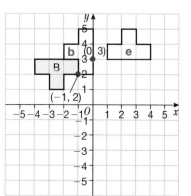

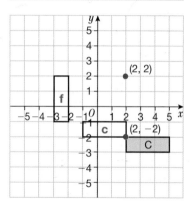

Answers

Exercise 17C

1 a Rotation of 90° clockwise about $(-1, 0)$
   b Rotation of 90° clockwise about $(0, 0)$
   c Rotation of 180° about $(0, 0)$
   d Rotation of 90° anticlockwise about $(0, 0)$
2 a Rotation of 180° about $(2, 1)$
   b Rotation of 90° clockwise about $(0, -1)$

Exercise 17D

1 a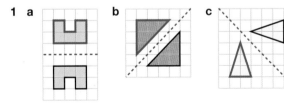

2 a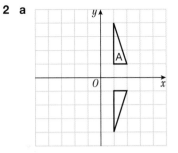

   b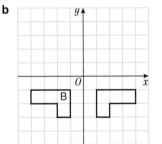

3 a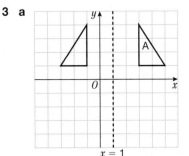

   b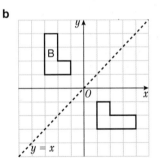

Exercise 17E

1 a Reflection in the x-axis
   b Reflection in the y-axis
   c Reflection in the line $x = 2$
   d Reflection in the line $y = -2$
2 a Reflection in the y-axis
   b Reflection in the line $y = 2$
   c Reflection in the line $x = 3$
   d Reflection in the line $y = x$
   e Reflection in the line $y = 3\frac{1}{2}$
   f Reflection in the line $y = -x$
   g Reflection in the line $y = -1\frac{1}{2}$
3 a Reflection in the line $y = x$
   b Reflection in the line $y = -x$

Exercise 17F

1 a, b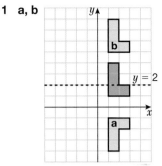

   c Translation by $\begin{pmatrix} 0 \\ 4 \end{pmatrix}$

2 a, b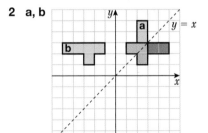

   c Reflection in the y-axis

3 a, b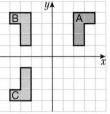

   c Rotation of 180° about point $(0, 0)$

4 a, b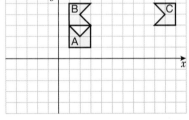

   c Rotation of 90° anticlockwise about $(6, 6)$

5 a

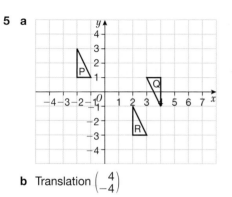

b Translation $\begin{pmatrix} 4 \\ -4 \end{pmatrix}$

Exercise 17G

1 a

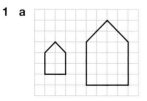

b

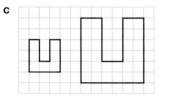

c

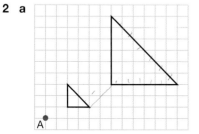

2 a

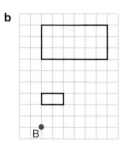

b

c

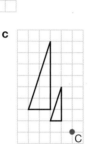

3 a

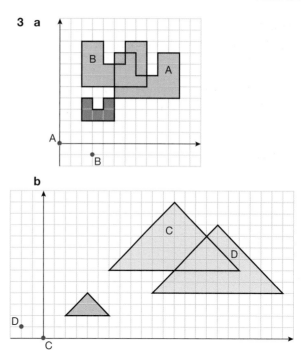

b

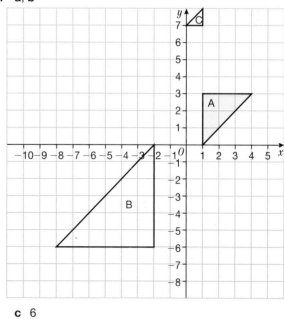

Exercise 17H

1 a, b

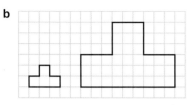

c 6
2 a Enlargement sf 3 centre (1, 3)
  b Enlargement sf 2 centre (9, 0)
  c Enlargement sf 3 centre (2, 2)
3 a Enlargement sf 2 centre (8, 8)
  b Enlargement sf 3 centre (0, 7)
  c Enlargement sf 2 centre (9, 4)

Exam practice

1

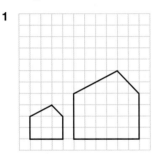

2 a, b

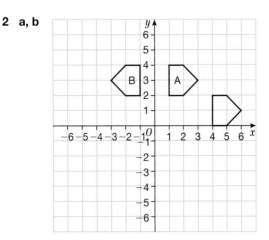

3 a, b

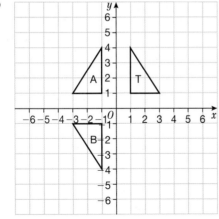

c Enlargement scale factor 3, centre *O*

4

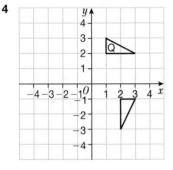

5 Reflection in the *y*-axis

6 a

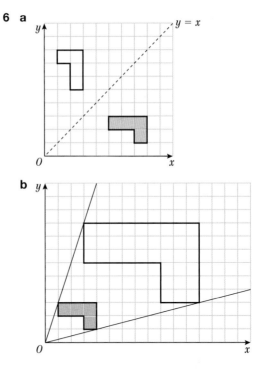

b

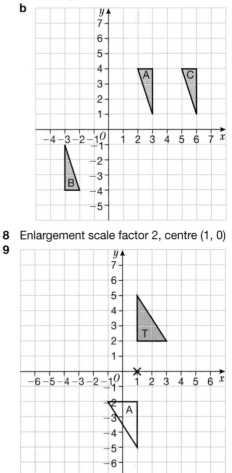

7 a Rotation 180° (clockwise or anticlockwise), about the origin.

b

8 Enlargement scale factor 2, centre (1, 0)

9

10 Rotation 180°, centre (0, 1)

11 a

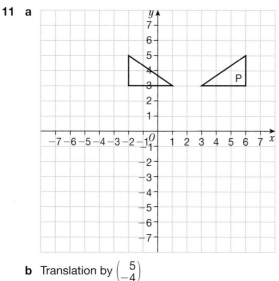

b Translation by $\begin{pmatrix} 5 \\ -4 \end{pmatrix}$

12 Rotation 180° about (1, 0)

Chapter 18 Answers

Exercise 18A

1 a $h = 13\,\text{cm}$ **b** $p = 5.83\,\text{cm}$ **c** $v = 8.38\,\text{cm}$

Exercise 18B

1 a 4 cm   **b** 0.7 cm   **c** 4.8 cm
2 7.35 m
3 a 33.2 cm   **b** 27 cm

Exercise 18C

1 a 5   **b** 8.49   **c** 10.6   **d** 11.4
2 a 14.1   **b** 15.3   **c** 11.4   **d** 9.43
   e 13.6   **f** 12.7

Exercise 18D

1 a 37.7°   **b** 46.2°   **c** 19.7°   **d** 40.1°
   e 47.1°   **f** 43.6°
2 a 36.3°   **b** 51.1°   **c** 32.3°
3 a 41.0°   **b** 57.2°   **c** 98°

Exercise 18E

1 a 5.47 cm   **b** 17.1 cm   **c** 11.6 cm
   d 26.1 cm   **e** 10.4 cm   **f** 11.3 cm
2 a 18.1 cm   **b** 13.4 m   **c** 10.8 cm
3 a i 9.96 cm   **ii** 8.36 cm
   b 5.30 cm   **c** 13.7 cm   **d** 68 cm²

Exam practice

1   10.63 cm   **2**   15.23 cm
3   6.71 cm   **4**   11.9 cm
5   56 cm   **6**   230 km
7   7.48 cm   **8**   18.4 cm

9   28.6 cm²   **10**   £54 000
11   AB is 10   **12**   6.39 m
13   39.3°   **14**   8.48 m
15 a 51.3°   **b** 10.5 cm

Chapter 19 Answers

Exercise 19A

1 a

Vehicle	Frequency
Car	卌 卌 卌 卌 II
Bus	卌
HGV	IIII
Bike	IIII
Motorbike	I

b Motorbike   **c** Car

2

Mode of transport	Tally	Frequency
Car		
Walk		
Bus		
Other		

3

Number of DVDs bought	Frequency
0–3	9
4–7	11
8–11	6
12–15	4

4 a

Weight	Frequency
$57 \leqslant w < 60$	7
$60 \leqslant w < 63$	3
$63 \leqslant w < 66$	5
$66 \leqslant w < 69$	5
$w \geqslant 69$	4

b $57 \leqslant w < 60$ **c** $60 \leqslant w < 63$

Exercise 19B

1 A: open, B: closed, C: open, D: closed
2 a No option for dissatisfied customers.
   New suitable question:
   What do you think of the new amusements?
   Very good ☐   Good ☐
   Satisfactory ☐   Poor ☐
   b Options overlap.
   New suitable question:
   How much money would you normally expect to pay for each amusement?
   £5–£7 ☐   £7.01–£8 ☐   More than £8 ☐

c Not clear what the options mean.
New suitable question:
How often do you visit the park each year?
0–2 times ☐   3–5 times ☐   6–8 times ☐
More than 8 times ☐

3 a Only asking the best students so the sample is biased. The sample is too small.
b The choices are all positive. The question does not reference *liking* mathmatics.

4 a What type of magazine do you normally read?
Celebrity ☐   Sport ☐   Nature ☐   Other ☐
b How many magazines have you read in the last week?
0 ☐   1 ☐   2–3 ☐   >3 ☐

5 Do you like the new layout? Yes/No

Exercise 19C

1

	Music	Drama	Total
Art	7	6	13
PE	5	12	17
Total	12	18	30

2 a

	Plain	Salt and Vinegar	Cheese and Onion	Total
Males	7	7	14	28
Females	5	6	12	23
Total	12	13	26	51

b 13   **c** 51

3 a

	Orange Juice	Grapefruit Juice	Total
Men	22	8	30
Women	18	12	30
Total	40	20	60

b 40
4 a 51   **b** 146

Exam practice

1 a It does not allow for sending no text messages. It does not include a time frame, e.g. per week.
b It only includes people of one age.
2 a The categories overlap. It does not include a time frame, e.g. per day. It does not allow for people who use their computer for more than 6 hours.
b It only includes people of one age.
3 a It does not allow for never visiting the cinema. It is hard to decide what the categories mean. It does not include a time frame, e.g. per month.
b On average, how many times do you go to the cinema each month?
0–1 times ☐   2–3 times ☐   4–5 times ☐
More than 5 times ☐

4 On average, how many times each week do you shop at this supermarket?
0 ☐   1 ☐   2 ☐   3 ☐   4 or more ☐

5

Country	Tally	Frequency
France	卌	5
Spain	卌 II	7
England	IIII	4
Italy	IIII	4

6 a Biased, because it only includes those working on the night shift.
b Not biased, because it uses a simple random sample.
c Biased because the question starts with 'Do you agree…'

7 51 children

8 a

	London	York	Total
Boys	23	14	37
Girls	19	24	43
Total	42	38	80

b $\frac{21}{40}$

Chapter 20 Answers

Exercise 20A

1 a 2   **b** 2   **c** 2.5   **d** 7
2 a 190 cm   **b** 186 cm   **c** 185 cm   **d** 20 cm
3 a No mode   **b** 131 emails   **c** 131.5 emails
d 170
4 a 4 meals   **b** about 100
5 a 28   **b** 38
c 64 (to the nearest whole person)
d The mean because it is the highest average.

Exercise 20B

1 a 36   **b** 28   **c** 47   **d** 18, 36   **e** 18
2 a

```
0 | 4 5 6 7 7 8 9 9 9 9
1 | 0 2 4 5 7
2 | 1 4 8
3 | 0
```
Key 2|1 stands for 21
b 9 minutes   **c** 9 minutes   **d** 26 minutes
e 7 minutes, 17 minutes   **f** 10 minutes

3 a

```
5 | 2 6 9
6 | 3 3 4 5 5 8 8 8 9
7 | 2 4 4 4 4
8 | 2 3 5 8
9 | 2 4
```

Key 7|2 stands for 72

  b 74 km   **c** 69 km   **d** 42 km
  e 64 km, 82 km   **f** 18 km

Exercise 20C

1 a 1 car   **b** 2 cars   **c** 2 cars
  d Assuming there is currently one space per household they should provide an extra 15 spaces.
2 a 65 g   **b** 65 g   **c** 65.2 g
3 a 6 to 8   **b** 6 to 8
4 a $1.1 \leq d < 1.3$ **b** $1.3 \leq d < 1.5$

Exercise 20D

1 1.5 breakdowns
2 11.125 minutes
3 42.5

Exam practice

1 a 3.5   **b** 3.6   **c** 4
2 a 65 kg   **b** 34 kg
3 30 mm
4 1, 4, 5, 5, 5; 2, 3, 5, 5, 5; 1, 3, 5, 5, 6; 2, 2, 5, 5, 6; 1, 2, 5, 5, 7; 1, 1, 5, 5, 8
5 a 29   **b** 46   **c** 46   **d** 45
6 a £22   **b** £34   **c** £46.70
  d The median is the best average here. The mode is the lowest value and the mean is distorted by the expensive dress (£180).
7 a Eating apple: mean 138.9 g, range 18 g
  Cooking apple: mean 148 g, range 26 g
  b On average the cooking apples are heavier, but they vary in weight more than the eating apples.
8 a

```
4 | 6 8
5 | 1 2 8
6 | 0 3 4 6 8
7 | 4 7 8 9
8 | 7
```

Key: 4|5 stands for 45 kg

  b 5 people   **c** 41 kg
9 a 67 bpm   **b** 26 bpm
  c Heart rates faster after walking, bigger median, median increases by 11 bpm.
  Heart rates more spread out after walking, bigger range, range increases by 11 bpm.
10 a 15 tracks   **b** 13.5 tracks
11

```
2 | 3 7
3 | 1 4 5 6 8
4 | 1 2 4 5 5
5 | 0 2 3
```

Key: 4|5 stands for 45 years old

12 a The mode is 7.   **b** 6.3 rooms, to 1 d.p.
13 The mean for males is 48 and the range is 48.
  The mean for females is 61.1 and the range is 70.
  On average the females get higher scores, but their scores vary more.
14 Meena must score $70 \times 6 = 420$ marks in total on the 6 tests to get an average score of 70.
  So far she has $64 \times 5 = 320$ marks.
  Therefore she needs $420 - 320 = 100$ marks on the sixth test.
15 If you want to show that the average is high use the mean (£30 000). If you want to show that the average is low use the mode or the median (both £10 000).
16

```
2 | 3 5
3 | 1 2 7 8
4 | 0 6 8 9
5 | 6 6
```

Key: 2|1 = £21

17 a 10 to 12 and 13 to 15 are both modal classes.
  b 13 to 15   **c** £13.50
18 a $31 \leq h < 33$ **b** $29 \leq h < 31$ **c** 30.36 cm
19 19 minutes   **20** 18.4 minutes
20 a $10\,000 < x \leq 14\,000$ **b** $14\,000 < x \leq 16\,000$
22 59.5 grams

Chapter 21 Answers

Exercise 21A

1

Time in minutes	Angle
Less than 10	$\frac{3}{30} \times 360 = 36°$
Between 10 and <15	$\frac{4}{30} \times 360 = 48°$
Between 15 and 30	$\frac{17}{30} \times 360 = 144°$
More than 30	$\frac{11}{30} \times 360 = 132°$

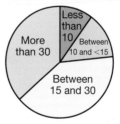

2

Category	Thriller	Classic	Romance	Non-fiction
Angle	$\frac{120}{540} \times 360$ $= 80°$	$\frac{60}{540} \times 360$ $= 40°$	$\frac{270}{540} \times 360$ $= 180°$	$\frac{90}{540} \times 360$ $= 60°$

3

Type of car	Ford	Nissan	Toyota	Renault
Angle	$\frac{24}{90} \times 360$ $= 96°$	$\frac{30}{90} \times 360$ $= 120°$	$\frac{27}{90} \times 360$ $= 108°$	$\frac{9}{90} \times 360$ $= 36°$

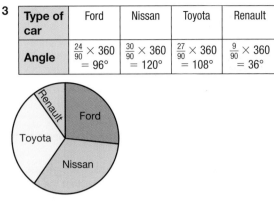

4

Day	Monday	Tuesday	Wednesday	Thursday	Friday
Angle	$\frac{7}{36} \times 360$ $= 70°$	$\frac{8}{36} \times 360$ $= 80°$	$\frac{10}{36} \times 360$ $= 100°$	$\frac{6}{36} \times 360°$ $= 60°$	$\frac{5}{36} \times 360$ $= 50°$

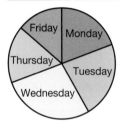

Exercise 21B

1 a Spain **b** 4° **c** 20 girls
d 108° **e** 27 girls

2

Activity	Angle	Number of hours
Sleep	120°	8
School	105°	7
Play	30°	2
Watch TV	60°	4
Eat	15°	1
Homework	30°	2

3 a 2° **b** 180 people
c Vanilla and chocolate. They have the largest angles.
4 a $\frac{1}{5}$ **b** 60 students

Exercise 21C

1 a 30°C **b** 33°C **c** G
d C and F **e** A
2 a 70 g **b** 10 g **c** Fruitbix
3 a Saturday **b** Thursday **c** 40

Exercise 21D

1

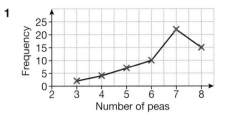

2 a $70 \leqslant d < 80$
b, c

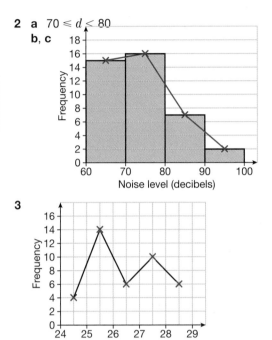

3

4 Girls, because their mode is 5 minutes and the boys' mode is 9 minutes.

Exercise 21E

1

Weight (w kg)	Frequency
$0 < w \leqslant 20$	80
$20 < w \leqslant 30$	80
$30 < w \leqslant 40$	100
$40 < w \leqslant 50$	60
$50 < w \leqslant 70$	40

2 a

Lifetime (l hours)	Frequency	Class width	Frequency density
$10 \leqslant l < 15$	4	5	0.8
$15 \leqslant l < 20$	10	5	2
$20 \leqslant l < 25$	20	5	4
$25 \leqslant l < 30$	15	5	3
$30 \leqslant l < 40$	6	10	0.6

b

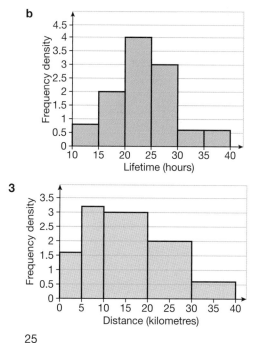

3

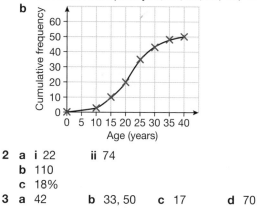

25

Exercise 21F

1 **a** Cumulative frequency: 3, 10, 20, 35, 43, 48, 50

b

2 **a i** 22　　**ii** 74
　b 110
　c 18%

3 **a** 42　　**b** 33, 50　　**c** 17　　**d** 70

Exercise 21G

1 Waiting times at Tudor Royal Hospital are much lower than at Bakefield General, median is smaller. The waiting times are more spread out at Bakefield General, the range is greater.

2 German test results are higher (greater median). French test results are more spread out (greater range).

3 Both teams are equally consistent, range is the same. Shaw Tigers score more points per game on average, median and mean are greater.

4 Picton Golf Club has more members in total and has more members in each category. However, Chad Golf Club has a much higher proportion of men than Picton and proportionally less women, less boys and less girls.

Exam practice

1 **a** $\frac{1}{4}$　　　　**b** 60 students

2

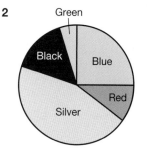

3

Drink	Frequency	Angle
Hot chocolate	20	80°
Soup	15	60°
Coffee	25	100°
Tea	30	120°

4 **a** 18%　　**b** 5%　　**c** 100%

5 **a** $\frac{5}{18}$
　b **i** 16 students　　**ii** 72 students
　c The pie chart doesn't give frequencies, only proportions.

6

7

8

Protein	Carbohydrate	Fibre	Other
6 g	16 g	5 g	93 g
$\frac{6}{120} \times 360$ $= 18°$	$\frac{16}{120} \times 360$ $= 48°$	$\frac{5}{120} \times 360$ $= 15°$	$\frac{93}{120} \times 360$ $= 279°$

Answers

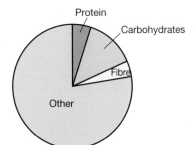

9 Students' composite bar charts
10 James. The angle for the combined proportion must be between the Year 9 and Year 10 angles.
11 a 88 people   b 38 years   c 54 − 22 = 32 years
12 From a cumulative frequency chart, the median for the men is £240. On average, the men spent more than the women.
13 a 21   b 10
   c Most of the high and low scores are scored by the boys. More of the girls scored an average mark.

14

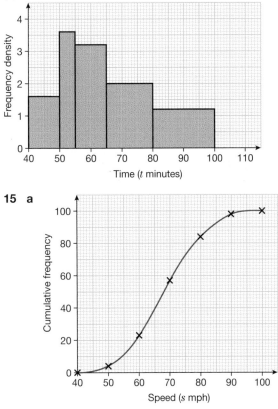

15 a

   b 88 mph   c 76 − 61 = 15 mph

16 a

Distance (d km)	Frequency
0 < d ⩽ 5	15
5 < d ⩽ 10	20
10 < d ⩽ 20	25
20 < d ⩽ 40	20
40 < d ⩽ 60	10

b

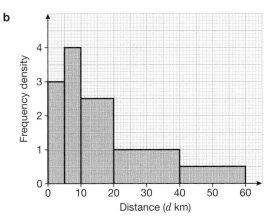

Chapter 22 Answers

Exercise 22A

1 a

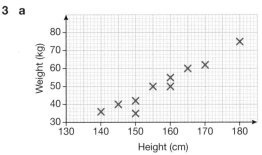

   b 7th hour
2 The higher the number of breaths per minute the higher the pulse rate.

3 a

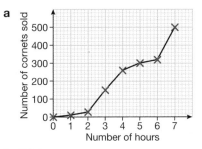

   b The greater the height the larger the weight.

Exercise 22B

1 a, c

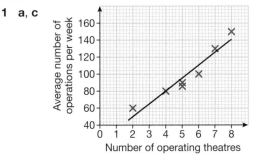

   b Positive correlation
   d The higher the number of operating theatres the higher the average number of operations per week.
   e ≈ 65

2 a Negative correlation
  b i 30 units **ii** 4.8°C
3 a 147 **b** 52 years
  c Positive correlation: the older a man is the higher his blood pressure.

Exam practice

1

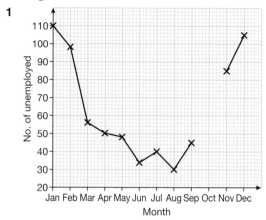

b 65
c August, because more people go to the seaside in the summer holidays.

2 a, c

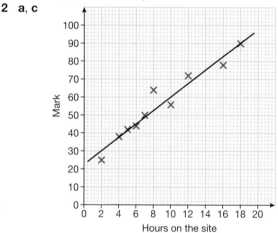

b Positive correlation

3 a Positive correlation
  b

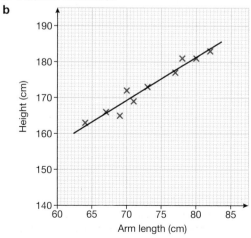

  c 175 cm

4 a About −1 **b** 9.4 minutes
  c Negative correlation
  d The older the apprentices the quicker they learn skills

5 a, c

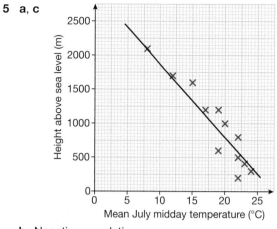

  b Negative correlation
  d 11°C **e** 1000 m

6 a Negative correlation
  b 120

7 a Positive correlation: the greater the weight the taller the height.
  b

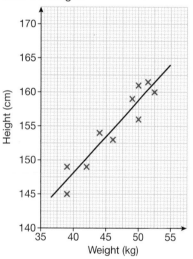

  c 155.5 cm

8 a Negative correlation
  b

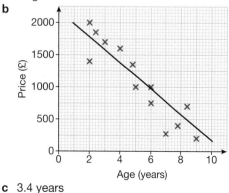

  c 3.4 years

9 a Approximately £9000
  b The one-year-old Mini is more expensive than expected. It may have extra features or a very low mileage.
10 a Plot point at (6.1, 32)   **b** Positive
  c Answer between 6.7 and 7.5 cm
11 a

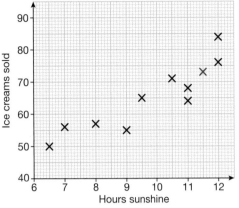

  b The greater the number of hours of sunshine, the greater the number of ice creams sold.
  c 67 ice creams

Chapter 23 Answers

Exercise 23A

1 a $\frac{1}{10}$ **b** $\frac{3}{10}$ **c** $\frac{2}{10} = \frac{1}{5}$
  d $\frac{6}{10} = \frac{3}{5}$ **e** 0
2 a $\frac{1}{6}$ **b** $\frac{2}{6} = \frac{1}{3}$ **c** $\frac{3}{6} = \frac{1}{2}$
  d $\frac{4}{6} = \frac{2}{3}$ **e** 0   **f** $\frac{3}{6} = \frac{1}{2}$
3 a $\frac{67}{120}$ **b** $\frac{53}{120}$
4 a $\frac{3}{15} = \frac{1}{5}$ **b** $\frac{7}{15}$ **c** $\frac{5}{15} = \frac{1}{3}$
  d $\frac{10}{15} = \frac{2}{3}$ **e** $\frac{8}{15}$ **f** $\frac{1}{5}$
5 a $\frac{13}{25}$ **b** $\frac{7}{25}$ **c** $\frac{3}{25}$
  d $\frac{9}{25}$

6 a

	Orange	Lemonade	Milk	Total
Sandwiches	5	7	1	13
Biscuits	4	4	5	13
Crisps	8	7	1	16
Total	17	18	7	42

  b i $\frac{18}{42} = \frac{3}{7}$ **ii** $\frac{16}{42} = \frac{8}{21}$ **iii** $\frac{4}{42} = \frac{2}{21}$ **iv** $\frac{4}{42} = \frac{2}{21}$
  c John is right.
    P(milk and biscuits) $= \frac{5}{42}$
    P(orange and sandwiches) $= \frac{5}{42}$
7 a $\frac{1}{26}$ **b** $\frac{1}{2}$ **c** $\frac{5}{52}$ **d** $\frac{7}{26}$ **e** $\frac{7}{26}$

Exercise 23B

1 0.85   **2** $\frac{50}{53}$ **3** 0.3
4 P(train is not late) $= 1 - 0.32 = 0.68$
5 0.3   **6** 0.1
7 a 0.17   **b** 0.81   **c** 0.64
8 0.25   **9** $\frac{1}{10}$
10 a 0.3   **b** 0.55

Exercise 23C

1

Dice		
6	(H, 6)	(T, 6)
5	(H, 5)	(T, 5)
4	(H, 4)	(T, 4)
3	(H, 3)	(T, 3)
2	(H, 2)	(T, 2)
1	(H, 1)	(T, 1)
	H	T

Coin

2 a $\frac{1}{8}$ **b** $\frac{1}{6}$ **c** $\frac{5}{12}$

3 a

Sheet			
W	(W, W)	(G, W)	(O, W)
Y	(W, Y)	(G, Y)	(O, Y)
B	(W, B)	(G, B)	(O, B)
G	(W, G)	(G, G)	(O, G)
	W	G	O

Pillow case

  b i $\frac{2}{12} = \frac{1}{6}$ **ii** $\frac{5}{6}$
4 a $\frac{1}{16}$ **b** $\frac{4}{16} = \frac{1}{4}$ **c** $\frac{6}{16} = \frac{3}{8}$ **d** $\frac{7}{16}$
  e 1   **f** $\frac{9}{16}$ **g** 0

5 a

Spinner 1			
3	(1, 3)	(2, 3)	(3, 3)
2	(1, 2)	(2, 2)	(3, 2)
1	(1, 1)	(2, 1)	(3, 1)
	1	2	3

Spinner 2

  b $\frac{1}{9}$
  c Because there are three ways of scoring 4 out of nine possible outcomes. So probability is $\frac{3}{9} = \frac{1}{3}$.
6 P(2) $= \frac{1}{2}$, P(3) $= \frac{2}{12}$, P(4) $= \frac{3}{12}$, P(5) $= \frac{3}{12}$, P(6) $= \frac{2}{12}$
  Scores of 4 and 5 are both most likely.

7 a

Coin						
H	(1, H)	(2, H)	(3, H)	(4, H)	(5, H)	(6, H)
T	(1, T)	(2, T)	(3, T)	(4, T)	(5, T)	(6, T)
	1	2	3	4	5	6

Dice

  b i $\frac{1}{12}$ **ii** $\frac{1}{2}$ **iii** $\frac{1}{6}$

Exercise 23D

1 a Students' results
  b i $\frac{1}{6}$ **ii** $\frac{3}{6} = \frac{1}{2}$ **iii** $\frac{2}{6} = \frac{1}{3}$
  c Students' conclusions
2 a $\frac{1}{2}$
  b, c Students' results and conclusions
3 50 times   **4** 30 times
5 a 15 times   **b** 45 times   **c** 30 times
6 a 16 games   **b** 14 games
7 a $\frac{3}{8} \times 60 = 22.5$; 22 or 23 red balls
  b $\frac{5}{8} \times 60 = 37.5$; 37 or 38 blue balls
8 95 claims

9 680 seeds

10 Students' numbers on star
(average of numbers on star = $x - 5$)
For example, if it costs 15p to play the game, $x = 15$.
Average win should be $x - 5 = 10$p.
Therefore numbers add up to $10 \times 6 = 60$

11 60 times

Exercise 23E

1 a
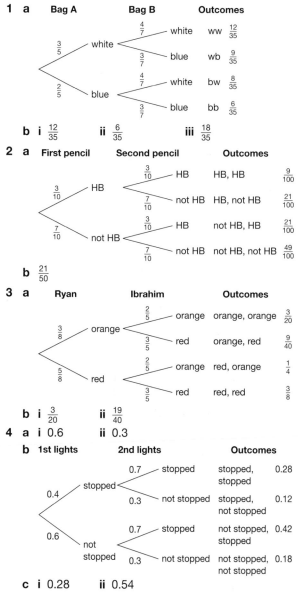

b i $\frac{12}{35}$ **ii** $\frac{6}{35}$ **iii** $\frac{18}{35}$

2 a
First pencil   Second pencil   Outcomes

b $\frac{21}{50}$

3 a
Ryan   Ibrahim   Outcomes

b i $\frac{3}{20}$ **ii** $\frac{19}{40}$

4 a i 0.6   **ii** 0.3
b 1st lights   2nd lights   Outcomes

c i 0.28   **ii** 0.54

Exam practice

1 a (1, H), (2, H), (3, H), (4, H), (5, H), (1, T), (2, T),
(3, T), (4, T), (5, T)

b $\frac{1}{10}$

2 a

	London	York	Total
Boys	23	14	37
Girls	19	24	43
Total	42	38	80

b $\frac{42}{80} = \frac{21}{40}$

3 a $\frac{7}{20}$ **b** $\frac{9}{20}$ **c** 0

4 a 0.2   **b** 15 counters

5 $x = 0.35$ **6** 0.4

7 $\frac{8}{15}$ **8** $\frac{7}{18}$

9 a

+	2	4	6	8
1	3	5	7	9
3	5	7	9	11
5	7	9	11	13
7	9	11	13	15
9	11	13	15	17

b (2, 9) (4, 7) (6, 5) (8, 3)   **c** $\frac{3}{20}$

10 a 0.75   **b** 0.2

11 a 0.25   **b** 0.45   **c** 60

12 Robbie

13 a $\frac{1}{6}$ **b** $\frac{1}{4}$ **c** $\frac{5}{12}$

14 a 97 or 98   **b** 7 or 8   **c** 30

15 a
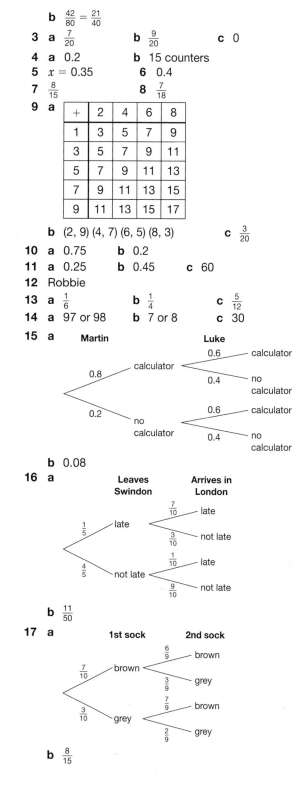

b 0.08

16 a
Leaves Swindon   Arrives in London

b $\frac{11}{50}$

17 a
1st sock   2nd sock

b $\frac{8}{15}$

Index

edexcel ▦▦▦

ResultsPlus *Booster*

ResultsPlus Booster is an online service offering targeted practice and assessment designed specifically for students aiming for a grade C.

- Questions regenerate with different numbers, allowing you to keep practising until you are confident.

- Guided practice questions feature instant feedback and links to learning aids to help guide you to the correct answer.

- Edexcel exam-style questions written by senior examiners allow you to test your progress.

- Study plan adapts, based on the work you have done, to show which topics need further study.

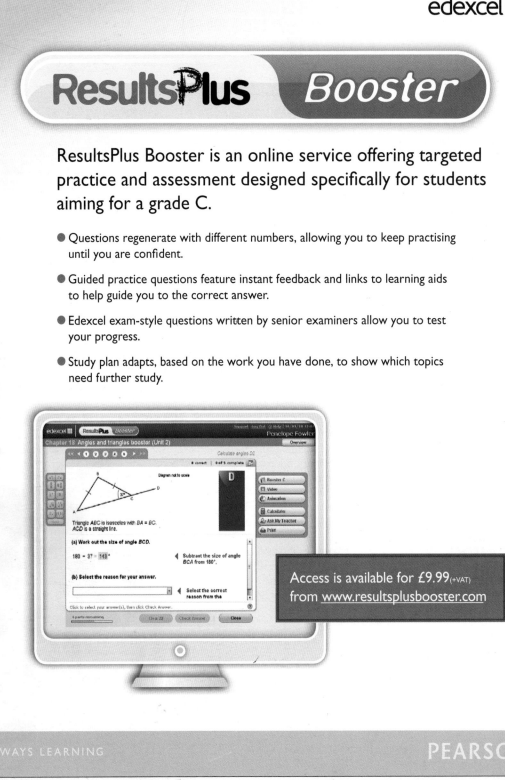

Access is available for £9.99 (+VAT) from www.resultsplusbooster.com

ALWAYS LEARNING

PEARSON